THE GOTHICK NORTH

A HERMIT PRAYING IN A WOOD
By Simon Marmion of Amiens (1425-1480)
(*See page* 324)

THE GOTHICK NORTH

A STUDY OF
MEDIÆVAL LIFE, ART, AND THOUGHT

BY

SACHEVERELL SITWELL

WITH ILLUSTRATIONS

BOSTON AND NEW YORK
HOUGHTON MIFFLIN COMPANY
The Riverside Press Cambridge
1929

The Riverside Press

CAMBRIDGE · MASSACHUSETTS

PRINTED IN THE U.S.A.

TO
MY BROTHER

CONTENTS

ILLUSTRATIONS

PREFACE

THE subject of this book has so vast a complexity that two principles have been easy to satisfy : that the things discussed should be non-Italian, and that they should be remote from ordinary experience and not too painfully present to the eyes. But this book, which does not pretend to be a treatise upon mediaeval art, has at least other intentions than that it should merely extol the strange and the unfamiliar.

The trend of taste has now altogether set in against the period in which my scenes are placed. So many books of a purely technical interest have been written upon churches that it is nearly impossible to consider their merit away from the massed opinions and facts in which they are embedded. Indeed, the strained and fidgety bulk of these huge affairs has made their beauty a little repellent in the eyes of our contemporaries. Such familiarities of France and England have been scrupulously avoided in these pages. But even the Moorish Alhambra, that typical instance of the elder discrimination, is denied its beauty by this present generation, and poet, or painter, is more likely to tread in his fancy the banks of the Congo than those filigree courts and coffered cloisters of Granada.

> " *At length burst in the argent revelry,*
> *With plume, tiara, and all rich array,*
> *Numerous as shadows haunting fairily*
> *The brain new stuff'd, in youth, with triumphs gay*
> *Of old romance.*"

Now this shock, this revelation, bursts upon the poet's brain from some other quarter. Empty shrines and deserted fanes have nearly lost any hold they ever had upon the imagination.

Perhaps the motive of my pages has been sufficiently set

forth in these opening words, but the method and manner employed may call for some explanation. The writing of this book entailed a delightful, if terrible, imprisonment in the past, and it is notoriously difficult to give life to any antiquity older than living memory. To take the supreme masterpiece of historical reconstruction, Flaubert's " Salammbo," it can be argued that the author's intentions and genius would have been better suited if the book had lacked characters. Matho and Spendius are nonentities ; Salammbo has purposely, inevitably, no individuality ; only Hanno has force and personality. The book would have been better kept as an essay ; and, best of all, as a film. The persons with whom Flaubert enlivened his study and seclusion in that African past meant little to him ; they had no contingency to himself.

In my book, then, I have called into being characters from our own present lives, using them to give argument to my purpose. But their old-fashioned point of view, and their association with my childhood, places them half-way into the past, for, after all, someone living only two years before one's birth is as distant from one as Pharaoh. This problem of what is dead and what is alive prompted all contemporary incident in this book, and led me to write its fictional and imagined chapters.

It has fallen easily and naturally into three volumes. First of all, a preliminary survey of what subjects suggested themselves to me shows my eventual choice out of those many possibilities. Then follow the history and introduction of my two characters. After this I am shown at work on the first shaping of my facts and ideas, and in the course of this investigation I catch up with the characters and meet them again while travelling round on my search for material. Finally, the last chapter of this volume represents the fruits of the journey on which I met them. This constitutes, in fact, part of the kernel and principle of the whole book.

The second volume, soon to be published, is separate and divisible, taking the form, practically, of a novel. In the third volume, the final instalments of my Gothick subject are given, and the characters are assembled for me to say farewell to them.

The Notes at the end of each volume give further information, where required, upon any buildings, pictures, or tapestries, mentioned.

In those chapters where the book deals with tapestries and miniatures the wealth of examples to choose from is so over-whelming that the most practicable course has been to select for discussion a very few instances of particular beauty. In the latter case the Library of the British Museum has been the most easily available centre of study. With tapestries, were it not for three books, my remarks could never have taken their present form, for lack of information. These books are " The History of Tapestry," by W. J. Thomson, London, 1906, and two books by George Leland Hunter, " Tapestries : their Origin, History and Renaissance," John Lane, 1912, and " The Practical Book of Tapestries," Lippincott, 1925. It is also necessary to explain my spelling of the word " Gothic " as " Gothick." This has been because the former word has now become so hackneyed as no longer to possess the character it originally implied, and so I have reverted to the older spelling of Walpole's time. In the last place, I must plead poetic licence for appearing in person, during Chapter IV, on one and the same day, at such widely separate places as the Château d'O, near Falaise in Normandy, and the Abbey of Vézelay in Burgundy.

In the chapter called " The Visit of the Gypsies," which is meant to be an interpretation of tapestry, its beauties, its sub-jects, and the admirations of both maker and client, the con-cluding episode is an attempt to show the effect that music would have on a world full of every kind of beauty except this. For such purpose a tapestry called " The Visit of the Gypsies " is made use of by me, but it has also been the occasion for an act of literary homage on my part. Something like eight, or ten, pages of my narrative are copied down from " Die Zigeuner und Ihre Musik in Ungarn," a book on Gypsy music by Liszt. I have taken them directly from the English version of Mr. Edwin Evans, senior, lately published by William Reeves, of London. This book, by the greatest virtuoso who ever lived, has passages of extraordinary interest and literary value, separated, since he

did not know how to put a book together, by many tedious and
dreary paragraphs. I have tried to group together his finest
passages, at the same time giving them a coherent form which
the author has not quite achieved. I am a fervent partisan of
this master, and my fantasy upon his themes has been the most
delightful labour to me, for, not having the gift of music, I am
unable to lay hands upon any of the rest of his Protean output.

Having made these few necessary remarks, it only remains,
now, to qualify the personal attitude of this book. In the writer's
opinion the direction of public affairs in the arts has lately been
usurped to the exclusion of everyone else by the painter and the
picture-critic. Undue prominence has been given to a profession
that does not deserve it, as anyone will agree who saw a certain
retrospective exhibition held in London last summer. The
foremost English artists of our day showed their finest work,
chosen from a decade of achievement, and the result would have
disgraced an annual exhibition of Swiss art in the capital of a
canton.

Dr. Burney, in his "Musical Tour," describes an encounter
with Voltaire in the garden at Verney. Voltaire's first remark,
on learning that he was addressing an Englishman, was an
inquiry as to what new poets there were. The same question,
in the same words, was put to me at Fiume, in 1920, by the
greatest literary artist of our time. So I am not alone in my
conviction that what poets think, in the foremost land of poetry,
is of more importance than the opinions of painters in a land that
has hardly produced one. The truth is that, not painters, but
architects and musicians are what the future needs, and what the
future will produce, and the nearly cancelled rôle of poet has its
necessity where these two latter are concerned.

In all, I have been occupied upon this book for some two
to two and a half years. The two characters who appear in it
had an authentic existence and may still, for all I know, be living
somewhere under their true names, which I have naturally not
divulged to the public. Their presence was necessary in order to
give the right perspective to this view of a writer engaged, over
many months, upon a long book of this nature. By their pre-

sence, real or imagined, some of the hardships of living for too long in the dead past have been mitigated, if only by the deeper pathos of their own attitude of unquestioning reverence towards it. There would be no hardship if only that particular environment and no other was admired, but for one interested in many more bygone histories, and, above all, in the present lying before his eyes, that Frankish, or Gothick, Age had its imperfections. These, as well as its beauties, were the more easily realized in their company, or its supposition.

A preface, coming at the beginning of a book, is always the last part of it written. I believe, though, that anyone who reads only the first few pages of it will accept my statement that it has been written, not as a concatenation of facts, or to confute the learned, but for the exercise of other faculties, which not even the most prolific of poets can expect perpetually to bear fruit. If there is some hint of this, and a foreshadowing of the harvest I hope for, my delight in this toil will be sufficiently rewarded.

Weston, 15th February, MCMXXIX.

THE GOTHICK NORTH

BOOK I

THE VISIT OF THE GYPSIES

BOOK I

I

CHOOSING A SUBJECT

I CANNOT be writing poetry the whole time, and must look about for a subject for prose. Twice, before this, have I found myself in the same dilemma. I saved myself from it, the first time, by spending what would have been, otherwise, the wasted days of some two years on certain unknown and uncared-for phases of the late and luxuriant South. But the material was nearly too copious and profuse for one book, and the next time I was in want of work I found it in vague and tenuous introspection, and expanded the dim smokes and mists of memory over another two years trying to make substance from shadow. Now, for this third time, I am in the same quandary and am looking which way to go. There are these paths to choose from, and many others.

The Patrician of Venice, water-borne, and riding that smooth glassiness to the council-chamber while the tied boats below the window toss their necks together like horses. This magnifico we can move out of the canal-mouth to much flourishing of the conch-shell, but all his days are ruled by caste, he may speak to but few of his own countrymen and to no foreigner. His water-Renaissance has had its aqueous character worked into the lagoon-art so that the silks are like marble wetted with spray, and the painter, who seldom thinks of the soil, for it is never below his eyes, puts the shapes that he imagines against clouds that will move like an easy machinery of screens for his background. The most of this shakes easily at a firm tread ; the Doge's Palace turns into its true character of town-hall filled with boastful corporation-pieces that the empty Italian eloquence has lifted bodily into an aether of cheap poetry. The empyrean flight of these emphatically heavier-than-air bodies is crippled by the terrestrial detail that Veronese loved, the spider's web, the lamb of purity, the gilded wheat-sheaf, that are all the imagery to accompany these myths. Yet it is one of the most wonderful of human histories, visually and potentially, and to do justice to its strangeness one would wish to be of some future and far-distant race—perhaps a negro from some African Empire of the next millennium when the music and the sculpture that will of a certainty thrive there impel a practical curiosity in this direction. . . .

But we could convey back a negro identical to this into some black kingdom of the past, into some part of the Songhoi Empire of the Sahara.(1) Their vast cities of mud-architecture, the clouds of their cavalry mounted upon Arabian horses and protected with quilted and patchwork armour, their swords and helmets copied from those the French crusaders wore under St. Louis in 1270 at the siege of Tunis, the slave-markets teeming with a hundred different tribes from the south—what a subject that black age makes to any eyes and senses that are a stranger to its note of mourning ! For the negroes, not excepting the standardized athletes of ancient Greece, are the finest physical type that has existed, and their gigantic basalt made yet harder by the practice of incessant warfare turns them into the most stubborn machinery of battle. And all this still lasts in a diminished life in the negro-sultanates round Lake Tchad that were visited two years ago by the Citroën expedition !

Then there is the Maya civilization of Central America, where the most interesting of all archaeological discoveries are now being made, and in a natural setting that stimulates even the ordinary traveller's books upon that region into a high note of literary accomplishment. They had the sense to worship Time, most reasonable of all cults after sun-worship, and the statues that they set up were in honour of famous astronomers, not of warriors or of useless kings. That strange feather-clad world where rare plumes were the prerogative of power, makes the finest of all subjects for the writer to describe, with the lush jungle creeping into the maize-fields, with the volcanoes smoking like towers on every horizon, and with the sword and hatchet blades of the cactus making a kind of vegetable echo to the warrior that those happy Indians so seldom saw. For their peaceful communist system and the absence of bloodshed among them, until, some two centuries before the Spanish conquest, they came under the influence of the bloodthirsty Aztecs and adopted tribal wars and human sacrifice, should have meant an entire absence of the " bogey " from their minds. But, as though to give, in this, a damning parallel to their, in all else, complete differentiation from other men, their towns upon the eastern coast (giving out, that is to say, upon the Caribbean Sea where they never sailed and where one would have thought a paradise of peace held perpetual reign) were walled and fortified against the black and cannibal Caribs. These monsters of a negroid type, and of much more powerful physique

B

than themselves, swept down, at infrequent intervals and with no warning, in their fleets of canoes from the unknown islands to the south. Then there was terrible slaughter ; many captives were carried back into slavery in the canoes, and others were the victims of a cannibal feast held upon the beach at clumsy-lit pyres, which beacons we may think of as being visible to relations who had fled into the hills.

But another subject much nearer to the eyes tempted me and set me thinking of its possibilities. It had always been my ambition and haunted my mind. This was the reign of Napoleon III. It was then that the photographer came to life with his facile answers to idle curiosity, and we can see Baudelaire, Manet, Gounod, Constantin Guys, confirmed and proved in all they had to say. The women in daguerreotypes possess the pose and shape of a Spanish Infanta, and clothes soon reached to a height of bombast and daring insolence that tallied with the re-born eagles and kettle-drums of the Empire.

We might come to our climax with a certain year, about the middle of the 'sixties, when we read of such fashionable material for parvenu dresses as shot taffetas, damask reps, clouded, spotted, checked, and marbled, merveilleux at sixty francs a yard, gold and silver brocade from Lyons figured with bunches of flowers in coloured silks, lampas figured with golden palms, brocatelles with embroidered flowers in gold and silver thread. " Women wore masculine attire, used men's paletots, collars, cravats, canes. They were seen in military coats of yellow velvet with Chinese embroidery, in red velvet mantles trimmed with black lace, in black tulle dresses with gold lace. They went back to the caracos of their great-grandmothers and chose to have them of flaming

red satin studded with gigantic steel buttons, or hung
with cut-glass; they wore the Diana bodice which left
one shoulder uncovered; and, added to this, their hair
had to be red like a cow's tail and curled like a lap dog's,
en bouton frisé or *en caniche.*"

But my thoughts fled away from those blatant and
military reds in search of some minor and swaggering
feudalism, and they hovered for some little time inquir-
ingly over Japan. I read Kaempfer's travels into that
quaint kingdom and found a triumphant, barbaric jangle
of march and countermarch, of Royal progress and Royal
return.(2) He devotes three pages to an enumeration of
the various forces that accompanied one of the chief
Daimyos on his yearly journey to court. Without
pausing over the details, we may quote the following few
lines : " It was a sight exceedingly curious and worthy
of admiration to see all the persons, amounting sometimes to about twenty thousand men, who compose the
numerous train of a great prince (the Pike-bearers,
Norimon, i.e., litter-bearers, and Livery-men excepted),
clad in black silk, marching in an elegant order with a
decent becoming gravity and keeping so profound a
silence that not the least noise is to be heard, save what
must necessarily arise from the noise and rushing of their
habits, and the trampling of the horses and men. On
the other hand, it appears ridiculous to an European to
see the Pike-bearers and Norimon-men with their shifts
tucked up above their waists, exposing their naked backs
to the spectator's view. What appears still more odd
and whimsical is to see the Pages, umbrella and hat-
bearers, and all the footmen in livery, affect a strange
mimic march, or dance, when they pass through some
remarkable town or borough, or by the train of another

prince or lord. Every step they take, they draw up one foot quite to their back, in the meantime stretching out the arm on the opposite side as far as they can, and putting themselves in such a posture as if they had a mind to swim through the air. Meanwhile, the pikes, hats, umbrellas, baskets, boxes, and whatever else they carry, are tossed about in a very singular manner, answering to the motion of their bodies. The Norimon-men have their sleeves tied with a string, as near the shoulder as possible, and leave their arms naked. They carry the pole of the Norimon either upon their shoulders, or else upon the palm of their hands, holding it up above their heads. While they hold it up with one arm, they stretch out the other, putting the hand into a horizontal posture, whereby, and by their short deliberate steps and stiff knees, they effect a ridiculous air of fear and circumspection."

This account showed many signs of promise, and looking for closer details in the architecture and painting of that time I found these themes described in some of the Buddhist abbeys that compare in wealth and splendour with the famous monasteries of Europe. They occur in apparently endless flights of rooms opening into each other and used for the Abbot's apartments, for meeting-halls for the monks, or for the treasure-rooms of the convent. The plum-room has sliding screens of blossoming plums, then come a series of bamboo and plum-tree themes, pines and plum-trees, eagles and plum-trees, peacocks under double-blossomed cherry-trees, cherry-trees under snow, white herons, cranes upon pine-trees, herons in a snow-scene, peacocks and golden-pheasants in snow, the corchorus room with branches of yellow Yamabuki, pink and white chrysanthemums, tigers in a bamboo grove, screens decorated with painted fans, great Imperial processions against a golden cloud blackground, bears in a snow-covered forest, grapes and squirrels, golden maples powdered with snow, and an altogether endless repertory made up of variations upon this material.

The rotation of flower-festivals in Japan justifies and explains this peculiar genre of art. The plum blooms in January, the peach in March, the pear and cherry in April, the wistaria in May, the iris in June, the lotus in July and August, the chrysanthemum in September and October, the maple in December. Apparently only February is flowerless, but perhaps the snow supplies this deficiency. It does so, most certainly, in their art.

We know that landscape well and can realize the amount of rain necessary to bring the fruit-trees into their fullness of blossom. An easy device of a ladder and a light bridge brings you right into these snows, where the different airs from each tree might be a hundred separate gales so voluble are the tongues of sweetness that sound and breathe forth in every direction. Out of this heart of all sweet breath there are other things beside scent to consider, and each spray as it climbs into the blue sky shakes its little rattle of snowbells in a trembling and vibrant manner, as though a bird sang from this perilous kind of leaf, so ready to shake down and dwindle upon the ground at a touch or any noise.

Apart from these various worlds of plum, cherry, or apple, that break out like a flowery artillery in their appointed months, the whole of nature has been heaped and shelved at a provocative perspective which stimulates and inspires. And where the landscape is straight and untroubled, at a level line of sea, for instance, this piece of coast that cannot afford cliff or rock breaks into a grotesque clump of fir-trees that twist thirstily out of the salt sands and break the air into a hundred levels.

Altogether, the scenery set against the swaggering, feudal warriors is of a more uniform design, and therefore more easily typical of its own truth, than those many varieties that could be found in Europe. The Castilian highland, the German Alp, the flat meadow of France or England, the cypress-hill of Tuscany, the brackish canal of Venice, all of these have an equal truth for my purposes and can make a background for my knights and monks, whereas in Japan the whole likelihood can be simulated by the French Riviera and the volcanoes of Naples and Sicily. The interior of the country, where it rises into ranges of hills and has convents, like those of Kōya-san, in the difficult green shades of the cedar-woods, would seem to resemble the mixed sanctity of Vallombrosa and La Grande Chartreuse. The spiked and resinous boughs meet above the low roofs ; they are sepia clouds during summer, and during winter those thousands of sharp needles in the hoarse, rasping wind groan and sigh and drip out their depression. Yet the low roofs below were the only refuge from iron rules of caste, or a perpetual military service.

Thinking the whole subject over in my mind, it seemed to me that the twisted tree-forms, the dwarf people, and the comic or even burlesque element in their lives, added to what a poet has called " the long, lacquered afternoons," made of Japan too quaint and tortured, often too ugly a material for treatment. I wanted to match this violent and profuse imagery, and scarcely expected to find it, but these items jumped before the eyes and persuaded me to write them down, so strange and unlikely was their provenance. They occur in a list of vestments bequeathed to the chapter of St. Paul's Cathedral in 1402, and then in use there : three albes and amices of linen cloth with orphreys of red velvet powdered and worked with little angels and the arms of England, given by Queen Isabella ; three albes and amices with apparels of red cloth of gold powdered with white letters of S and with golden leopards, the gift of John of Gaunt ; six copes of red cloth of gold with blue orphreys with golden-hooded falcons and the arms of Anne of Bohemia ; a suit of blue cloth of gold powdered with gold crowns in each of which are fixed two ostrich feathers ; a cope of red velvet with gold lions, and orphreys of the collar of the Duke of Lancaster and a stag lying in the middle of each collar.

This hunting after fact and incident led me into yet deeper fields of imagery. Such were the trophies of every moment of their day, and at night their beds were a house within a house. The following items are drawn from the accounts for the great wardrobe of Edward III during the four years, 1345–1349, and they give a list of the beds made for him during this short space of time. They explain the wealth of the King's furniture by an occasional reference to his everyday clothes and appurtenance. They include charges for making a bed of blue taffeta powdered with garters containing the garter motto ; for a bed of red worsted given to the King by Thomas de Colley powdered with silver bottles having tawny bands and curtains of sindon beaten with white bottles ; for forty clouds for the King's garments, embroidered with gold, silver, and silk, with an E in the middle of the gold, garnished with stars throughout the field ; for a doublet for the King of white linen cloth having about the sleeves and edges a border of long green cloth wrought with clouds and vines of gold and with the King's word : " It is as it is."

We give a few final specimens in order to close this list-making of metaphor and simile. Edmund Mortimer, Earl of March, dying in 1380, left his bed of black satin embroidered with white lions (the badge of the house of March), and gold roses with scutcheons of the arms of Mortimer and Ulster ; Joan, Princess of Wales, left to Richard II, her son, her new bed of red velvet embroidered with ostrich feathers and leopards' heads of gold with branches and leaves issuing from their mouths ; Thomas of Woodstock, Duke of Gloucester, left a great bed of gold, coverlet, tester, and soler, of fine blue satin worked with gold garters, and three curtains of tartryn beaten with garters to match ; also a large bed of white satin embroidered in its midst with the arms of the Duke of Gloucester and with his helm in Cyprus gold.

In the same list the following items are found : a bed of black baudekyn powdered with white roses ; a large old bed of green tartryn embroidered with gold griffins ; fifteen pieces of tapestry for two rooms of red worsted embroidered with blue garters of worsted with helms and arms ; twelve pieces of tapestry carpet, blue with white roses in the corners and divers arms ; a large bed of blue baudekyn embroidered with silver owls and gold fleur de lys ; a green bed of double samite with a blue pall (stripe) of chamlet embroidered with a pot of gold filled with divers flowers of silver ; an old bed of blue worsted embroidered with stags of yellow worsted ; a bed of blue worsted embroidered with a white eagle ; a coverlet and tester of red worsted embroidered with a white lion crouching under a tree ; a single gown of

blue cloth of gold of Cyprus powdered with gold stags ;
a single gown of red cloth of gold of Cyprus powdered
with mermaids ; and three curtains of white tartryn
worked with green popinjays.

There is no need, here, for any Italian mythology to
come in and replenish the artist's fancy. In this one
field of heraldry, alone, there was endless material from
which to draw inspiration, and the traditional English
reticence, true even in those days, prevented anything
approching the " excesses " in which Germans, or
Spaniards, indulged when they had the opportunity.
But the numerous examples just given have been quoted
in order to show how the most truthful and least vain-
glorious of designers were unable to resist the occasion
and arrived at a strange and perverse complexity without
realizing the brazenness of their doings. Enough has
been said to show that these English barons had as brave
a setting for their persons as any Daimyo, and that this
tough and copious repertory collected for their renown
was far from remiss in its efforts after their fame.

So this is the imagery of the Gothick North, and now
it can be seen how our path is set among the knights and
monks of that day. But the cathedrals and the primitive pictures are never touched upon and their assistance
has not been asked. Instead, I have tried to investigate
the Gothick North in directions where it is less known,
but none the less true to itself. Tapestries and miniatures have been consulted, and the great monuments in
stone are only called upon for evidence where what they
have to say is not too familiar.

So this book is to be a study, if not a defence, of the
fair-haired races that have imposed themselves for a
thousand years upon all the countries of Northern

Europe, and, in fact, upon everything that is not Slav or
Italian. Besides this, it is to be a study of the arts
produced by the mediaeval church when it worked in
Gothick, and not Italian, modes. It must be, in part,
then, about monks and monasteries, about the triumphs
and defeats of celibacy. All my life I have wondered at
that strange and neutral existence still led in our midst,
but it is monk more than priest that I am studying ; the
celibate shut close within walls is my subject, though I
may go outside this into the streets and lodgings where
priests dwell. Yet I have been interested in churches
and not in prayers, for those long hours were a penance,
and so far as I am concerned I have no beliefs and they
were wasting their time. Their millions upon millions
of mumbled breaths I have left uncounted ; I have little
interest in ritual, and only care for superstition when
it is answered dramatically, or has coarse or brutal
eccentricity.

If, added to their more ordinary dimensions of length,
width, and height, the famous buildings of Europe were to
be expressed, like battleships or liners, but in terms of the
air, not water, that they displace, the Gothick cathedrals
would exceed every railway-station, every town-hall,
everything except these very battleships, or liners,
with which I am contrasting them. But many of them,
whether it be with or without the restorer's aid, are old
black steam-engines standing in lonely squares like waste
machinery in a railway yard. Their façades, lodging-
house window-lace gone black with age and dirt, the
spikiness of their ornament, the slave-work of their
intricate sculpture, all this would seem to have been born
of a dead and soulless age. When new is it reasonable to
suppose that their effect was any better than it is now ?

Later on in the book I hope it will be possible to suggest what might have happened had Gothick continued, had no breath of the revived learning ever taken effect outside Italy. There was no reason that Gothick should stop ; it b oke into Renaissance at the very height of its achievement and with no real decadence inherent in its practice. Had it continued, our notions of the picturesque would have been far different, and Mr. and Miss Corder would be at work for ever on the endless intricacies of worked grills, spiral openwork staircases, carved wooden doors, sculptured tombs, and every other mediaeval elaboration whose development the Renaissance cut short.

But the mention of their name reminds me that the hero and heroine who launched me on my present path are waiting for me at a country inn for their dismissal, and while I prepare for a morrow that will no more be troubled by them, I must excuse their presence here by an explanation of how they came into my life.

II

ACROSS THE COMMON

FOR five years of my childhood I was at school in Surrey. A line of chalk hills ran East and West behind the house and made an abrupt horizon to our eyes. It was along the ridge of those white cliffs that the Canterbury Pilgrims rode, having by this point forgotten the towers of Winchester in their longing for the spires of Canterbury and the first sound of the bells, and here we used to play once or twice every week, always keeping a piece of chalk to bring home for the blackboard when the master's back was turned. There were some great crater-like hollows, steep-edged, and with fir-trees growing in unexpected bare spots upon their slopes, and here all the realities of football field and asphalt playground faded before a new and startling perspective. It was something outside life and yet at the same time nearer to what life should be than the two samples I have just mentioned as being chosen for a child's background ; indeed, our walks along the top of the chalk hills were the nicest things about each term, and even the most disagreeable of school comrades took a turn for the better in this environment. There was little else I can look back upon with pleasure except a row of great bound volumes of the *Illustrated London News*, dating from the 'forties, the earliest years of that publication. I can still remember many

20

of these, among my favourite passages being the visit
of Louis Philippe to Eton and Queen Victoria's sub-
sequent stay with him at the Château d'Eu, only three
or four years before the King's ignominious flight from
France under the disguise of Mr. Smith, which tragi-
comedy was also to be seen described and drawn in
woodcut in these pages. I used to turn over the volumes
while I sang to myself some of the sad airs of the music-
room which lay just behind the library and below the
sempiternal boughs of a cedar tree that smelt resinous
and made one's thoughts turn at once to piano and
violin. The same little tunes practised over and over
again and showing, even after three months, but scant
improvement in their playing made a surprisingly fit
accompaniment to the diurnal happenings of so long
ago that seemed then so important, and now were only
tolerable because quaint and improbable. But I need
go no further since this is not meant to be a book of
childish memories.

Instead, I will pitch at once upon my heroine—if the
rôle that she plays in this part of the book can be said to
satisfy that claim for her. She taught drawing in the
school and her name was Miss Corder.

She came every Friday afternoon, spending from four
to seven o'clock over the different classes she had to
teach, and the very day of the week on which she appeared,
bearing with it a foretaste of Saturday and Sunday,
made one think of art as the prelude to the only pleasant
part of the week, and, probably, when one had left
school, to the only pleasant part of life. I must give
an outline of her appearance. She was thirty-five,
or thirty-six years old, I suppose, and fulfilled in every
detail what a foreign caricaturist would require of an

English spinster. She was tall and very thin, had an exceedingly pale face, and wore, not pince-nez, but steel-rimmed spectacles. Her dress was pathetic in the extreme, and I remember her very long, thin hands and the curious, accustomed way in which she sharpened a hard lead pencil, while the noise made by this implement in the process of " shading " comes back to me as soon as I think of her drawing for our correction a miniature of the task we had been set in an upper margin of our drawing-books. It would be a chair, a table, or a few cups or glasses ; but, often, as though to give us a fore-taste of what lay before a finished master of the art, we copied lithographs out of a big portfolio that she brought. In their close imitation of pencil or charcoal these were meant to show what " sketching " could attain to at its highest development.

There must have been two or three dozens of these drawings that we were set to copy, and nearly all of them were of foreign scenes. One or two were of ruins in Norfolk, or Suffolk, and both these and several of the foreign subjects were by Cotman. These latter, without exception, were of places or scenes in Northern France, presumably in Normandy and Brittany, some of them, as I say, by Cotman, and others by Samuel Prout. As I used to spend one at least of my holidays every year with my parents in Italy and saw no more of France than the mere railway journey from Calais to Paris, the rest of the transit being accomplished at dark of night, I associated these drawings that we were set to copy, even then, with a sad and forlorn kind of travel quite at variance with the blue skies and sunny architecture that I had discovered for myself. Such, then, were the pleasures of Miss Corder and her kind, and I used to prepare a very different paradise for my own maturity.

One of the things we noticed about her was her unfailing punctuality ; she was never so much as a minute late for a lesson, and indeed she was to be seen hovering about in the drive near the entrance to the schoolrooms for some five minutes before the clock struck. She used to walk over every Friday from the twin town to that in which my school lay, a distance of some two to three miles, the town in which she lived being associated in my mind with only three things, that her lodgings were there, that it was the first, or on other alternatives the last, station between school and home, and that one of the largest and reputedly the most dangerous of lunatic-asylums was situated near there. The road she came by led out of one suburb of brick villas across the common into the similar suburb of our own town, and I suppose the walk cannot have taken her less than forty minutes each way.

In childish curiosity I asked her one day why she did not take a cab and was answered with the frank remark that her yearly fees from the school were some eighty pounds and she could not afford to throw away nearly half of this upon cab-fares ; so she chose to walk. This, then, was why for a great part of each year she wore goloshes, in which at the end of our French lesson she could be heard padding softly round upon the fallen and damp needles of the cedar tree while she waited for the clock to strike four o'clock. Very often, of course, she would arrive dripping wet and would remove her goloshes and mackintosh, and then seem strange and unfamiliar from the fact of her appearing among us hatless and, therefore, less impersonal than usual.

Her remark about the expense of cab-fares had the effect of breaking down barriers in my understanding of her situation, and I was able, now, to see her in a truer light and to approach nearer to life as it existed for her. For instance, the reason for her extreme punctuality must lie in a nervous horror of what would happen to herself were she to lose, through any negligence on her part, what amounted, I expect, to her rent and a good many of the necessaries of her life combined. The particular master who was generally in the background was an exceptionally nice man and treated her when he was in the room with an exaggerated politeness that must, it seems to me, have been born from sympathy. She was a sad object, it is clear, and the precision and effort of her attempts to keep going must have touched anybody who had a moment to spare in thinking of her.

Her other sources of income were these. She taught in a small girls' school, she took one or two private pupils from the town, and during her spare time, chiefly in the school holidays, she painted a few water-colours that she sold, however miserably, at a better rate than the best poets can sell their poems. All this, it will be seen, amounts to but little, and I should say that on a good year she was contented with two hundred to two hundred and fifty pounds. She lodged in a couple of rooms above a grocer or newsagent, and I expect that she herself prepared nearly all her meals at home, glasses of milk, cups of tea, and cakes or buns being her mainstay, while every now and again it would be an egg or a piece of fish, and very occasionally, on a Saturday for preference, she would eat a light luncheon at the Popular Café just down the road. I do know that her rooms were lit with acetylene and that she took in one newspaper a day, though I admit that other details of her manner of life I give as being probable more than definitely ascertained.

Why had she come to live here ? Why, indeed, had anyone, for these two towns had no history, no trades or manufactures, and were miles, even, from a river, that most primitive of geographical reasons for a town's existence ? But this very question tells us so much about Miss Corder's antecedents that we must delay here for a few moments.

Her father, so I discovered, had been an artist of some renown who lived the greater part of his life in the town in which I was born. It is true I had never heard his name, but Miss Corder knew mine well. Collectors in the North of England still pay good prices for her father's water-colours, and even better for her grandfather's work. Some years ago her father had determined on a bold move for fame and went out with his son, then about twenty years old, to paint a panorama of the Grand Canyons of Colorado, complete with the Red Indians and their villages, which work, or works, were publicly shown in London and rewarded his labours with a small fortune. Henceforward he lived near London, only visiting the North very occasionally, and in the summer it was his practice, but he was now an old man and almost beyond such an effort, to come over by train and paint views of the common which, considering it was but twenty miles from London, seemed remarkably wild and remote. He had always liked pines and fir-trees, while on a lucky day there might be a gypsy encampment to add a glamour to his sunset effects, for I gather that he worked all day upon trees and landscape and only threw in the sun at

c

its last moment of life rather as you might drop the
remains of your dinner into the pond on the banks of
which you had been dining.   He often took his son or
daughter to sketch with him, and in this way over a
period of years they had made some friends and become
familiar figures in the landscape, so that when Miss
Corder accepted an offer to teach drawing in the school
it did not take her long to decide on living in this town
where she saw it would be possible for her to support
herself and not have to depend any more upon her
father.   In the holidays she went over and stayed with
him, or more often took a room near her brother's studio
in London.   She was often in London, then, at Easter
and Christmas, but in August and September she
generally arranged to go over to France for a month's
sketching, where she made enough pencil drawings to
give her material for colouring and selling for the remainder of the year.   Dorothy Perkins, or Red Rambler
rose, Miss Corder seemed never to have seen ; anyway,
she ignored them in her art; likewise she never painted
a herbaceous border, or, unless actually sketching with
him, trespassed upon her father's preserve of pine and
fir tree entangled in setting sun.   In fact, her drawings
more nearly resembled those of her grandfather ; they
belonged to the Early English school, with acknowledged
paladins like Prout or Cotman as leaders.

One Friday she announced that her brother was coming
over the next week to help her with our lessons.

He was taller and of much better physique than his
sister, being like her to look at, but with everything that
was cadaverous in her changed to a Teutonic broadness
with him.   It was, perhaps, in recognition of this that
his Christian name was Carl, but in spite of his big build

what should have been muscle was not strength in his case. The blue serge suit that he wore sagged in a critical way at those points where in schoolmasters, who are chosen for private schools more for their athletic record than for any other reason that one can see, the powers that urge on foot, cricket, and golf ball can be noticed in ugly protuberance. Just at those particular moments, as I say, his clothes bridged untidily over a sunken hollow, and our masters, even the one who tolerated Miss Corder with kindness, were unable to disguise their feelings towards him in a certain stiffness of manner. So, where the sister could be forgiven for being too feminine, the brother erred unforgivably by not being masculine enough, and one could even feel them longing to get him out in the cricket-ground at fielding practice, or " nets." It is easy to imagine that merely because of this atmosphere by which he was surrounded one felt a deeper interest in him than was likely to be incurred by any of the 'Varsity products that had been chosen as models for our chase after foot-ball or cricket-ball.

But here I withdraw both brother and sister from the grounds of the school and will not think of them any longer in that environment nearer than the gate leading into the drive from the public road outside. I have explained how I met them both and we can think of them walking over to their work together without pausing any longer over the details of that work. They were the first artists I had ever met, or even seen, and I am not likely to forget them for that reason.

There was three or four years' difference in their ages, the brother being the younger of the two. He was now about thirty-two and had been working on his

own for some five or six years, painting a certain number
of portraits and doing innumerable pencil and charcoal
sketches to illustrate books with such titles as " Picturesque Normandy," or " Peeps at Brittany."   Also,
in the world of dealers, he had his father's and grandfather's name to help him, so that, all things considered,
he was in a far better position than his sister.   What
hardships there were, such, for instance, as the fact that
even brother and sister together could not afford a cab
on the wettest of Fridays to save them that three miles'
walk, he was able to treat, remembering his other advantages, as so many picnic inconveniences, the sort of
difficulties without which you could not really say you
were an artist.

Indeed, to my mind, as I think of them both walking
over the common at sunset on a winter's evening, they
carried with them, merely in virtue of their profession,
an air of festivity in the background, bands playing, a
fair in progress, or a dance in a marquee, and the fact
that they were always walking away from this, that they
were staying away from the feast, invested them with a
sort of halo of regret that matched them admirably
well with the evening mist and the first spikes of the
frost.   He used to carry the heavy portfolio for her, and
there cannot have been much to talk over save lost
ambition and those festivities I have described as always
in progress behind them and in which they never shared.
They were both still so close to those lights, near enough
to feel their warmth, and almost to catch the glow of
any contemporary success among their friends.   I am
not suggesting there were many meteors among their
colleagues, but in these surroundings anyone with the
merest sign of a life of his own, artistically speaking,

seemed to burn like a bright fire on the common. Like
the gypsies' encampment, it would no longer be there
next morning if you came back to look for it, and for the
old boot and the stones blackened by fire that you would
see there I doubt if I could find at home in my chest of
drawers so much as an old pencil or a drawing of my own
corrected by Miss Corder or her brother, yet these two
unfinished shades led me to all the solaces and the only
purpose of life.

At other seasons than that I can think of Miss Corder
by herself on her way across the common, and I should
not like to choose which was the most congenial sadness
in the months for her background.   The full, broad glare
of a summer evening in May or June made an aching
and heartless wall-paper to her little room of vision
that she pushed slowly in front of her through steel-
rimmed spectacles past low bushes heavily spangled with
eglantine, with the grass on either side entirely powdered
with daisies, and any hollows there might be upon its
surface filled to the brim with buttercups.   The artificial lights of any human festivity could not but look
trite and feeble out of this, though they became tuned
to a better harmony when the days had shortened and
sunset could be depended upon either at the end or the
beginning of Miss Corder's transit home from her work.
As to the deep authentic winter nights when she was
engulfed in complete darkness the moment she had left
the cone of light thrown forth by the opened door, and
was only guided on her way across the common by an
occasional lamp that blinded like a lighthouse anyone
who came within its orbit, these dark and tragic screens
that took up new places round her wherever she looked
did at any rate carry her without other interruption

than that of her own thoughts straight back from her work, past the shuttered villas, and into that street of a few shops where she had her lodgings. Then it was simply a matter of the latchkey, of feeling her way up dark stairs, and of fumbling for matches upon the mantelpiece where she knew she would be within reach of the acetylene.

The only difference between what the light showed her and that which would have been true of every hired apartment in the whole of the country was a few of her own framed sketches upon the wall, and these seemed gently to break down that convention and contradict its truth. Also, her room was less tidily arranged than the average, for Miss Corder was one of those people who have little talent for comfort and do not, therefore, make the best of their surroundings ; indeed, she seemed never to have unpacked properly, as though expecting at any moment to be called away. Books were untidily arranged upon the table, from a mere corner of which she was satisfied to eat her meals, and through the open door into the bedroom beyond you could see a confused tangle of clothes and her two suit-cases pushed into the corner where they would be ready for her the minute she wanted them. Her copy of the *Daily Mail* lay, still folded, upon one of the books on the table, for this was her daily accompaniment to supper, while, even then, I remember her confessing to me how little it interested her and that she had no appetite for news. A book or two from Boots' Library lay on the table, but these she never read at supper and kept till they could claim her undivided attention after the meal was over. Even so, potted meat and bread, an apple, and various cups of tea, could not be delayed over for more

than half an hour, and by the time the clock had circled
into that other quarter of the wind and appeared to be
moving upwards under a new and younger impulse, she
had pushed her two plates and cup aside and drawn the
armchair up in front of the fire which her landlady,
by a special arrangement, lit for her at half-past six every
Friday evening during the winter.   There was an hour
and a half to read in before a last cup of tea and her
resigned retirement through the inner door into the
bedroom, and this hour and a half was most certainly
the best part of the whole day.   At least there was no
task she had to prepare for to-morrow and there was
even another advantage that she deeply appreciated,
that there was no exact moment in the cold morning
at which she had to be ready and dressed for work.   All
her duties were in afternoons, so that she had the whole
morning to herself and could spend it in writing letters or
finishing the sketches she had made during the summer.

Of course, during the time that Carl taught with her
they had supper together on Fridays, and I expect that
he caught a late train back to London which would get
him to his studio by midnight.   For these occasions she
took a little more trouble over her rooms and increased
the supper by some fish or a few cutlets, while she prevailed upon her landlady to send out for a bottle of beer
for her brother's supper.   By the time he had to catch
his train it was late enough to go to bed, and in any
case she would not want to sit thinking alone, while the
unusual sensation of having had a companion to talk to
during the whole evening made the idea of reading a
book quite impossible.

Her pupils' holidays were looked forward to eagerly
by Miss Corder, but I imagine that when they came

they brought with them more acute financial worries, for all her daily expenses seemed to be sheer extravagance which she could not justify by counting up how much she had earned that day, or this week. These troubles were only smoothed over when the enjoyment that she derived from her expenses became increased out of all proportion, when she could feel that for very little more than living cost her in England she was existing in better circumstances and with the most acute enjoyment of every moment of the day. These particular pleasures only came, as I have said, once a year, in August and September, and I must not forestall their charges upon her small sum of happiness.

Instead, we will leave her having supper with her brother and as far removed in spirit from all that was tiresome in yesterday and to-morrow as I am from all the details of school life that I have tried to forget in order to raise up out of that debris just this one figure.

I have a legacy waiting for her and can, therefore, enlarge for a little more upon what must now seem to have been the early discomfort of her life. We can think of her walking over the common once again, a plain without a symbolic river for her to cross, and no nearer approach to it than a duck-pond choked with chickweed, a pool of Siloam in which even the brown and white ducks did not prosper, for by the time its waters had brought their condition to perfection they were instantly sacrificed for Christmas. It is as un-inspiring a background as can be found even in Surrey, perhaps the tritest part of the whole world; but, indeed, it is for this very quality that it has been chosen. Veranda on veranda, trellis on trellis, form, as it were, the only images that the most inspired pair of eyes could deduce from their surroundings ; and the intrusion upon these of any figure or object out of the different and preferable worlds of beauty would seem like a bat flying about in the daylight, or a crocodile found in a trout-stream. It would strike a ridiculous and incongruous note against the tepid and inane background, and anyone possessing firearms would be out after it as soon as sighted. Miss Corder was in herself rather inappropriate to this scene, for trellis, veranda and the hope of pretty fair-haired children would seem to lie within the reach of all villa-dwellers ; while I find it impossible to think of her mowing the lawn or playing tennis.

But I have chosen her precisely because of the symbol thrown by her long, thin shape. She was, as I have said, the first artist I had ever met, or even seen, and she sprang for this reason into an instant importance. Her whole shadow seemed to me to throw back into the past which that convenient telescope of history enlarges into detail for us, and then shuts back again into one level plane, so that when we are not tying down our thoughts to one particular figure, all the dead are simply dead as opposed to the living. They seem to us all to be dead, and dead at the same time, while clanging tram and motor-horn tell us we are alive. Miss Corder as an artist and as a person had still some vestige left about her which carried her through that transparence out of the present into the past. There was a little resemblance, a visible relationship, between herself and those geniuses one was led to believe were now extinct, though, to state it in terms of fact, Miss Corder was towards one of these real paladins what the dead and mummified monk you see in a Capuchin burial vault in the South of Europe is

towards such figures as Cardinal Wolsey or the Renaissance Popes, in whose veins the blood might still be
running, so fresh and vital do they seem to us. There
is not, speaking of personalities, much more than the
bones and the monk's cowl left of this particular skeleton,
and yet we can recognize it and know whence it came.
Such dry and brittle talismans lie between the dead
and the living, for the skeleton belongs after all equally
to these two states, and it seemed to me that Miss Corder
occupied a truer medium towards those two extremes
than anything else that I knew of, for she was here sitting
at my elbow and at the same time was gone a century
or more away where I could still see her in the midst of
my own life.

Over a period of years Miss Corder and her brother
had disappeared entirely from my memory, they may
have come into my mind for a fraction of a second in
each year but they took up no more space in it than that.
Their father died not very long after I last saw them and
left a sum of money which was sufficient for them both
to give up teaching and take a small house together in
Cornwall, from which, as we shall see, they followed their
old custom and crossed over every summer for a sketching
tour in France. Thus they suffered the most unhoped-
for perpetuation; they understood their good fortune
but did not dare to make inquiry of it, accepting the new
turn of their lives unquestioned.

In order to make a keener contrast with her happy
fate, we will leave her for the last time in the middle of
the common on her way back from the evening lesson.
We can see her shape getting smaller and smaller against
the grey and darkening road, though long before it
dwindles into nothing she is swallowed up whole, as it

were, by the night. Somewhere ahead of us she is pushing her way forward ; her little room of vision being narrowed down to a few feet of animate and moving blackness as the pitch-black night strengthens and holds her. From where we stand we cannot see one of the sparse lamps that map out the road or we should find her darting into that bright light for a moment, thrown back suddenly into a dazzled life from which she would seem, apparently, to take the earliest escape into the darkness again.

Though this is the last thing that Miss Corder would believe, she will never walk across here again with her brother ; but she would give no more credence to it than I should have done, in those days, to a rumour that the winter-term was to be called to a sudden end in the middle, say, of November. And had such a story been true, the last afternoon of games, as, with Miss Corder, it was the last Friday lesson, would have passed into a kind of excited pleasure such as I had never experienced before. This would have prolonged itself in her case into her supper-time, and have occupied all her brother's thoughts in his train back to London, and even during the cold walk from the Underground to his studio.

The road across the common was dead and gone for her ; just as dead in its way as the Pilgrims' Road along the top of the white chalk cliffs above the two towns. It would be frightening to have to walk along there after dark, and the far inferior and more managed darkness of the common would now alarm Miss Corder were she to find herself once again within its grasp. She would wonder how she had ever contrived those lonely and double crossings of its exposed blackness every week, during most of the weeks in the year, and into the deep and black heart of the winter.

Meanwhile, the Pilgrims riding to Canterbury upon that high, white bar above the plain were terraced, almost, as if upon a ridge of clouds. Every night they tethered their horses and mules at the appointed stopping-places and slept in the great barn-like stone barracks built for their accommodation, till the trite and metallic bugle of cockcrow woke farmer and pilgrim in the drab winter morning. In just the same way the placid church bell in St. Agatha's flint-set tower chimed down the street of mean shops, and must have hung for a moment of time above the grocer or newsagent's shop near the corner. But when its cold note woke Miss Corder she opened her eyes to very different surroundings from those in which she had just been moving down her old mazes of measured life, remembered in an autumn dream that seemed to explain all its illusions by the warm mist upon the pane, and the fruit trees hardly visible through the mullions, and the droning bells.

III

A FIRST SKETCH

THE droning bells against the mullion's glass cobbles, together with the fruit-trees just seen through the gentle mist, took me into a present so true of the past as to make a continuity out of which I could break at any point I chose. Of course the door into this, as well as out of it, led through the orchard below my window. The bells working through this mist and under the loaded fruit-boughs seemed to lose their hammering insistence, the brief and catastrophic lilt of their leaden burden, and they flowed evenly into the most lovely of melodies that poured themselves unceasingly into fresh shapes, and then moved with those very limbs of poetry they had evolved into more firm and brighter changes. A rhapsody, or heroic mood, with its drums beating to a fierier measure than any heart or breath could bear, would turn in the very throat of its own pace into a languorous and hardly flowing pastoral, and then quicken from those sighing sheaves to a held and insistent monotone, some thicket of sly whispers, or a fountain's voice hushing the words behind its shade.

That shade of sound and not of sight, for the thin crystal of its jets made no screen, sparkled traitorously through the trees ; indeed, there was nothing for it to hide. Instead, its gay and dangerous glitter showed a young lady at the fountain-brim with her ankles and pale feet in the water. With one hand she held up her clothes so as not to wet them, and with the other, she poured rose-water from a jug into the chill and scentless pool of stone.   This was as provocative and bold a sight as those days could afford, for no greater nudity than this was ever seen away from the nuptial-couch.   The two elders to this Susannah walk, gravely talking, among the near boughs.

Look closely at the enchantress !   She is tall and thin with long hands and blue veins of birth.   Her pale face and fair hair make her unsuitable for any fictions except this present, or its contemporaries, and she has appeared in no previous poetry or imagery whatsoever.   This castle-bred woman has come down in descent from some distant and far back fjord where she may have waited, looking, then, like a Scotch fisher-girl, while the black boats slid, hissing, into the waves and another pirate expedition was launched.   But in her present form there is little of the open-air about her and she has lost the carroty hair, or too emphatic, as if bleached, blondness of the Scandinavians.   Her present physical condition comes from castle-confinement, and the steep towers in which she lives have for their object the protection of the marriage-bed.   Her long flat sides, the thought of which has caused a master of poetical imagery to compare the gold-fish in a pool to princesses out of a fairy-story, give her the stiff and angular look that comes from no lack of perspective science on the part of the artist but is true of her in the same way that a fine photograph of a Chinese landscape justifies and condones the Chinese convention.   It is typical of her purposes and ambition that she will prefer her portrait to be taken when she is swollen with child, and is, according to her mind, by that the mistress of perpetuity.

THE TAPESTRY 'SUSANNAH AND THE ELDERS'
In the Victoria and Albert Museum

How different, even, are her ideals of courtship from those prevailing in any other place or time! She keeps the climax of her admiration for an armoured and clattering ghost who cannot rise once he has fallen to the ground and is a half-man, an embryo, away from his plated horse. Even when this tartaruga has had his shell unbuckled and the page has carried his armour away limb by limb, she is but little nearer to him. His long and thin legs may be shown in tights, but his body is encased in the thickest of woollen pleats and folds. Anything that followed the semblance of the nude body was as absolutely unheard of as the actual nude itself, and this so-called mediaeval age that seems cruel to us with its tortures was more prim and painstakingly virtuous than any other culture of which we have knowledge. The naked athletes of Greece, the gladiators of Rome, the population of statues by means of which the whole classical world knew and attached no degree of shame to the human body, all that logical bareness is unheard of and unknown in these lands of slant roofs built against the snow.

For the still safer security of their women, the elaborate game of chivalry was invented. This was a play of move and countermove, a hazard of retreats and advances towards or against the perpetuity of family, which seemed, then, to be the main object of life among the nobles. In order to mass enough weight and put enough swirl upon the importance of these pawns, long mythical ancestries from the North had to be invented and whole cycles of legend were developed. King Arthur and his court sprang into a realistic present, apparently hardly further back, so vivid was the detail of their presentment, than the memory of grandparents. These mated easily with Charlemagne and his paladins, and with the old German folk legends strengthened for the occasion into a firmer focus and the wild-beast skins of the Teutons improved into shining, if cumbrous, armour. The Norman barons, and their Spanish and German contemporaries, availed themselves to the fullest degree possible of these airy benefits and tied them on like a heavy tail behind their own descents.

Very soon these ideals were matched on an admirable playground against just the luxury-loving enemy with a few chivalrous conventions similar to their own that they would have chosen; while the difference in religion made him a declared and perpetual foe. The Crusades, strangest and most pathological chapter in the history of Europe, lasted for a couple of centuries, but unfortunately they came too early to leave a record in any but the literary arts. But what effect they had was one that made this new kind of Eastern and Christianizing adventure, pleasantly and piously disguised as a duty, into a memory that tallied with those mythical and purely literary-made deeds of the Northern paladins. In other words, they helped to furnish out the mythology on which art is fed and a new row of heroes remained to be celebrated, where Bohemund and Godfrey de Bouillon took their places beside Charlemagne and King Arthur. But these filled ranks finish the grand and epical days of construction. The great stone doxologies that they built for cathedrals are completed, the developed Gothick has come forth from the Norman or the Romanesque and, itself, died in due turn to give place to the Flamboyant and the Perpendicular. Meanwhile, the peculiarities of the Northern social system have become developed into their greatest extent; dynastic rule puts Spain,

England, and France, at entire variance with the commercial democracies of Florence or Venice, and Kings and barons have set themselves up on a scale that still keeps them in two out of these three countries as the ruling class. Coming first as aliens, they conquered by military prowess, and then set up a permanency in which the church aided them with its promise of immortality to the poor who were patient enough to bear their lot and would then be admitted without more ado into a perpetual paradise with the rich, who attained this no less easily by their wealth and the lessened worries that this insured.

The whole of these written legends by which Kings and barons set their seal upon lands they had taken over from an alien peasantry must be considered in their right relation to the personages that they celebrated and thus established. The stories in the Arabian Nights can be compared with them with this difference, that these latter were intended primarily as an amusing after-dinner entertainment, to which must be added their aphrodisiacal properties and their appeals to the personal vanity of kingship by an oriental over-emphasis upon ordinary and redundant flattery. But the legends of the North are colder and less pleasing to the harem; it is combat after combat, battle after battle, with strange emphasis upon the male virtues of strength and courage, and none of that dithyrambic praise of female beauty which fills so many pages of all Eastern poetry and epic. Though never written by themselves, the mediæval epics composed for the nobles by bards, professional and servile scribes, or the eunuch fancies of a monastery inmate, copied to a surprising degree of truth those exact qualities and that particular style King or baron

D

would have effected had the simple and humble mechanics
of writing been known to him and not relegated of necessity to one of his subordinates.   In fact these stories
made a kind of rumination, a half or waking dream, upon
the baron's wishes, his ideals, his paradise, and the extent
to which he has realized them.   They have an immense
psychological importance to his personality, and we can
read into them an interpretation of his abstract as well
as concrete ambitions.   They make an index to his
character, and I find I can best express my meaning when
I refer to the last chapter in Joyce's " Ulysses," where
Mrs. Bloom gloats in a horrible, macabre manner upon
her own soul, and the intensity and length of that self-
examination and self-exaltation show us an indulged
and flaccid nonentity in the same perfection of detail
in which we can see all knightly ideals and all chivalric
ambitions shown in these mirrors that make a pretence
of flashing back into an uncharted past and really show
an unbridled and true present.

Up till now it is their only art-form, for the church has
so far the monopoly over all expressed imagination.
The barons live in the primitive state of their castles,
not yet thinned into steeple-roofs or fretted into pinnacle-
work, and the illustration that I give of a ranting hero
from the melodrama of a century ago gives as good a
suggestion of them as we can get from tomb or carving
in those early centuries before any attempt at portraiture
was made.   The genius of George or Robert Cruikshank
can be relied upon for a spiritual, if not historical, truth ;
and the green grass of the foreground, the pillar-box
castle at the back, the plated and lobster-like armour,
the bristling moustachios of this knight, are a good
rendering, keyed into theatrical intensity, of the sort

A GOTHICK KNIGHT
By Robert Cruikshank

of figure that might have issued from the portcullis at Carnarvon or Conway castle, or from that most formal of all toy-forts, the Tower of London.

By now, another art had been perfected for their praise, and we find the knights accompanied in all their acts by a display of heraldry, forming a kind of certificate of genuineness for these paladins, who, but for such banners and emblazonments, might be mistaken one for the other. But the very armour they wore distinguished them, and in the tournament they were known for their different suits, that probably cost them in proportion as much as the modern sort of magnifico will spend on his Rolls-Royce or Hispano Suiza. Their crests, from simple plumes, grew into the real rendering of their devices, so that a knight encased in heavy plate might be seen in the lists supporting above his head a swan with out-stretched wings, or a stork upon her nest.

For the Gothick knight was invested during the short two centuries of his existence with a fine and poetical panoply of his warlike power. In this, the most material help to his renown was this same art of heraldry invented solely to record his pride of birth. As the most primary instance of this we can take, in our own country, the badges of the great families : the bear and ragged staff of the Beauchamps, the portcullis of the Beauforts, the crescent of the Percys, the swan of the Bohuns, the mermaid of the Berkeleys, the sickles of the Hungerfords, the knots of the Staffords and Bourchiers, the malets of the de Veres. Sometimes the herald's art made use of the rebus, a punning allusion to the family name. Thus, the seals of the Longespée family show long swords ; there is a boat on the seal of Hugh de Veere ; sheaves of oats on that of Aver of Rochford, while Thomas of

Gloucester, a son of Edward III, who was born at Woodstock, used the stock of a dead tree as the badge upon his seal ; Richard, Lord Grey of Codnor, used a gray, or badger ; William, Lord Bottreaux, used buttresses ; Lady Margaret Beaufort a marguerite ; and Thomas, Lord Ros of Hamlake, had a hemlock for his badge.

There are many examples of barons and prelates marking their buildings with a rebus. Bishop Walter Lyhart put a hart lying in water upon his chantry in Norwich Cathedral ; Bishop Goldwell in Wells Cathedral used golden wells, and Bishop Beckington, at the same place, a beacon on a tun ; in Ely Cathedral, Bishop Alcock had for his rebus a cock on a globe meaning All the World ; at Canterbury, Cardinal John Morton had an eagle standing upon a tun which was lettered Mor, and Prior Oxney, an ox with *ne* written upon him ; at Exeter, Prior Goldstone II used gold stones, and Bishop Owlham has an owl with a scroll lettered Dom; at Westminster, Abbot Islip has an eye and a slip of a fig-tree with a man falling, which means " I slip " ; at Fountains Abbey, Abbot Darnton has a dem on a tun, and Abbot Huby, a hobby, or small hawk.

Such specimens as these are capable of infinite multiplication before it is necessary to leave our own country and search for like instances in France, Germany, Spain, or Italy. But the few I have given are sufficient to show the kind of imagery in which the lives of the great priests and nobles were led. They were accompanied all their days by incessant reminders of this symbolic importance given to them by their inheritance ; for they wore it on their clothes, and it was always before their eyes on a servant's livery, on their furniture and textiles, and upon the trappings of their horses.

The herald's art had its great opportunities at a wedding, a funeral, or a tournament, when there was obviously no limit to the possible conjunctions out of this range of mythology that was open to them. Strange pitches of personal stridence were arrived at in these boastful attempts for pre-eminence, and we may imagine a church hung with gay or funereal tapestries, or else a whole encampment of gaudy pavilions vying with each other in proud violence of imagery.

Sometimes, as in the illuminated Froissart of the British Museum (Harl. MS. 4380), the pavilions have had their roofs raised into pinnacles and little windows, while the gables above these mock-turrets are gilded and carry pennons with arms upon them. In front, the lists are built ready and knights and their squires are riding to take up their places before the spectators. The chargers they have mounted wear steel head-pieces and have steel coverings to their manes which are jointed and arch with every movement of their necks. They are still wearing long brocaded horse-cloths that trail upon the ground and are only taken off them for the few moments of the fight, after which they are quickly replaced to guard against cold. The knights look fixed and implacable in their armour with their visors down and the steel beaks pointing forward with the eye-slits all but invisible; they carry shields with their arms upon them, and above their helmets great badges are fixed. One of them has a high red cap with a swan rising out of it, the other has his helmet ending in a woman's black steeple hat, like those of the ladies who look on in the background, from which a whimple flows down his shoulders on to the horse's back. Behind the knights ride their pages, without armour, and carrying spare lances to replace

the splintered ones that their masters will soon
hold.

Indeed, we can look back with an amazed astonishment
upon this new, pointed and floriated art of Europe that
was rising out of the gigantic, blurted shapes of the
Romanesque. Then, there was so much to say that
sometimes speech failed. Great towers of sound rose
trembling out of the ground and every horizon was
crowded with statues. All these imperfections came
before the small completions of Gothick development
when the heroic age was over ; but art, instead of
tumbling in that one, unobvious direction might well
have continued to its own logical exhaustion.

I speak of imperfections because the age of the gigantic
could not, of necessity, delay very long over anything
but its own climaxes. Then, every kind of accent was
pulled into effect and a whole maze of metaphor spoke
volubly from the stone. In a later part of this book I
speak of the Abbey of Vézelay in terms of a poetical
masterpiece which the sculptures, themselves, dictated,
for they flowed so easily out of the stone into metaphor
and image. Every part, there, is of the utmost value
and no detail has had to be hurried over in order to reach
to some more interesting field of action.

But it is no diminution of their total to say that
certain mediaeval masterpieces possess an excellence out
of all proportion to that of the others. I find it difficult
to admire, as a whole, any one save Chartres out of the
famous and great cathedrals of France. Rouen stands
black and grim in its square, while the triple, spiked
porch of St. Maclou and the pinnacled Palais de Justice
recall the buildings of Burma ; Amiens is a sooty engine
standing alone, unhooked from its train ; Bourges, which

looks so imposing upon its ridge from a distance, is hardly interesting as to its interior, so bare is it of anything save stained glass, much less splendid than the windows of Chartres.

We have already begun to restrict the picturesque in our rejections. Many hundred easels have stood in patience before certain objects ; now we try and persuade their owners to move with us into a more congenial angle, where the neck is less craned and the eyes become delighted as they strain. At present they are sketching some still and tiny frost-flowers above them, where no hand can reach, and even the eyes will hardly melt them into obedience to the pencil.

Where the building is a great cathedral in some large and populous town, not only the general planning, but every detail in the two or three centuries of work that so big an affair entailed had to be submitted to, argued upon, and passed by, the whole corporation of townsmen. As always, where it is a question of committee resolutions, the slowest and safest opinion has been arrived at after every wild or rapid fancy has been lamed by argument. No sensational battles have ever been won in this manner, and that any effects of art have been arrived at in this way is a matter for wonder. We find the more famous of the cathedrals praised, then, for the time, labour, and money, expended upon them, and according to the very ratio of these extravagances they are the more likely to have been watched over with the jealous eyes of the corporation and the whole mass of the townspeople. That wonderful results were arrived at in spite of these restrictions is so true as to be a platitude, but this book searches for extreme instances and not for the average, and therefore the typical cathedral has been avoided.

Instead, I have chosen the two most personal fields open
to investigation, and the tapestry and the miniature are,
here, exalted from wall and bookshelf into heights more
worthy of their individuality. In a companion chapter
to these two studies, when I have worked the material
into a strength sufficient to bear construction, I examine
one particular phase of Gothick building where certain
peculiar features have been carried to lengths that have
been realized in no other time or place, though, alas !
this is church and not secular perfection.

To put the shadows in their appointed places we must
extol with the very same breath in which we condemn.
I have detailed some of the drags upon inspiration, but
it is the great miracle of the Middle Ages that all their
accomplishment was reached in the teeth of these
obstacles. This can be proved, later on, in even so
vague and impersonal an art as that of the tapestry-maker.
Where these strictures are untrue, their very opposite
came into operation with just as dangerous an effect.
A miniature painter, for instance, might well be engaged
for some five or ten years upon a small book, during all of
which time he was immune from comment, or from any
fresh influence which by changing his manner would spoil
the even and untroubled fancy along which the paintings
of a missal should progress. Once the method had been
established in the first few pages no transition could be
allowed, and the whole work must proceed on a logical
development out of its own foundations. Thus, in an
even truer sense than the reality, was the illuminator,
monk or professional painter as he happened to be,
immured in the cell where tradition imprisons the
scribe. Such works as his are fine in proportion to their
expression of sustained and unflagging powers.

These remarks can be applied to tapestry with the same potency of truth. That process of building, where the units of design are so small as to be hardly visible to the eye, had to progress in an even development that no false changes could interrupt. It is a slow and tortoise-like poetry that is born by such long pregnancy into immortality, and youth and freshness of effect are its proofs of miraculous origin.

If Rome, Egypt, or Assyria, are compared with these Northern civilizations this very slowness of production, which is comparable with theirs, then contradicts any similarity by aiming at precisely an opposite effect to that which these older cultures hazarded and achieved. The eternal, expressed in terms of wealth and bulk, was their ambition, while the Gothick artists tried for a more human kind of eternity. The figures that they carved are so often young, and are fixed by this into a pathetic and clinging mould of humanity. Their very buildings have turned something transitory into a permanence, for these strange elegancies and floriations would seem to have the thinnest and most perilous of lives. Yet those few springs and summers live on uncrushed by the snow and rain that are their enemies!

Such a building as Chartres would seem, after the Colosseum or the temples of Karnak, a most unlikely trial for permanence so jagged is its outline and so fretted and pinnacled its detail. Also, the extraordinary amount of sculpture seems to be a proof of an innate longing for documentary evidences of divine interference, while, at the same time, the invention of printing is foreshadowed in that intense hunger for information and knowledge. The cloud of witnesses has as many figures in it as a bible has pages, and over and above this set number we can think of the superfluous shapes as so many leaves of other books than the bible, leading into more authentic histories, or the false realities of poetry. Karnak, or the Colosseum, have no such indications in their plain substance, and the Egyptian conventions of painting and carving carry no other messages than obedience to the Pharaoh, prompt payment of taxes, and a mummied tomb life, too like prison. There is no kind of development out of the straight, box-like buildings of life, and the rock-cells of death, into any flowering of the arts of living. It is the same with Roman buildings, except that here there is a bigger democracy of slum-dwellers to cater for, so that categorical and drastic spectacles have had to be provided for their diversion, of which bloody drama we find an echo in the heavy trophies of sword and trumpet that make the items of their decoration.

All this was now dead, so dead as to leave a bare tradition of laws and roads behind it, which meagre material might be fortified into deeper probability by the discovery of a few yards of Roman wall, or a stolen and dropped handful of coins. In its stead we find this strange flowering of habit and idiosyncrasy that we have come to examine in its final form before the return into that imaginary and reconstructed Italian past. This must be, therefore, a statement of ideals and an index to ambition, and where facts have been improved into fiction it offers the finished alternative to the gradual Italianization of the arts. The different Cæsars of Spain, France and Germany, lived, but had not taken up their titles, for we can deny the German Emperors before Charles V and take from them anything but an Empire over heraldry. But by this very act, by marriage and by counter-marriage, they achieved their aim, and

Charles V, the most important of European kings between Charlemagne and Napoleon, owed his Cæsarian position to inheritance, and not to conquest. He was born into a Gothick world and died in an established theatre-craft of Roman imitation, so that his reign is the watershed between these two seas. Here, in this book, we are definitely to the far, or Northern, side of these mountains, and there is a great landscape before our eyes.

It is the green meadows of the Ile de France from which itinerant artists started to all quarters of Europe, taking with them the same principles of building and design which were capable of endless development into a mysterious kind of spiritual affinity with the countries where these French products flowered into shape. From the initiation of this movement in the latter part of the twelfth century the exodus began into foreign lands, and the great age of activity in France itself, and outside, lasted for at least a couple of centuries. The Normans, turned into more martial and sterner Frenchmen, conquered England and Sicily. The French themselves, in the guise of Crusaders, covered the Holy Land, Syria, Greece, and the Greek Islands, with French churches and castles, while more than one attempt was made towards a permanent occupation of Egypt and Northern Africa. French barons assumed the crowns of Jerusalem, Constantinople, Athens, and Cyprus, to mention only those colonies whose importance merited kingship. Greece has, to this day, some of the most splendid mediæval castles, while Rhodes and Cyprus have Gothick buildings as fine as any to be seen in France or England.

A few instances may be given of this spreading of French culture. Guillaume de Sens was the architect of Canterbury and died there in a fall from a scaffolding.

Eudes de Montereau went with St. Louis to the Holy
Land and raised the fortifications of Jaffa.   Philippe
Chinard, a French architect, held a permanent post at
the court of the Emperor Frederic II and must have
been largely responsible for the Castel del Monte, the
greatest castle of the age, near Andria in Apulia ; another
Frenchman, Pierre d'Agincourt, worked for Charles of
Anjou in Sicily and built the Castel Nuovo in Naples.
A master-mason from Troyes built churches, convents,
and commanderies, in Cyprus.   Villard de Honnecourt
and Martin Ragevy built churches in the most distant
parts of Hungary ; Matthieu d'Arras, a native of Avignon,
built the great bridge at Prague.   Germany, Spain,
Poland, Finland, and Sweden, employed architects from
France.

The monks of Cîteaux and Cluny raised monasteries
of their peculiar pattern in every country of Western
Europe.   In Italy they built the great abbeys of Fos-
sanova, of Casamari, and of San Galgano ; in Spain,
Poblet, Veruela, las Huelgas, and Santas Creus ; in
Portugal, Alcobaça ;   there were eighteen monasteries
of the order in England, more than forty in Germany,
eleven in Austria, and six in Norway and Sweden.   This,
even, is but a phase of monastic building, for there are all
the buildings of the Benedictines, of the Dominicans, of
the Franciscans, and of the Military Orders, Knights of
Calatrava, Templars, Teutonic Knights, Knights of
Thomar, and a dozen other varieties of military ascetic.
It was the greatest period of building activity that there
has ever been, and no mere catalogue of names and places
can convey any idea of the strength and quantity of its
products.

A dozen different civilizations were safely established

on that firm foundation of which the four corners are king, baron, priest, and monk. In France these four conventions lasted till a century ago, in Spain they still exist, and a half of the four, though diminished in power, have yet some authority in England. But we must narrow down the arts by which these figures were surrounded until they come out of the historical background into some kind of reality with our own life of image and its opposite or answer, truth.

For the subject suffers from its profusion, there being so much work of first-rate quality that the second best is difficult to choose. Churches in such remote parts of Europe as Norfolk and Suffolk, Somerset or Lincoln, come out of what is essentially a permanent and geographical provincialism into the centres of their own unique and peculiar styles. This is true of all Europe, and not only of the more bucolic parts of England. Galicia, the most westerly province of Spain, flowed with riches owing to the pilgrims who visited Santiago, and, in consequence, had a great flowering of architecture; the three finest mediaeval abbeys of the whole continent are to be found in Portugal; there are magnificent Gothick remains in Dalmatia, and in far off islands like Gothland in the Baltic. Indeed, the spread of Italian architecture and Italian craftsmen during the Renaissance took the new ideas no further afield than the area covered by this earlier culture. Also, its hold upon the population was much stronger and deeper; it affected all the details of life and not merely the external air of priest and noble. Yet its life was perhaps a century shorter than that of its Italian successor and rival.

Its peculiar qualities are far from being accidental in their origin; indeed, they start from rapid and organic changes in concept, for every ideal was altered, and bent or straightened out of its accustomed line. Yet it was no age of alternatives, there was enough work for the imagination along lines that could not be avoided, and there was no need to waste time upon a complete new start. That is why the change from Gothick into Renaissance was accomplished with so little difficulty, for this one art at its highest pitch of delicacy and execution flew off along those new lines and for some little time was too busy at its work to notice the change of direction. It must have been, at first, just an addition to the stock of ornament, and the change worked down from the surface into the heart, not killing the body of which it had taken possession until there was a certainty of success.

The epoch came to a finish with a series of transcendental exhibitions of technique, one or two of which are to be found in every country where the style had flourished. These do not conform with the criterions of modern taste, which, having gone back to the primitive, now distrust these sensational exhibitions. This class includes such buildings as these: the chapel of Henry VII at Westminster, the chapel of the Constable of Castile in Burgos cathedral, and the Cartuja de Miraflores, near that city ; the unfinished chapels at Batalha ; St. Maclou at Rouen ; the churches at Louviers, Brou, and Rue ; San Juan de los Reyes in Toledo ; and a number of other small affairs of this kind upon which every trick and resource have been allowed licence.

After these it was too late. The whole of that great movement tilted over and there was nothing left of it that they respected, being prepared, as all real artists should be, to sacrifice it at once for their convenience. Whenever there was sufficient money they were ready

to pull down these old evidences and put up something
new as a proof of their contemporary skill and importance.
In Spain, it is only the richness of material, the marble
or gold used upon it, that has saved many a Gothick
masterpiece from destruction, for the Spaniards, who
judge of a work of art by its value and have, therefore,
always preferred a statue to a painting, being most happy,
indeed, when they have been able to combine both these
arts in polychrome sculpture, showed no mercy to work
the Gothick intricacies of which they could so easily
surpass in the Plateresque or Churrigueresque fancies of
the day. Only one other thing, save their value of
material, has saved them, and this is the problem of
distance, many formerly rich towns being nearly deserted
when the great days of wool-trade, or other similar
industry, were over.

So it is to Spain that one must go in search of the
finest details and the most complete remains of the age ;
and the expansion of the house of Hapsburg into a world-
power, coinciding with the expiring Gothick, ensured
the most complicated of effects for this really high and
bare table-land with little to recommend it save a cloudy
kind of patrimony over alien lands.

In this, our final return to its generalities, if we want to
discuss the poetry, or even the very appearance of that
age, we find it more easy to attempt our reconquest by
diminution. In fact, we take away from it those
qualities, the absence of which in their day made the
greatest and most abrupt difference between that age
and the full Renaissance of a generation later, and we
find the Gothick period paler and more easy of understanding from this loss.

First of all, we find no music there, and this at once

deprives the mind of half its machinery of imagination.
The church music of the day had gone no further than
expressed faith and stubborn belief can be carried in
terms of music ; while the songs of ordinary life were
nursery rhymes with endless verses, or else easy love-
catches, the sound of the words having hammered themselves into a tune. Secondly, the art of printing had
hardly begun, and so books were a fine rarity that only
the scholar could affirm to be a chief factor in his life.
They were, indeed, books of reference, a kind of chained
oracle always there to be consulted, and not life-long
accomplices without whose assistance no day could be
lived through happily. It is doubtful whether many
nobles of the time were much better at spelling out the
inscription upon a tomb, or above a door, than is
the present product of public-school and university at
the deciphering of a date in Roman numerals. In
fact, written words, even in one's own language, were
practically sentences in a foreign tongue of which a few
syllables could be recognized and stammered out with
difficulty. That they were insisted on all the more for
their intricacy, and that a long inscription in the thin
and spiked letters of the time was considered the most
important adjunct to posthumous fame, all the more
because if suddenly woken from the grave you would,
yourself, hardly understand this label upon your ticket
into immortality, is a most obvious truism and one which
nothing in the mentality of that time can afford to
contradict.

Sounding a false alarm and having thus summoned
him to the spiked door of his chapel, we may, while our
deception lasts, look closely at this product of our Northern
soil who has made such a firm establishment for himself

above the anonymous and trampled crowd. He is in full armour, enshrined in this greatest article of his expense as he might be shown in this century seated in a motor-car, but with visor raised, as it might be the window lowered, so that we can see his face. He has a straight nose and a long, fair moustache moulded in the lines of all his contemporaries to a degree that makes this type of face into a kind of mask of his likelihood, of the average of his appearance, its meaning, and its probabilities. There is not much room in that small but long head for anything but bravery, skill in the hunting-field put into terms of battle and campaign, and a certain romantic liking for the rests from this activity, for flower-gardens, games of chance, and a rather mournful love-making made more tender by its chances of a violent end in battle, tournament, or at the King's displeasure.

Behind him there is a vast and endless flight of arches, the stone truths, as they might seem from their numbers, out of a whole world of mirror. It is a ceaseless repetition, one arch after another catching this echo and then repeating it into its neighbour. These huge cliffs, hollowed out by the strait of light that flows through them, run silent and tideless out of sight, and are the unparalleled epical works of but a generation or two before his lifetime. There is this gigantic past to his present meticulous finish; these huge, hurried energies and then the slow and nerveless persistence in execution as a contrast to that speed. The backs of these buildings are raised high enough to break the wind in the same literal sense that a harbour-wall shatters the waves, and, for the boats lying safe in that shelter, here there are houses of three and four stories built close to the church in order to tread its cloak of shadow in the summer and

E

share its warmth and dry shade during winter. The minster-roof above is no flat terrace, no parallel to the stone floor below, but it shelves steeply from either side into a narrow ridge garnished with a row of metal flowers that grow, thus precipitously, far from any possible reach of hand. Wherever there is room for them, the parapet is crowded with monstrous animals that lean out defiantly into the weather and would seem to live undisturbed and with nothing to fear among the towers and pinnacles.

It is, therefore, an architecture with all the simulacra of life that this knight has round him. But these graven images fixed forever in a stone pose have nothing of theatrical life about them, for the theatre was dead, and, so far as they knew, had never been born. So there is no " make-belief," and everything is still, being shown in a kind of catalepsy with no indication of how this trance can be shaken off and its lethargy broken into movement. Nothing is sketched, and every figure is given the full detail of is own depth. They either walk with human tread, or hover, when there is celestial assurance, in a manner copied too obviously from the flight of birds, and they are never seen, like the work of a later century, moved along, or marching to music. If shown dead, they lie prone at full length and do not recline ; if standing, they are sentries and not actors waiting for their cue to sound ; there is no agency to move them quicker than the walking pace of horse or man, achieved in either case by the clock of the heart, that always returns into its own pace, and by the lungs, that can never stop pumping air into their pipes.

This slowness, and their ignorance of all artifice, give the works of Gothick builders an intrinsic importance

over and above any of the achievements of those later
centuries of theatre-craft, though this value, that consists
in expenditure of time and does not reckon any of the
more rapid and certain beauties of the theatre, is denied
the sparkle and much of the poetry of the baroque.
This lumbering metal tortoise, but with its slowness
fired into a metallic brilliance that belies its heaviness
and lack of pace, stands by the spiked door of his chapel
and is a clanking engine, a noisy piece of machinery,
beside the finished and wigged shades that cloud his
future and will be his descendants.   Out of those
elaborate personal fences made of manners, perfumes,
embroidered clothes, it is most certainly a descent into
his representative in this present age, whose straight hair
and short head, in the uniform of tennis, golf, and night-
club, is idiotically curbed by school and university into
a wish to be exactly like everyone else, only, if possible,
more ordinary still.   It is near to the end of a long
trajectory, the spent and finished deadness of the flight
before it just falls by its own weight, and is now but a
little way above the mud out of which it raised its head.

It is probable that these steel knights in their full
panoply of armour were at a greater advantage in the
lists than in the battlefield, for the ground had to be
most carefully chosen for their charges, the horse being
too heavily laden to cover anything but the smoothest
of fields.   The edge of a wood, or a short plain easily
covered by an army, were the most likely chessboards
for these advances and retreats.   Bare moorland or green
meadow make a dead and dry scene for the Gothick
Knight compared with the sort of nature that could
easily be summoned for his support.   A vineyard will
be the simplest of improvements and is a probability

in three out of the four countries with which this book is principally concerned, but that rather tame and mild betterment of a plain can be exaggerated into a congenial and apt violence. We may think of great flower-banks and of mile upon mile of blossom, the stiff and pungent air being fortified out of the ordinary into accepting these bursts of strength. The lotus, the magnolia, the more ordinary fruit-tree, become the undergrowth through which the arrows are fired, and the light infantry, precursors of the gradual and then thundering impact of the charge, come through these low bushes on to the petal-strewn ground outside their dense thickets. Then, hoarse trumpets are heard out of the darkest shades, and there is a lull of nothing but the flight of electric feathers through the air, till the goose-plumed arrows meet their aim and hammer against something harder than shining leaf or soft flower-heart.

They strike with a clatter and a tang against the hard husks of iron horse and iron rider who come out from the shadows and reveal themselves as the most likely insects to inhabit the trees of flowers by which they are moving. Their armour, swollen to preposterous joints at knee and elbow, urges forward each quilted and embossed charger into a lumbering, blind canter just sufficient to carry it into that steel thicket of spikes and points set opposite to it for the charge and moving, now, with a like speed into iron contact. Their lances shiver in the same moment, one against a shield, and the other upon the smooth and steely, nearly female, breast; the pages hurry with the auxiliary spears, but it is too late; the shielded warrior pushes down the other with the weight of his rearing horse, and he falls out of the saddle into a tangle of reins and horse-cloths, which, from their armoured plates, catch more heavily on to his feet and prevent his turning on the ground. Then the other leans out of his saddle with a spiked mace lifted high in his hand and brings it down in two terrible crunching blows on to that steel head, which is battered in and shows the crumpled features of the knight between its dents. He is banked up towards the mace, against the back of his struggling horse, nicely propped for these blows upon the lively and kicking pillow of the horse's body, which, while he falls in deadness over its haunches, has the spinal marrow in its neck pierced with a dagger by one of the knight's attendants, whose duty it is to behave like a quadrilla of bull-fighters to the knight's matador.

In three or four minutes all his potency is spent and the horse has come to a standstill behind a line of spearmen ; he is lifted down from it and his armour is unbuckled to give him air and ease the terrible weight on his hips and shoulders. The remainder of the battle is left to light cavalry and light foot to complete, while, now that this stage has been reached, any enemy knights there may be on the field are carefully attended to and carried into shelter ; but the more dangerously wounded of the enemies' infantry are either left uncared for, or are finished off in mercy with a thrust of spear or dagger. So far as the knights are concerned, the most bitter and sudden moment of danger now turns into a kind, luxurious safety where everything possible will be done for their comfort by this alien simulacra of themselves. The more uninjured, the greater the ransom, and the end of captivity may well be merely a question of exchange and not of payment. Any of the knight's attendants fortunate enough to have been captured with him are released at the same time as their master, while the more menial of the infantry are no more thought of than the jaded hacks who start a bull-fight by tiring out the terrible horns with their crippled bodies.

The valuable armour is packed carefully and carried on a line of sumpter-mules through the fields towards some castle in the distance where imprisonment will be nothing worse than a few gentle months of hawking and poetry. For this very sport of falconry the castle is certain to be hidden away in a maze of woods where no peasant is allowed except to fell timber, and where the act of poaching draws down a death sentence upon the offender. The tracks through this wilderness are only wide enough for a couple of horses to ride abreast, and they are crossed by such frequent contradictions that no one unfamiliar with the forest would know the right direction to keep. A light mist, like blue smoke, hangs among the autumn boughs and prevents any more than the near prospect of stems being seen, until a sudden line of clearing coming in from the side shows the caps of a great range of towers standing up above the tree-tops, and now the track turns suddenly, as if it had been purposely misleading all this while, and veers round against the front of the castle, which lies a hundred yards away across a cleared space where there is nothing to interrupt the eye.

But it is a pity to compress the journey of many days towards this castle into a ride of a few hours through its woods when the very park itself is such a cosmogony of the senses. We will turn aside from that path along which they are returning from the war and go into some other part of the wood where those same towers and their black caps of slate are seen from another angle through the trees. Those walls, built thick for war, protect the only secular and non-religious arts of living. They symbolize, therefore, all the perfections on the one side of life, and, as an image of the different happinesses they stand for, a castle comes into the background whenever a painter or illuminator climbs from the deep ruts of religion into any suggestions of the more material and more easily won beauties of the living.

In a wonderful manuscript, that will be referred to again in this book, we find a castle coming into the background whenever there is any excuse for its presence. Where two peasants are shown felling trees for firewood there are castle-walls shining white as any lighthouse above their bowed heads ; a little further on the vines are being trimmed down close to the ground, and in a mood of enthusiasm the painter has put in, not one, but two, castles in the distance as a tribute to the blue clusters that will soon climb upon those gnarled stems ; a shepherd plays his pipe to a dog who dances on his hind feet, behind them the sheep are cropping the smooth field and a castle climbs up at their back into the cooler air of summer ; at a later page in the book the peasants are hoeing in an enclosure fenced with wattles that are shown gilded with sun, and there is the castle, as ever, making, this time, an almost painful comparison of its luxury with their ceaseless labour ; the summer, for all these miniatures are medallions for the calendar of the year, burns towards its greatest heat, and the village boys are seen bathing in the stream, with the castle high above the banks and a still and exquisite pool for bathing hidden, to all probability, in its walled garden ; and now the harvest comes and a man and woman are reaping the corn with method, for its yellow and clearly cut comb stands stiffly where their sickles have worked, red poppies and blue cornflowers grow here and there in its body, it is a hot September afternoon, the gold lightning breaks out of a cloud that hangs ominous above the labour in front of them, and the castle stands on a little hill in the other direction, quite safe from the storm that would seem only to threaten the peasant and his crops and never menace the castle-dwellers. Yet that mimicked war, louder than any battle of theirs, for shouts and the mere sound of steel are no match for thunder, shows us that this path we are treading, so near to the castle and yet so far, it would seem, from that other track of captives and returning warriors, is separated from its sister only by an angle of these towers ; in fact, it is but the castle-walls and the skill of the builder that have made these woods into a safe haunt for the hunting-party.

Following a stag through the green glades was the most romantic possibility open to those days, for, then, the young men could show their skill and strength, the party was often separated by the trees and the speed of the chase so that conversation was possible where it never could be in room or garden, and because in riding the women showed themselves to more advantage than in dancing the slow measures of the time in dark castle-halls. The romantic fever bred of these autumn days in the wilderness caused a legendary emphasis to cling to the unhappy stag they were chasing so that this animal typifies the most difficult and distant poetry that could be attained in a day's journey from the castle arbours and their more immediate beauty of flowers and blossom. The stag is a favourite animal for tapestry, or the herald's art, and is carried into such extreme conceits as the tomb of Sir Thomas Markenfield in

Ripon Cathedral, who, in allusion to his name, wears a collar to his armour that is made of park palings, spreading out at the front of his neck into a fenced space where a stag is seen lying.

The Hapsburg ancestors at Innsbruck are a gallery of bronze heroes showing every conceivable extreme of the armourer's skill, and it is here that the machines of metal into which the great men of the time aspired to turn themselves can be seen in the greatest variety of their fancy; the most realistic rendering of the blue and shining steel that they wore is in the triptych by Conrad Witz at Basel (3); and we can safely leave to the regions of Germany and Central Europe the credit of having produced the most emphatic iron shades of this Nietzschean prophecy. But for the more romantic and less bloodthirsty emotions it is necessary to move towards the West, where the patience and the fast inspiration of Fleming and Frenchman worked together in the production of tapestry. We leave that art for a later point, and part from the huntsmen as from the warriors, though the sound of distant, and yet more distant, horns announces that they have found the scent and are off into the unexplored shadows.

Instead, we will find ourselves, once more, by those huge white towers that in their bare expanse of wall to so little window seem to be a great ship bleached by the waves and raised mysteriously nearly out of this green water of the grass meadow that runs by the walls. A deep moat, tall enough to drown, guards the castle-foot, and to reach this there is the bare and exposed grass to cross under a cloud of arrows, but the portcullis is lowered and the gate unchallenged.

Every few miles down the countryside there are these

bundles of towers lived in by this race from the North, who have acquired an additional paleness in the dark halls where they pass their lives. They come out from them to hunt, or to fight, and for this latter expedient they appear perfectly encased in armour, where, in theory, they should be as safe as inside their castle-walls, but, with the gift of movement, the siege and capture of these lively pawns has become quick and likely, and so caution keeps them safe behind stone walls as long as can be. Here we may find for their leisure tapestry, or carving, but no pictures, no books, little music. There is nothing else out of these degrees of their wealth except the nearest monastery, and with that we are not, now, concerned. The ideals of the castle-dwellers were handed down through the lines of inheritance that make a safer average of their likings than is probable of a monastery, which, though it may have been inhabited for a thousand years by the same order of monks, changes, with every new generation of a few years, while the consistent and unchanging patterns of perfection towards which the barons aimed their lives ensure a longer continuance of what was typical of themselves. Some points of breeding were expected of their physical appearance in just the same way that one kind of horse, a racehorse for instance, differs in certain obvious directions from a cart-horse.

They must be a race apart from the peasants, or from the town-dwellers ; they must have thin, white hands incapable of, as they are unused to, labour ; long and thin faces with noses of a distinct bridge ; tall, long-waisted bodies ; long, thin feet. Towards the production of all these specialities they offered every kind of artificial encouragement, and even exaggerated them in their clothing so as to draw attention to what they had achieved in this direction. Great rings make thin fingers look slighter still ; pointed shoes are drawn out into rats' tails and to such a length, sometimes, that they had to be fastened by gilt chains on to the knee-cap ; an emphasis is given to the lines of the face by skilful swaddling, so that folds of the complexity of the most elaborate oriental turban are seen swathing the features and framing them for this advantage ; hoods fall so low that they are like the empty clothes of another body carried upon the back, and give, by this small contradiction of a live body in clothes with those empty trappings carried so near to it, a contrast in which the living body is seen to be long and thin and held tight in its clothes ; sleeves are cut and tapered like the edges of a leaf, or the fins of a fish ; all of these were so many cheats towards the effects at which they wished to arrive.

These qualities of the tall and the thin are true as well of their rooms, and where wealth allowed it they would never have a flat roof, but let it be arched into a thin cone, or a wedged apex above their heads. They were buried in the most extreme versions of their clothing, and this was copied in the tomb above their bodies, below the vast flight of arches that I described, that, in their mirror-like repetition of each other, but in the hardest of stone and not in glass, carry out the ideal setting for a human-being into a corridor for giants.

Coming out of these castles and forests, we can leave their dead heroes in the emphasis that they liked and come down to the smallest things of life, things that were not dead and fashioned by their hands but alive, and yet not with that degree of life that an animal possesses but with the dumb and pathetic life of the

tiniest domesticities of nature. The flowers of the
garden, that were, then, so few in number compared
with what they are now, would appear to have crept
into the walled enclosures with knowledge and sense of
their appeal. They were mostly single flowers with
rayed petals like the groining of a roof, and with centres
like a purse of scent. Sometimes they were parti-
coloured like the York and Lancaster rose, which flower
is a miracle of nature in its miming of the diapers and
parti-colours of its age, and with its extraordinary
prophecy of the swashbuckler of the next generation
who was to blow out of those bold and insolent colours.
But for the most part the flowers were single and of one
colour, of the sort that could easily be held in the left-
hand while the right copied them in their true colour
into the pages of an illuminated missal. Also, there
were one or two chief months of scent, for the science
of delaying flowers was little known to them and the
tendency is for everything to burst out into flower in
the first two months of spring, leaving little for summer
except the redundant shapes of the trees and the eventual
harvest of cherry, apple, and pear, with, last of all, those
latest fruits hardly deserving of the name, for it requires
a frost to bring their qualities to perfection.

Every one of these fruit or flower-shapes is of a nature
that complies easily with their other canons of taste,
having the principles that they applied to the chief works
of building expressed in miniature but with no dropping
of its scale in details. Thus they reached to a homogeneity as complete as that of the Japanese, but which is
not so obvious to us because we have come out of it, and
are, therefore, still a little under its cloak and not freshly
set in front of that strange and recondite set of fancies.

So final was the fullness of all their forms that no other culture need ever have existed, so lacking is this in any memories from another, and so entire is its dependence upon itself. The little flowers, the fruit-trees, even the tame rabbits and the swans upon the moat, have been pulled by this happy coincidence into a harmony with their masters.

That same voice of water is sounding out of the lion mask into the stone pool below, and it is a cool song to such fiery lips of summer. The falling water hardly breaks the matrix but flows away in little blue ridges against the stone rim, making a perpetual and lapping music beneath that steady voice above.

Yet once more the cool transparency is figured into two snowy feet, and this same young lady sits at the fountain brim with her ankles and pale legs in the water. With one hand she holds up her clothes so as not to wet them, and with the other she pours rose-water from a jug into the cold and scentless pool of stone. One of the castle-towers shakes on the water and pierces into the little trees in its true self before it has reached the water-face; and to look at first the castle and then its towered reflection has an ineffable and mute sadness about it, as if you had consulted first the declining sun and then the dwindling sand of the hour-glass. The droning bells, truest answer to dying time, leaned out of their towers and gave a giddy emphasis to the vesper-hour which now sounded on other bells far away into the distance. The maze of fruit trees dropped one by one out of their gaudiness into the ghostly forms that they wear during the night, and the fountain and its lion-mouth were hushed and hidden away.

So every kind of life in this moment between day and

night fled into the lit mullions of the house that had just flickered into being, and the old abbey and the château d'O, from my next chapter, were reflected there, so far as I was concerned, with as much life as Susannah and the Elders had possessed in this tapestry that I unfolded in the apple-wood. And now these lighted windows took me back to the goose-village that I knew lay in front of their fire, and to the pair of shadows that I expected.

IV

A CASTLE AND AN ABBEY

NEXT day, the honeycomb morning filled the whole air. It stretched out in every direction save where its comb was cut into by the sharp line of a wall, or pushed back by the towers and sails of an avenue. The dark shadow below the wall felt cold and empty away from that almost animal warmth, while the trees made a sombre tunnel with their windows and the blown spaces between their sails just beginning to fill with the morning light. One-storied houses, low attics, step-tiled roofs, stood on either side of the road and showed no more life within them than a wood-fire could give with its thin, brackish smoke, for there were no children and no peasants about and there was a dumb and inert deadness of everything human. All down the street little files of white geese were waddling close on each other's footsteps, crossing from side to side and busily disputing such scraps as they could find with a few hens who from their hurried walk and the intentness of their gaze resembled the women shoppers at a bargain sale.

Little did the geese know, while at their social duties, the whole purport of life's mysterious kindness towards them, and that their whole happiness and contentment had been arranged so that death should reach them on the day it was least expected. The rare beings who set foot among them came to feed and supply their wants, though the sound of steps from its infrequency still caused some little alarm among them. But, on this occasion, it was a motor-car with its driver scattering terror before it that drove down their muddy pastures, stopped to take on board some other human shapes, and then started once more upon its course, going quickly out of sight, and, so far as the geese were concerned, out of mind.

Within a few seconds we were deep within that sombre tunnel of the avenue, though the road was now a shining river-bed along which we travelled at a great speed, reaching sometimes to a point of tension in our pace that made us appear to be standing perfectly still in the middle of the track, so absolutely motionless were the past and the future to either side of us. But then some particular tree-trunk on which the eyes had fixed as being immovable and unapproachable came suddenly with a violent swing, as if pulled, straight towards us, and then fell back again into its old place, but behind us. Time and distance became so many notches that we waited for and then at a convenient opportunity pulled past us and disposed of, so that it was a relief to the eyes and the nerves when the avenue came to an end in a decided and peremptory manner and we found ourselves in the full tide of sunlight beyond.

Vineyard and orchard mingled together without any prejudice to their fertility and the fruit hung ripely and heavily upon both. There was but this little difference in their manner, that the low vines, cut close to the soil, had a violent and twisted thrust into the air in order to hold up into the sunlight without their touching the ground those clustered and shining pyramids that they must have found, apparently, in the earth at their feet and straightway held in air as high as possible for rain to polish and sun to ripen and make sweet ; while the fruit trees had engendered their pears and apples from the direct mating of sun and rain among their boughs, so that these air-born and sweetened phantoms hung like a breath about the leaves until just this month of the year when the very accumulation of these light burdens shook down one and then another upon the grass, and those that remained turned from lightness to dying heaviness. Pears and apples were now so ripe that they fell at the slightest touch and a whole cluster could be scattered and thrown down with a wave of the hand to meet again but once more, at the cruel and stony lip of the cyder-press.

The morning became magnified into long days and no nights by the beauty of pear and apple wood. Whole days of poetry could be passed in their shade with the golden bread of sunlight and the crystalline rain for food. Out of the green heart of these orchard trees you could see nothing else except this wood of sisters, for each tree was as like to the next as a twin and the whole concourse of them were so many moving and nearly animate divinities, pagan goddesses that thrived in each other's blown shadow, and in this same gentle wind moved apple-breast and apple-cheek to that sleepy voice from the hills. But coming to the edge of the wood there were other factors just as beautiful, for a fast-flowing and cold brook ran between steep banks and held back the ranks of vines from the green walls of the orchard trees. This was the sword that Lysander and Hermia laid between them when they slept by this barrier

F

through the summer night. That sharp coldness and nothing more separated them, for all the winds and every sighing branch lulled them ; while those very boughs that then breathed out sadness over Demetrius and Helena now showed their fruition in bowed branch and loaded vine. Yet the same chill stream ran to-day between orchard and vineyard, and the outermost apple could but roll into the water and never reach that other bank of grapes.

Whole days could be spent between these two divinities, watching their maturity come to them and seeing their daily changes down to the night that at this time of harvest-moon was a mocked and burlesqued day with the sun aped at his duties by the barley-god who could ill-conceal her pregnancy in that fiery armour. When day came again they would both shine together for a space from opposite ends of the world until his steady climb trampled her into the Western marshes and she went down without a trumpet out of the sky. Soon after this the sun had mounted so high that only his general radiance and none of his beams came down through the thickened orchard roof, and there was nothing to do in the immovable silence except sleep and dream of the soft hands and strange hair that might waken one in this sacred grove. But after the long and faunal noon the slanted rays came in again and woke one before the end and death of light, while that strange and obdurate comedian came out through another wing of the world from that into which she had disappeared, and once again mocked him in his declining strength. Time after time this happened till she changed into a deeper travesty, half negro-masked : and then wore the horns of deception as a mockery to his far-off strength.

Such were the hours born of minutes in that countryside. Later on, the eclogues and the oaten tunes of the
harvest sounded through the steep hours of midday.
They played on either side, and so far as the eyes could
see over gentle and rolling hills, for the corn held the
whole country in subjection and in its turn obeyed only
the sun, who raised its stature the better to see him
in his burnished armour, and the wind, who ran among
it and played in its ranks like a dog who runs, now and
again, into the shallow waves, chasing a bird along the
shores of the sea. These were the harvest's only interruptions until the day of slaughter dawned, when, just
as the sky kindled, the work of massacre began and all
the gilded and trembling corn-heads were struck down,
making no resistance. They were tied together in their
companies and left standing, shackled, upon the battlefield until the rising of the harvest-moon which held all
the colour the reapers could never take from their
prisoners when the mill-stream ground them into pale
flour. To-day the slaughter was but begun and the
corn still stood in its massed ranks so far as the eyes could
see, while the oaten pastorals sounded with but a breath
among the corn-stalks. A few feet away, standing at
the edge of this cut honeycomb, where the reapers had
changed their direction and gone over the brow of
the hill, a little fistful of wind would fall about a stone-
throw ahead in the field and at once with that encouragement the bearded corn blew together and its chattering,
dimmed voice came through the still noon to our halt
at its frontier. This was the only interruption from all
that golden horde, and for the rest they stood there in
their millions waiting for death to strike them down,
quite helpless from excess of numbers, and ignoring the

first scythes that flashed out as they were lifted under the hill where we could only see the brandished swords and not the reapers who held them.

On the slope of the next hill there were some large rocks coming out of the corn, and this was the first sign of an entire change in the whole country, for the corn-fields came to an abrupt stop, and on the other side some stunted trees grew that became a forest filling the whole valley and running out of sight. There were no poplars lining the road and making it into a dark and sombre tunnel like that down which we had travelled on first leaving the town; instead, the trees stood back at some distance from the road, and lay not too close to each other, so that it was possible to see a great way down into their depths. Very soon it seemed as if we had never passed through anything else except forest, so complete was their dominion.

We were on our way to a castle and a ruined abbey. Both of these were in different clearings in the woods, and we hoped to reach the first soon after midday and the second some time in the evening on our way home. We had passed several little villages identical with that from which we had started, save that these were smaller and even more silent and deserted. The day, although already doomed by the crossed meridian, seemed as though it must always last in its freshness and beauty like the sweetest smelling flowers cut close to the soil that are unhurt by this semi-death and have a more piercing fragrance for their last evening. An acute and pleasant melancholy filled these last hours, for there was hardly anything they called to mind that was not enjoyed and finished, or else impossible and never to be. The golden bowl in which we were living must surely be

broken before sunset, or we must reach to its rim and
see what lay beyond! Meanwhile, these more bitter
sort of conjectures, which amounted to criticism and
complaints at perfection, were netted and brought back
to us by the trees that were so beautiful in themselves
as to let the mind think of nothing else except their
high and dazzling towers, or the reflections these would
throw in water. Thus we were confined strictly within
one kind of world, subject only to its changes and to
what variations these could attain to upon their quiet
and peaceful material.

Goose village after goose village had come and gone,
leaving those slow white fleets in complete and undisputed possession of their ponds, to, or from, which they
were all the time repairing for planned and deliberate
regattas. Few men and fewer women were to be seen,
for they were busy about their various harvestings till
nightfall, and in the wide fields were outnumbered and
only visible when their voices could be heard calling to
each other. Yet they must have developed the extraordinary richness of the country by concentrating upon
first one and then another of the many harvests. One
week they would be in a band about the cyder-press,
and the next be sowing corn on the furrowed fields while
they kept the rooks away with a posse of scarecrows.
When the time came for the geese to be killed the
whole population, men and women, would be in and
out of their houses all day long busied about the slaughter,
but that day was not yet come and lay far ahead in the
heavens; indeed, it was always heralded some days in
advance by the goose-feather snow that mantled the
roofs and the window-sills when the grey morning
broke. To-day the villages were deserted and there was

not a footfall to be heard except that webbed and strict procession.

We had come, by now, a good distance from our starting-point, about twenty miles, which up till a century ago would have meant at least a day's journey. The place we had started from, the bedrooms we were to go back to that same evening, were unrecognizably remote, too far away to be worth considering in their relation to the present. We were without a home, in a strange immediacy of air and time that could be anchored and tied down more easily to the past than to the kind of present associated with being back at the hotel, ringing for the chamber-maid, and walking into the dining-room for dinner. It was better to keep return out of mind and to think of a battered stone wall for shelter and of one of its fallen pieces for dining-table.

A few roofs came into sight, and in a moment or two we were in another village street. Although, as I have said, these villages are all the same, they have in themselves some strange and pointed details that they share in common with all other villages over a great stretch of country; in fact, up till that region where big hills lift their rolling, heaving bosoms out of the sea of plain. The roofs of the houses, and more particularly the roof of any barn or farm-building, are pitched and slanted at an angle that makes the height of the roof out of all proportion to the height of the building. This is not so much, as has been suggested for the roofs of their churches, in order to let the snowfall slide off and prevent it from collecting and breaking down the roof with its solid weight of massed swan-down, as to make a convenient shelter to keep the logs dry that they saw up

during the winter for firewood. Sometimes in the high
lofts of a barn whole stacks of straight young trees can
be seen tied into bundles and standing up in their natural
position with the denuded stems reaching, at the point
where their leaves should have been, into the blackened
daylight of the dark barn-roof. Whichever of these two
reasons may be the correct one for this abnormality,
the high and stilted roofs of the villages make their chief
characteristic and even seem to leave a mark in other
traits of this particular race of men. The elongation of
their loaves of bread, the slanting angle at which they
cut their rolls into slices, and, more still, the sloping line
of their handwriting, would seem to be symbolical and
characteristic of the people who dwell beneath these
steep roofs. There is even a kind of nervous passion for
exactitude and arrangement expressed about these details,
for it is to be felt here, as it is about their actual character
as a nation, that everything being tidily arranged, their
affairs will prosper and they will be contented, whereas,
one log displaced from its bundle, a letter ending dis-
courteously and without the accustomed formulas, or
a badly-cooked meal, may plunge them into a nervous
despair which can be the prelude to something disastrous
and final.

Just at the end of the village street a little lane led off
at right angles to the road and was edged with a strong
white wall that ran back, eventually, into a semicircle
filled with fine iron gates. A plot of grass parted by a
gravelled drive came forth, and the eyes ran along this,
through the wrought-iron patterns to the Château d'O,
beyond.

The gates were opened and the castle lay some hundred
yards in front, holding itself out of the waters of a mere,

though on the drawbridge side that sheet of water had thinned into a moat. It was hung, as such a castle should be, with turrets, and had been built in the century one might have expected of its romantic queerness by a family, long ago extinct, whose name was the letter O. Since then it had passed through many hands, and the present proprietors were staying away, which gave more leisure and greater opportunities for its study.

Walking round the banks of the mere to see all sides of the castle, we came to a point where the fortifications, obviously considered to be unnecessary at this distance from the shore, ceased altogether, and the house broke into a row of quiet arcades, while there was quite a green lawn formed out of the island quay, and the pillars of the arcade were clustered heavily with flowering creepers. In fact, the family probably had tea out there in the summer, and sat and talked in the arches during the summer night. Just opposite to this, two sketching-stools were pitched and the backs of a man and a woman could be seen who had reached that preliminary stage of drawing where the pencil is held up in air to apportion the scale of objects.

They looked round on hearing footsteps, and I at once recognized them, while their curious looks towards me showed they remembered something. After we passed, I could hear them talking together and I expect they were searching their memories, thinking through the hundreds of children they had taught.

So here were these very scenes I remembered in charcoal and lithograph set up, and, as it were, hand-coloured by nature. And there, in front of them, sat Miss Corder and her brother, building up, and then demolishing with bread or india-rubber. There were two pasts and two presents, and from inside this double rainbow the colours were so many glasses to magnify or diminish.

The sighing brakes, the turbaned bulrushes, these made the setting for this water-castle, just as much as a crane does for a Japanese screen. For the snow upon green pines we have the sunlight flashing off those wet reeds and the thousands of little blue ripples broken into golden crests as they move.

But so far as the two artists were concerned it was all dead, as stony dead as hard pencil and hard paper. No amount of drawing would ever fill one of the turrets with a live person, even in so unromantic a shape as one of the present proprietor's servants.

Heaven only knows who the d'O family were; their history is a little string of bucolic marriages and bucolic births, until death diminished them all together and left nothing except this castle and their name as a curious plaything on account of its proud and simple spelling !* Now it has become just an object to draw, like the upturned boat and the fishing nets, the group of fishermen and the sad coast, or the group of elm trees and the mill-stream. It climbed with all its turrets out of the lake in the middle of mile upon mile of that extraordinary and diverse harvest I have described in the process of arriving at its gates; and where everything else was turned to profit it alone had no life and was a bundle of old bones. Yet it was easier to sketch than cornfield or orchard and had as much poetry stored in its decaying cells. But nothing could be done about it; the castle had to be looked at and then passed by. Whereas I did not appreciate the two sketches I saw being made, it seemed to me that the castle photographed

* The last of the d'O was one of the mignons of Henri III.

remarkably well ; in fact, it was a postcard off a revolving stand in a tobacconist's shop that gave me the idea of hunting it down upon a map and setting out to see it. In fact, a camera eye prevailed upon a Corder eye, and I don't suppose that they ever felt so uncomfortable, when upon a sketching tour, as in front of a postcard stall. Crocketed and pernickety did the castle look in their sketches, with all the sombre fussiness of the fifteenth century expressed in its angles and corners, while the sepia finish of the postcard was kinder to the troubled contours and left them alone without any emphasis upon their quaintness.

We ate our luncheon upon the banks of the lake and gave all the crumbs to some swans and to a tribe of ducks with richly variegated chests and throats who had about them something of a municipal air as though they should be pensioned off on a comfortable permanence to some duck-pond in a corporation garden. Their eager quacking caused the artists, once more, to glance in our direction, and then it was time to be off again and to look, for the last time, at this castle rising out of the lake.

We were back again among the harvests and were soon in a bigger and more broken country. There were no orchards, no cornfields, and only vineyards, that thrive particularly upon a burnt and reddish soil such as this.

I began thinking of the two artists once more, for nothing is more strange than a sudden renewal, such as this had been, of something of fifteen years ago, at the most curious height of childhood. I wondered if they had managed definitely to tie me down to any one particular child they could recall, and, still more, as to whether I should ever again set eyes upon them. The towers of the water-castle, the wide expanse of the mere, and the green brakes of reeds, made a sad scene of music for their memory and they faded out upon those sluggish undertones.

We must be near the abbey.

Away in the tumbling, wide country there was a conical hill covered obviously with a town, because many roofs could be seen, and at its top the hill became more pointed still from the dark bulk of some great building. It was a long way removed in spirit from the rat-tail shoes and steeple-hats of the Château d'O, and the burnt slopes of the hills answered with a loud and martial ring to the sunlight upon their bare flanks. Presently when the town had loomed high enough above the road to throw a shadow and hide half the sky, the only trees in the whole landscape, some poplars, came into sight along the banks of a stream, and out of their clouded branches a tower could be seen. This was the church of St. Pierre just outside and below the town. At each corner of the tower there stands an archangel sounding some dire and final proclamation by trumpet into the varying winds, and the sky is for ever marching its torn flags past one or other of those alarms. Below, there is an arcaded porch of astounding beauty and invention leading to an interior of little interest. Nevertheless, there are signs in the cold stone within which justify the arcade outside and the four archangels above, for in the abbey of Vézelay (4) there are the finest sculptures in Europe.

This latter building has that supreme merit of not attempting a façade, for most certainly no such experiment could hope to succeed, as an introduction to what lies within. There is the more reason for this because the inside takes the form of an interior within an interior, there being a great porch in which processions were to collect and form before they marched through the sculptured door into the church beyond. This doorway is the most wonderful triumphal arch ever invented or conceived, for it has none of the dead and unbelieved-in deities, or the banker-journalist Cæsars, of Rome portrayed upon it, but every species of triumphal and intoxicating march has been worked into its stone until the sacred figures themselves tread and dance to those fiery measures. There is nothing to compare with it ; the most famous Romanesque work of its kind, the Portico da Gloria in the Cathedral at Santiago da Compostella, betrays too clearly the vaunted twenty years' labour expended upon its details by the sculptor, Maestre Mateo, when compared with this swift and live-born masterpiece.

If the doors beneath are wide open the white vessel of the church can be seen beyond, filled with a clear and chalky light that shows every detail as though snow lay heavy on the ground outside. The capitals of the columns and the sculptured bosses high upon the walls beneath the windows are, each and all of them, on the same plane of energy and invention as the finest poetry. Each one of the capitals is treated as an object to be looked at from every angle so that there can be no excuses and no weak moments in its circumference. Its scene, therefore, has had to be considered as a fan that never shuts and the whole story told without waste words in a language easily to be understood. So great were the sculptors who worked here that it is next to impossible to choose between the different capitals, not one of them has been hurried, not one of them has been lingered upon. The first sight of these marvels evokes an absolutely new feeling and new atmosphere, and one far removed from that which even the finest Gothick art produces with its stone laces and stone brocades.

I have visited nearly all of those old, black steam engines standing in lonely squares like waste machinery in a railway-yard, and in the whole lot of them, Rouen, Amiens, Notre Dame, Sens, Bourges, there is nothing to think of for a moment with the hours in which Vézelay can be remembered. Their façades, window-lace gone black with age and dirt, the spiky chapels near by (St. Maclou at Rouen), the damp and cheerless interiors, the slave-work of their intricate sculptures, they belong to a dead and soulless age contrasted with these other days of music and poetry. Chartres and Beauvais come far outside that orbit and are exceptions, being master works of science and engineering; while Chartres has the finest sculpture after Vézelay, and the most beautiful glass in the world, and Beauvais is on such a scale that it can really intercept and divert the winds. Let us forget those blackened and damp ruins and only take out of them those two that we have just excepted!

Two hundred years after the building of Vézelay the French were producing just that kind of apposite and self-characterized work that I prophesied a few pages back from their steep roofs and slanting handwriting. The flying porch tied on to that astounding brick castle, the Cathedral of Albi, work like that at Vézelay of a golden age; the flying porch of Louviers, so often drawn by Cotman; the house of Jacques Cœur at Bourges; the chapel of St. Hubert at Amboise, where the spire is decorated with gilded stag's horns; the tower of Caudebec with its battlements pierced with gigantic words of praise; this is the mediæval decadence, pleasant to

study and perverse in its influence, if we would listen
to the same voices that condemn Bernini and his Italian
and Spanish followers.

For what our own eyes can see we have the best support
and proof in the tapestry and miniature painting of that
age. If, now and again in Flanders, or by the Palais de
Justice of Rouen, the modern buildings of Burma are
recalled, and the one kind of tortured crocket does not
seem to be far different from the other, it must be
remembered that in an age of such continual experiment
there was a great deal of failure mingled with their
success, and tapestry or miniature must be consulted
for proof of this contention. Those brand-new Troys,
or Jerusalems, possess a kind of beauty that runs directly
into poetry, and poetry of a green, sappy age, long before
the perfections of green leaf and nice metre. The
miniatures by Jean Foucquet that are preserved at
Chantilly, and the Livre d'Heures of the Duc de Berri,
at the same place, will show these different poetical
perfections at their highest point.

We are back again at the Château d'O ; but it is hardly
finished ; there is still some scaffolding about the turrets,
and the castle that we saw only this afternoon is magnified into a whole world of no other achievement save
this for wealth, or piety.

There are so many towers that the castle has become
an encampment of stone tents, and in their giant intricacy the effect that they give is more that of an ivory
carving, something worked down to out of the block,
than anything built up and laboriously applied, stone
upon stone, brick upon brick, out of the soil. There
are no gardens save those that are walled, and, except
for a few rose-trees, their idea of this kind of beauty is

a stone fountain, some low beds of simple flowers more wild than cultivated, and many fruit trees; of these latter, almond, pear, plum, apple, and cherry, grow in their spring clouds of white, pink, or red, at the appointed time and in their day suffer a disintegration that no cloud has ever known, and while they feather the ground with their eyed and honeyed snow-flakes the embryo fruit comes from the very mouths of that broken sweetness. These different archipelagos, standing beside their sister trees, or along a wall's stone coast, come into leaf one after another and are transformed into Djinns of the East who break out of the ground laden with gifts.

Meanwhile, beneath those boughs, the more lowly flowers are showing their brilliant coats against the grass, and all of them are models for the borders of a manuscript, being small enough to be held in the left hand while they are drawn and coloured with the right. The rose-trees can thrust up no higher than some lover's face held still in young arms, and the whole of this Hortus Conclusus divides itself into how many poems can be written upon green branches, loaded boughs, and the heavy air cloyed with a hundred mingled scents.

The tall, pale-haired men and women of the castle come through the portcullis on horseback, hawk on wrist, and they vanish into the wood's dim glades until a distant horn but deepens their mystery. Dark and swarthy peasants in their hoods are at work in the fields, under the keel, as it might be termed, of the towering castle above them upon its moat. They can be seen after this fashion at all their different labours for the sum of months in the year, while their lords, if not hunting, may be seen moving chessmen in a mimic tournament upon a chequered board, walking in that same autumn garden of nuded boughs, or sunk into a proper winter lethargy of feasting and piled fires. The red and white flames in the castle kitchen leap high into the hooded chimney and their velvet lips and serpent tongues turn them into a living and fanged bed of flowers more violently alive than any growing in the garden outside. By their light the scullions are turning great spits and lifting huge cauldrons for the feast, while a number of young pages in piebald hose wait by to carry them, who, in the words of Rabelais, will be whipped like green rye for a dropped plate or spilled gravy. The hangings of the banquet-hall carry that prospect of hard knocks and school severity into a positive battlefield of heraldry.

Such is a calendar of the months, and their slow and full rotation can be studied in many manuscripts, while those loaded days, for each day portrayed had to have a month of labour in it, have been poured into an immortal mould in Brueghel's pictures of the months, of which there are only four left in existence. Most wonderful of these is his famous snow-scene, standing for February, with the huntsmen coming down with their dogs from the hills, while in the late afternoon the villages in the plain below are just shutting up for the night, the labourers will all be home in their cottages, and the little boys sliding on the ice have come back to their mothers. The trees are trebly blossomed with the snow and so are the roofs and the whole landscape for mile upon mile down the Burgundian plain. The winters of the whole mediæval age between the time of Celt and Goth, and the days of Bourbon and Hapsburg, are here cast into a final and eternal form that requires nothing added and can allow nothing to be taken away.

Tapestry is a more hedged and cumbered poetry than this. It was never enough to tell one story at a time. But these are the master works of the North, as beautiful in their finest examples as the works of the best Flemish painters. They are another instance of the anonymity of nearly everything mentioned in this book, because, even when the designer of the cartoons is known, their interpretation into tapestry required an extraordinary invention of detail, and the flowers and little animals, very often the details of the robes worn by the figures, had to be supplied out of the weaver's mind during the long years required in their making. Thus no one person can ever be said to be responsible for the whole effect, and often the credit must have been divided, over a span of years, among as many artists as there were actors in the drama under construction. The patrons of that day reckoned the value of a work of art in terms of the amount of labour expended upon it, and, particularly where a set of tapestries was concerned, simplification was unheard of and would never have been allowed.

The steep, narrow composition of a tapestry, more often than not higher than its own length, serves to tighten and compress its tall actors. Their dresses are further elaborated into the stiffest patterns standing quite still before the eye, beside a plethora of little woodland flowers that in their happy lack of perspective are sown between the castles and the trees, and down by the fountain-foot among the figures gathered there. In their midst are two knights in plated armour with chain sleeves, and this pair of slow and clattering ghosts are but waiting for the herald's horn blowing into a nearer fanfare than the huntsmen in the forest to enter the lists and mount their armoured horses. Yet the

G

hunting party, but a few threads away, have gone a great distance into the acorn-wood, and there is a swineherd near them whose language will be so uncouth that they cannot understand him and must drop their questions as useless and go down the glade where the stag's last belling was heard. This will lead them at the end into some quilted hills with rocks where the stag can hide and never be found; or he may stand in the stream so that the hounds have no scent.

Even where the figures are fewer the elaboration is just as marked. In the history of the Unicorn, among the loveliest of all Gothick tapestries, the scenes take place in a tremendous depth of woodland; where the lady is playing her virginal the wild flowers are numerous as a bed of stars, and the unicorn behind its fence of wattles does not appear to be any more relevant to the design than the rabbits and the little birds and animals that are playing in the same glade. The Chatsworth hunting tapestries, and the Gothick tapestries to be seen in Spanish cathedrals, such as Palencia and Zamora, where they are so perfectly preserved and so clean and fresh in colour as to appear no older than the products of the Kelmscott looms, all of these bear out the same rules of elaboration; indeed, it is about the only field of art where the critic dare not condemn prolixity.

Coming out of these castles and forests we can move for one little moment right out of France and think of the amazing conceits and refinements practised elsewhere. After the bad realism of Claus Sluter at Dijon, and the kind of work for which Nuremburg was famous with Veit Stoss, Adam Kraft, and Peter Vischer, it is a remarkable experience to go to Burgos where the sculptures by Gil de Siloe go beyond any imagination

in their ability to combine the most solemn and austere
kinds of beauty with every sin of over-indulgence and
overacting. The Cathedral, by Juan de Colonia, and
the chapel that it contains with the tomb of the Constable of Castile, designed by the same artist and his son
Simon, would keep the pencils of Miss Corder and her
brother at work for ever, so endless are the intricacies
of worked grilles, spiral openwork staircases, carved
wooden doors, sculptured tombs, and the reredos, most
typical of Spanish inventions where religious art is concerned. In particular instances at Burgos a kind of
varnished or lacquered colour has been applied to the
carving, a most hazardous but successful experiment,
which is interesting if only because the elaborations of
Spanish Colonial Architecture, where the churches are
positively vibrating to the eyes with their Churriguer-
resque altars, instead of offending with too much gilt
as might be imagined, are more often treated in this
manner. Their gilding is sharpened with shrill touches
of metallic lustre, an effect which is obtained by mixing
the colours with a transparent varnish medium applied
over a ground of gold-leaf. In this way ruby and
emerald-green effects of great violence and brilliance are
procured ; and perhaps Burgos is the only place in Europe
where these effects can be studied. But, without leaving
this continent, architecture just as strange as that of
Mexico can be seen in Salamanca, at the Casa de las
Conchas, in Guadalajara, at the Infantado Palace, and
in the Manoeline abbeys of Portugal.

All such works seem to have been executed by laymen ;
the day of the monk-architect and the monk-sculptor
were over. If some person of another race than the
European were to go round in the dim future making a

study of the Gothick period, always supposing that these
remains still existed and that he possessed the power to
appreciate them but was ignorant of their history, as
we are of the discoveries of Maya remains being made
at this moment, he would, beyond any doubt, ascribe
them to a slave population working for a tall and fair-
haired race above them. Whenever in a fresco or picture,
on a window, or in a coloured sculpture, there appear
figures more richly dressed than their companions,
these are always shown with golden hair as though this
was the race both admired and obeyed by the rest. They
would appear to be few and yet all-powerful, filling the
position, perhaps, of the Englishman in India. We can
find, indeed, a supreme instance of this kind in the
Austrian rulers of Spain, who preserved their flaxen
Teutonic appearance by constant intermarriage, and
made by these reasons an abrupt and physical difference
between themselves and their subjects. But these days
of which we are talking were before the Hapsburg day
of power and the advent of the Landsknecht, which
latter kind of Teuton was to exert great changes in the
ideals of tapestry. From the moment this large and
bearded man of thirty, or thirty-five, years of age appeared
in history he seems to have been accepted as the canon
of masculine beauty, and he comes into tapestry to the
exclusion of the older and more wiry sort of hero. He is
in the battle pieces, the hunting parties, and the tournaments, of Charles V, shown everywhere in his striped and
waspish strength.

Then the field becomes more open ; there has to be
room for his manœuvres ; these woven histories become
more true and bare ; the clouds, always ignored before
this, take up a quarter, or a third, of the tapestries' height ;

and we find ourselves walking away from those giants
into that old and intricate forest from which we emerged.
We come back to the castle again, find little comfort
there, cross the moat once more into the woods beyond,
and find ourselves for the second time in that white and
chalky light of the church.

We have left those strange and wilful conceits; the
crowded tapestry blown forward, as though its figures
moved, by a sly draught; the spiral stairs riddled out
of stone; the tombs of petrified wax; the parapets
writing words on to the sky; the coxcomb men and
the aquiline, fair women; the sibilant, pithy eclogues
of their poetry; their extraordinary miracles over glass,
where they have projected visionary heavens and earthly
hells on to a sky that they have controlled and fixed;
their loaded and indestructible figures upon panel;
their carvings in wood that they have born into as many
figures as each tree had leaves, and gilded the whole of
them as they never could be by a summer day; their
warriors like iron insects that can never rise once they
have fallen; their extraordinary heraldry and pomp of
birth, inventing a whole sharp mythology from the seed
of the nuptial bed; the lions, leopards, castles, lilies, of
these fancy hazards, borne before them like sails upon a
stout mast; the steep towers of their safety in lily-
wristed lakes; we have left those deep and endless
poetries and come back into this clear and sharp answer
to the trumpet.

For, in 1146, St. Bernard proclaimed the Second
Crusade within these walls of Vézelay.

The moving feet of the crowd, and the heralds' horns
from outside the porch, blown as a warning of the arrival
of each paladin in order to make a path through the mob

for his armoured tread, these seemed to me to surround
and suffocate those two lonely stools, pitched now upon
the cold, white floor, careless of draught and damp.
And there they both were, sitting head in air, hewing out
a capital again and blackleading it on to fibred paper !

This peculiar pair of spiritual witnesses had contrived
their arrival at the very moment it was best calculated
to dispel any illusions that might have gathered during
their absence.   They were doomed to one's derogation ;
like the housemaid tapping with her brush in the passage
at the height of some poetical metaphor, when the
whole of that airy bridge between two worlds collapses,
and the point at which this happened, and many other
such points, could be marked with a red pencil through
the poet's work.   They were there, like the skull in pictures of St. Jerome, in order to remind one of mortality
and the vanity of all ambition, even in so airy and unsubstantial a form as poetry.   Their poverty ; the pathos
of my memories of them through those long years of
Fridays, enough in the case of Miss Corder to make some
three or four months, so I calculated, of that one day
alone ; the obvious enthusiasm and the evident difficulty of their work ; all these phases in them came out
the moment they were seen, and were sent, so it seemed,
expressly to humble my fancy.

From the other point of view, at the back of their
pathos, they were acting, not in my direction but towards those things of which I was thinking, as the very
hands of time upon the clock face.   Even while they
drew, the past receded a little further from us, and
between their glances at the object they were drawing
and the drop of their eyes on to the paper the hands of
time had changed a little ; the ship that we might

have seen with our eyes had moved just a few feet, but this took it below the horizon and it did not so much fade from view as definitely fall out of vision. They had come near to this point with their sketches, and by that much closer to myself. For I had been far enough away from them both in all conscience, but now they had come into my life again and they occupied this horrible station between myself and my imagination. But it was tempered because of their pathos with a kind of halo not so very different in tone from the aureole surrounding the other things of which this book treats.

So this was what the past was left for ; these were the reasons for that dead continuance! And it seemed to me that men would do better to burn their houses at death. But Mr. and Miss Corder had crept among these dead bones and were determined not to leave without the value of their adventure. This consisted, as I have said, in copying some of the splendid statics of the past, some of those strong towers of beauty, on to drawing-paper, according to the formula of their own spectacled eyes. Well, for all it mattered to me, this permission to sketch was a cheap tax on immortality, and I was off again on my own journey, quite enjoying, meanwhile, the feeling of this brake upon my speed!

To be back in this first master work, long before the very thought of tapestries, or fine and detailed painting —to be on the other side of all that interested me— enabled me to come back quickly to myself through those delights, or else to linger among them sure of a safe return into motor-car and the table d'hôte. I was both beyond and to this side of everything, and so the two sketchers could be left at work undisturbed, for, after all, it was their paradise as well as mine, and it was just the contrast in our interpretations of it that delighted me.

I wondered how much the externals of life had altered, whether the structure of men's faces was different then from what it is now. This must certainly have been so, though in some cases there would be people so amazingly like the hostesses, or the servants, to whom one is accustomed that it would be difficult not to treat them like those copies of themselves to whom one was used. In the same way, in a Latin country, a porter or a waiter in Italy or Spain will so much resemble some poet or painter one has met that it is hard not to expect the like intelligence from his foreign facsimile. On the other hand some of the people who came into this church will have been strange and incomprehensible even to their contemporaries. Swineherds out of the great forest, who came here perhaps but twice in their lifetime, will have spoken a dialect of so small a scope that no townsman, monk, or knight, could understand them, and the fierce bestiality of their faces will have exceeded anything devised by " Peasant " Brueghel.

As for the cripples or beggars of that time, we may feel sure that their terrible dramatic sense left them in no need of language. Neither, for that matter, did these sculptures want a title or a legend to them ; but just as I was wondering, if this be so, why my two artists had chosen to disentangle the sculptures and tie them down on to paper, I noticed them far away making towards the door, and following them at a respectful distance, for I hoped to see them walk away together, as I had so often seen them do before, they climbed into a motor char-à-banc and eluded this ambition of mine. There was a knot of other passengers taking their places, and I had only time to see that the destination of the char-à-banc was the same town to which I was myself returning before a typically noisy Frenchman " cranked " that spluttering monster and it lurched forward, carrying my two friends out of sight.

So I came back into the cold and white shell of the church for a moment, but found its interest deadened for me by my encounter, and so, leaving it for the last time, came out into the golden evening and started upon the road home. In a few minutes we overtook and passed the char-à-banc, but the noise and the dust together quite prevented my seeing them and I almost doubted their reality. Before very long we were back again among the droning bells and the fruit trees, while for the morning mist against the mullioned windows we had the evening shades creeping like ghosts towards us. And so we were beneath the same roof once more.

V

THE VISIT OF THE GYPSIES

THE first sound each morning is the rumbling of a horn. This is blown with thick and hoarse breath as though it were a conch-shell, fresh found, with all the water not yet shaken from its lips.

The snow has not fallen, but everything is frosty and indistinct across the moat. A pool of hounds is baying round a huntsman. Their red tongues and smoky breath can be seen. The distance comes clearer and there is a pool of deer under the antlered trees, but these are for ornament and not for the chase.

Everything stirs and is hurried. Slippers sound in the stone passage and heavy doors are unbarred. A man crosses the bridge carrying two wooden pails of milk. A scullion comes out from an archway to take them from him. Some mules are tied ready to the stable door, while the less hardy horses are harnessed within. By now, the hunting horn would seem to have perfected its sonorous and shrill cries. They are suddenly silenced, as though put away. But the chapel bell begins through the cold mist and the muting of that metal voice is more easily understood.

People are hurrying by. There is not a glass in the whole castle, or else we might see them in a mirror as they pass. To themselves this would be their own first revelation, for even vanity cannot stay long, or whenever

98

it pleases, in front of polished wood or above the shadowed water.

These are the ladies. They are all fair-haired, and the four or five of them less richly dressed have green gowns worked with different flowers. Their fresh mouths and fair, or blue, eyes betray them. That mantling of colour to those soft faces means that each is hoping to be taken apart from her companions into some quiet glade. Once there, her shy words and clothed steps will make this or that girl difficult to tell in the twilight from the green sleeves of the wood. But they are in attendance upon two queens or princesses.

One of these wears a dress with much gold thread in it and an embroidery of marguerites which we may take as a hint of her name. The other carries an enormous and towering head-gear and has a fine blue dress with the inscription, "Monte le desire," worked in golden letters upon it. Each is aquiline of feature and more haughty than the ladies who wait upon her, so that she seems entrenched and fortified in the splendour of her dress.

They are both so much alike that there is no doubt they are the same person.

Some Saracen gentlemen are to hunt with them. They wear a peculiar, chequered dress of woven cord, as tough and strong as armour, and over it a bright blue, sleeveless hunting robe. They carry javelins, wear turbans, and are to ride barefoot mounted upon camels. As for the Christian knights, they are bravely dressed as though to compete with this Eastern magnificence. One huntsman wears a blue, sleeveless robe, bordered by a band of alternate red and white squares, with sprays of flowers embroidered across the chequers. All of them

have strange shaped hats with something leafy and overlapping about their form, as though these were the heads
of men dressed to be like trees, or to hide for their game
among the bushes.

One young nobleman, who is leading three dogs upon
a leash, has a dress of incomparable beauty. This is
imaged on his right sleeve and shoulder into a device of
a cloud shedding drops of rain, or tears.

The whole year has been passed at the castle and there
has been a hunting party every day. It is not possible to
describe them all, for the narration would be a brake upon
the speed which is the aim and purpose of each day. But
this can best be symbolized by the feathered arrows flying
from the bow, and by the falcon who is as steady in the
sky as upon some unseen wrist and then drops like a
pointed stone upon his prey.

But the horn sounds again and the mules and horses
are led forth to be mounted. The ladies climb on to
their mules from a stone block, and the knights lift one
foot into the stirrup and leap proudly into the saddle.
They turn to look at the camels, who are made to kneel
down till the bearded caliphs are ready, but the camels
lift them like still statues and they are carried along with
the rest.

They have ridden away for the whole day, or, if we
please, for ever, for each day is such a twin to its dead and
unborn sisters that a day's hunting is equivalent to a long
life spent among the forest glades. The woods stretch
away for many leagues round the castle and every kind
of game is found in them. In the same way that we met
the queen, or princess, twice over in different dresses, we
must expect to find the various incidents of the hunt
shown side by side and as though in a continuous narrative.

It is a panorama celebrating the triumphs and romances of the chase, a simultaneous exposure of their histories with the true sequence left to be discovered by your own eyes.

It begins in the very shadow of the castle, for the lords and ladies have ridden away, all except one knight and his lady, whom we may imagine as kept here against their will by some affairs to do with the harvest just taken in. The gardener's and groom's sons have asked permission to go water-fowling in the castle moat. The boys have put a rough wooden ladder against a swan's nest full of cygnets. The parent birds have attacked them, and while one boy wrestles in the water with a swan the other has been pushed off his ladder by the flapping wings of the second bird. Another boy is taking off his stockings to go to the rescue, while a woman is belabouring the swans with a long stick.

Far away, beyond the castle, two more boys are raiding a heron's nest in a tree, while a maid-servant gives one of the brood to the knight and his lady, who have done with their business and come out to breathe the evening air.

Nearby, the same lady is seen, on another day and in a different dress, killing one of the birds with a baton.

The whole strangeness of that age has been reduced into a static and timeless dream by the sound of a water-mill with its sighs and sad crankings. It has tied everything in mind to its heavy tread that never hurries and never takes it any further, being merely a pointless exposition of an arbitrary measure, as meaningless as a live clock in an empty room.

But the miller's daughter steps out of the house and becomes part of the legend. One of the men, who has been fishing with rod and line higher up the river, comes to talk to her. The miller is away selling his flour, and there is no one in sight except a dunce shepherd who is busier playing his pipe than minding his sheep. As for the shepherdess, she dreams the noon away under a tree and has forgotten the clown who is her work-mate.

Suddenly the wind breathes out loud and water seems to pour for the first time, now it has been noticed, through the holes of the mill-sluice. Little flecks of foam drop from the prongs, as it were, of this comb that all the waters have to pass through, and this sudden life above the mechanical heart-beat of the mill shows the miller's daughter, lights her ruddy hair and incarnates all the tales of deserted places.

No two beings are too strange to find themselves neighbours in these trees; and hermit, dragon, monster, or the ghost of a great stag, may appear at every step and be too certainly true to need any proving.

All at once a horn sounds, mysteriously near, yet in the uncertain distance. It is answered over an arc of the near horizon of woods, and the instinct is to hide.

Now a couple, or more, trumpets blow a regular fanfare as though riding before a procession. It is a mournful and long-drawn tune, and the wind seems to scatter its blown authority as a warning of the forest and its perils. Everything is absolutely still, there is a sudden darkness, and then the storm begins upon the drum-like leaves, explaining that loud rushing of water through the mill-sluice, for such noises have their start in the stillness before rain comes.

Lightning powders the forest and the whole air, and yet reveals nothing against its whiteness; while thunder, crashing and jostling at the back, flings rain down through the boughs.

But the storm has lasted long enough to draw breath, and now a hundred horns from all round proclaim their own safety and ask for news of each other. The royal trumpets keep together like a bodyguard. Their pomp and massiveness of numbers must mean that there is a king with them, and his crown will be no further than the sumpter-mules. The huntsmen, to judge by their flourishes of brass, must have changed into armour. Horses' hooves can be heard, and the whole procession moves down the woods, frightening the wild animals by their noise as much as by the terrors of the storm. The reeds and rushes of the river bank tell them they have lost their direction, and they decide to stay here under the deep trees till it has cleared.

The mill is across the river, but the miller's daughter has gone like a ghost.

The patterned queens and princesses we must think of as dimmed till it is light again ; the spades and hearts of their dresses have faded out and left them. The noise of their trampling has stopped, for the horses are tethered, and this withdrawal of what served to explain the trumpets by some other mortal sound only darkens the mystery of those fanfares and forlorn calls.

For their alarms have never stopped, yet the trumpets sound with a mournful and threatening pomp, as though there was nothing but death to proclaim.

The great and fearful drumming has rolled away upon the wind, and now there is a long space between lightning and thunder. One quarter of the sky is falling in golden rain, the grass steams in the sun, a fantastic glass-like bridge springs across the valley. Shapes come out from the trees, a horn blows to rally them. The otter-hunt begins.

A nobleman, standing on the river bank in splendid, if inconvenient, dress, drives a double-pronged spear into an otter, which turns fiercely upon him with a second spear already embedded in its back. The master of the hunt winds his horn, sounding the " mort," and in his other hand he holds a long spear from the point of which an otter is dangling, while a pack of yelping dogs struggles below. Nearby is a group of lords and ladies standing against some holly bushes and young oak trees. A knight is talking to one of the ladies in green dresses, and he carries a ferret. Below them is a hollow tree-trunk with five or six pegs close to it that must be used to keep a net in place, as is done in rabbit-hunting with ferrets.

More thrilling still is the bear-hunt. This begins at the border of the forest where there are rocks rising out of the grassy soil. The sky is cloudy, with a deeper blue breaking some of its piled layers and more rain driving out of the West. A continuous line of foliage stretches under the horizon to show the forest's extent, and at either end of it there are castles. From one of them a party of hunters has come out on horseback and on foot accompanied by two of the ladies in green dresses.

It is another day, and perhaps another season of the year.

The bear is standing over a Saracen, who lies on his back with his legs nearly encircling the animal. He has pierced it with his scimitar and the point projects several inches from the animal's body. His Saracen companions have ridden up to his rescue on their camels, and more than one of their javelins are embedded in the bear's flanks. He is still further threatened by another hunter with a long lance. Near him, a man drags the cubs from their den in the rocks and a Saracen stabs them as they come out with his sword. A little bear-cub, looking

over his shoulder with an expression of agony, is trying
to shuffle away into safety. A group of lords and ladies
is looking on, and an Eastern princess sits on the rocks
above and throws down chalk flints at the bear.

The huntsmen are gathered by a blast of the horn and
the bear-hunt starts in an acorn wood. The animal is at
bay seated on his haunches, and while two dogs attack him
in front, a huntsman at the back tries to drag him from
cover. No sooner have the eyes taken this in than, but
an inch or two away, the bear is seen vanquished and a
prisoner.

He is being dragged forth by dogs ; one of them holds
each ear in his teeth and another dog from behind drives
him towards a huntsman who has levelled his spear and
is ready to kill him. After this, his dead body is disposed of,
and it can be seen lifted on to a pack-horse and led away
while a nobleman and two ladies look on.

They will pass by a little brook. This is crossed by a
rustic bridge, and on the far side, holding a dog-cord in
one hand and what seems to be a loaf of bread in the other,
stands the young nobleman whose shoulder and sleeve
carry that beautiful device of a cloud shedding drops of
rain, or tears.

He is talking to the lady with the huge head-gear and
the dress worked in golden letters with the words " Monte
le desire." Just behind her, and in attendance upon
her, is another lady in a splendid red dress lined with
ermine. A huntsman kneels in front of them, and his
dress bears the initials " A. H." in a spray of flowers.

The mystery of these devices is still further developed
when this same lady and gentleman are seen as lovers
meeting on horseback. Not only does her dress carry
that design of marguerites, but the trappings of her horse

H

are marked with the initial " M." Later on, their betrothal, or marriage, has taken place, and they ride off together mounted on the same horse.

The lady has been identified, because of these things, as Marguerite of Anjou, the wife of Henry VI of England, and these different scenes that have been invented for her are taken from the four Chatsworth hunting tapestries. They date from the middle of the fifteenth century and were probably made at Arras, although the name of their designer is unknown and it is only possible for expert knowledge to point to some resemblance between them and the miniatures in the Hunting Book of Gaston de Foix, now in the Bibliothèque Nationale in Paris

Nothing is known of their history. They were found in fragments at Hardwicke some twenty years ago, having been brought there, it is almost certain, when Lord Burlington's house at Londesborough, in Yorkshire, was pulled down early in the last century.

They are woollen tapestries, masterpieces of design and incident but carried out in an adequate manner far removed from the silken and golden triumphs of the art. So their interest, which is not essentially a matter of technique or detail, lies in the extent to which they interpret ideals of leisure, and for our purposes they are an imaginative fiction, no more improbable in their time than the situations in a modern novel, and with only the difficulties of perspective to make their truths impossible of realization before the eyes. They make, for this reason, a most interesting comparison with the hunts of Maximilian, woven some sixty or seventy years later and representing the alterations of taste over two generations.

The manly and bearded chests of the Renaissance are

there foreshadowed, portraiture is attempted, not too
many incidents may happen at one and the same time,
and persons and objects have sorted themselves out into
some approximation to those truths to which eye or
mirror can testify.

But, as well as the accidents of ignorance, the
Chatsworth tapestries have an intentional romanticism.
Just as the church had two servants, priest and monk, so
were there two interpreters of the martial spirit, the
soldier and the hunter ; hunting was a field for half of
the masculine virtues and a ground of practice for the
rest of them.

All these qualities are here displayed in this perpetual
and tireless hunt, continued over the four walls, as it
might be, of some great hall or banqueting-chamber
which is opened in this way into the four winds. And we
must, ourselves, start off from this headquarters or focus
for our movements.

The Royal Hunt passes down the woods again, but
this time its notes have an air of challenge and the
inherent menace hides behind it. This ancient, traditional pomp has something in it which strikes an
inherited importance and terror into the heart of the
beholder. It has a symbolic value of its own, the mere
sight or sound of which has its peculiar, unique hold upon
the emotions. The mitre of the priest and the handcuffs
on the prisoner's wrists, here are two more instances of
things which have this same, timeless effect upon one.

The hunting horn, preluding far in front of the main
body, announces the procession riding away into the
shadows. The romantic poets of a century ago throw
open their casements, pull on their doublets and comb
their long, troubled hair, for this is a dream come true.

There is only one other sound to compare in its power of mystery with the entire bodyguard of trumpets that now ring out together, flurrying the airs with their importance. This other sound is the first muezzin the traveller hears.

It seems to be the middle of a black æon of night, and is really the new-born light, weak and trembling, rising out of the cedar hills. The window can only frame the mewing, puny beginning of light, but that fanatical voice cries out from its tower, and now, far away, other voices begin calling. As the eyes look for them and see not one of them, the tall tree below the window dies like a ghost at dawn. All the snowy blossoms that made its beauty shake off the boughs in an instant, and then, before they reach the ground, open wings and turn into a flock of ibis flying away from their sleeping-place on the branches for the mud of the river bank where they spend the day. Just as this happens, the minarets and fretted roofs of Fez can be seen, and the muezzins are little more than specks upon the green towers of the mosques.

This happens night after night, day after day, and the very first thought it gives, fortified by the constant and identical repetition, is this. How must the voices of the early Moslems in their days of faith and power have sounded if even these threads of that tremendous cloak have such fire and colour ! What must the terror and assurance of each sunrise have been !

The Spanish and the Persian, those two ends of the Moslem world, worked their difference and their mirrored likeness into those few syllables. If the same snowy mountains and the same hot plains were true to them both, the one had its vaults of stalactite and honeycomb, while the other heaped the flowers of the garden on to the marble, or onyx, pavements and then fired them into permanence in the potter's kiln, thus procuring a more lasting and cloying sweetness, as though honey, the delicacy of the nomad and desert-dweller, was here stored up, not in the comb, but in the very flowers that held its essence.

The poet's Indian and Caucasian vales found in those few phrases an answer to the halcyon and nenuphar. The lotus pools, and the bright and beaked winds that played there, were here embodied in a more material truth than that of any song or poem. The languors of the misted air floated down from the thin, marble spires with some note, perhaps, that this was an alien creed set up by violence in a world of placid Hindu peace. But this was the decadence, the last and ultimate conquest of the faith, for its fierce, dire days were behind it.

All the Moslem world, kneeling to the East or West in their prayers to Mecca, lay between these two extremes. That sound, heard anywhere, once in a lifetime, can never be forgotten; even if the muezzin be a modern Turk in a cloth cap. The potency of its effect is certain and inexplicable, and its cadences have a mysterious import far beyond the few monotonous words they form.

So it is with the Royal Hunt. The trumpet calls floating on the wind have a mysterious, sombre melancholy, for this is the old prerogative, the timeless privilege of the King, a ritual unto itself and one far older than that of the Christian church. There is little stealth, for terror is the weapon driving the wild animals from their cover; terror, and a challenge to any creature brave enough to fight to come forth and meet its fate.

This, and something like a confession that the same thing may overtake the King fighting in battle if he meets his equal, is the message of those incessant flourishes and fanfares. But it is impossible to conjecture what varieties this same limited shape must have shown in its time.

The hunts of Napoleon III at Compiègne and Fontainebleau had about them something of operatic mediævalism. They started after guard-mounting in the courtyard of the palace, when the Cent-Gardes, or the Guides à Cheval, moved in slow time to the trumpet marches written for them by Rossini. He had retired for thirty years, and only pressure from dandies and epicures had persuaded him to break silence in these loud, brassy tones.

The Imperial hunts were fakes, or revivals, however curious this attempted resuscitation may have been, compared with the genuine, if dangerless, excursions that Louis XV undertook into the woods of the royal domains. Those were picnics and romantic episodes followed by suppers in panelled cabinets. Out of that gallantry there was little occasion to hear the furious belling of a stag on the edge of the castle moat all through the night. Such was the chance of the castellans in the Chatsworth tapestries, but their fanfares, already described, have to give place for antiquity to the Royal Hunts of the Greek Emperors, and to the Great Kings of Persia hunting the lion.

Then, they rode in chariots that galloping horses drew like rough platforms, or little floats, over the surf-like roughness of the plain. The weapon was a bow and arrow, and the stallions flew into battle with snorting nostrils and eyes that shot fire upon the tawny, slinking game. The trumpets were appropriately curt and roaring to summon help when the lion had sprung and the stallions kicked and plunged in a fight that their teeth and hooves sometimes won. The sand was as yellow as the lions, and in a circus-posture these huge cats, like a fire of sulphur, maimed and seared everything they touched.

The great King was bearded to his waist and had a hat as high above this, fixed like a crown and never moving, while his beard blew in the wind and speed and seemed to balance the forced poses of his body as the chariot was tossed to and fro in the fight. His hooked nose was an emblem of cruelty and a sign of his sway over an army of women kept prisoner in his palace. There was no other rich person in the country except himself, and his brothers and sons he poisoned or blinded as quickly as he could. No one withstood him but the lions of the desert, and his conquests of them were carved in stone to give him a religious sanctity. When he rode back from the hunt, his men wore the lion skins on their bodies, a paw on each hand, the mask above their heads, and the hind legs and tail as a saddle for their horses. It was a triumphal return, and an imperious summons on the trumpet drew the people from their houses as by command.

This tradition of lion hunting descended to the Byzantine Emperors. The much exaggerated art of that capital has received but little attention on its musical side, religious and military. The chanting at the festivals of the church, the tunes to which the soldiers marched, the popular songs of street and wineshop, these are more interesting to think of than their tiny churches, incessantly facsimiled, and their agglomerate convents. Their music must, too, have profited by the same accidents of ignorance which have helped their architecture into its popular degree of barbaric naïveté, for these are qualities that have a more ready success in music, where force of inspiration can conceal a great deal of technical ignorance.

Mosaic, the Byzantine art, is preserved to us in only one half of its scope, for nothing but religious subjects are in existence. But the Imperial palaces were decorated with huge mosaics celebrating the battles and the hunts of the Emperors. In these, the elaborate canons of formalism that governed their treatment of holy legend were not followed. It is said that the last, and to judge by his military exploits, probably the first Emperor over a long period of years to practise lion hunting was Heraclius (A.D. 575-642). This monarch, the scourge of Persian and Arab, was the first Christian feared by the Moslems, who, up to this point, had met with no opposition in their onslaughts upon Syrian, Egyptian, or Armenian. His lion hunts may have remained visible in mosaic even after the conquest of Constantinople by the Crusaders. They will have been the only works of art to compare in beauty with the four hunting tapestries from Chatsworth.

There were thousands of years of tradition behind them, for, if the Assyrian bas-reliefs were buried in the sand and forgotten, the Sassanian Kings of Persia had hunted after this same manner until the time of Heraclius. Their trousers, so strange a sight after the Greek and Roman world of toga and kilt, the cloaks flying from their shoulders, their steep and terrible, swollen-looking hats—distended like the body of an octopus, or as though the high wind from their speed had inflated this curious balloon-shaped object worn above their diademed foreheads—the filleted hair blown back

in curled ringlets by the wind, the dressed and per-
fumed beard, all these can be seen in the bas-reliefs by
Lake Van, and they form the greatest works of sculpture
in the world.

Some element of them will have entered into the
mosaics. In their rendering of the lion hunt the Greek
mosaic worker had certain advantages rising directly
out of his material. The glittering plain, not quite
desert but sanded as thickly as the circus by dust storms
out of the hot South, lent itself naturally and admirably
to the indispensable gold ground of mosaic. And so
did the stiff, brittle plants of the plain, as much like the
cactus as these fasting ascetics could make themselves
before the iron men of Mexico spread all over the world.
Then, thickets of aloe and cactus came to fulfil the Greek
landscape. Groves of statues, built up piecemeal and
as easily lopped off, limb by limb, grew on the rocky
plains and on the stone hills. The gods and heroes of
that naked world cannot be imaged in the mind without
this hard echo to their beauty of form. But in the later
Greek mosaics, at Monreale, for example, this thing
wanting from the old world, until America was found,
has been remedied by the fig-tree, the date-palm, and
the ordinary palm-tree of the South. So the plants of
the plain were sufficiently hard and dry to match its
yellow glitter with the gilt manes of the lions crouching
in their lair.

We may think of the scene as rendered like a Persian
triumph, for Heraclius, that real milestone of an Emperor,
was also the last Roman to ride back in a circus procession
from his campaigns. On certainly one occasion he was
drawn in a chariot by white elephants, and in the mosaics
of his lion hunt there will have been the same emphasis

on the return of the hero. The plains of his victory, and his battlefield with the lion, shared the same clouds, and ran their waters through the same deep-hollowed chasms. The lion-victim wore the long locks which were the mark of royalty with the Persian Kings, and his warrior waist, and the majesty and strength of his arm that struck down the enemy like a mace, all of these attributes will have been rendered in the grained and gilded ground of mosaic.

Its little cubes were bolder and not so fine as the threads that tapestry is made of, but the mosaic work is more broad and confident. These mosaics of hunting will have been the only works comparable to the great tapestries of the chase and they must have shared many points of beauty with each other. The landscape, and the whole surface of the known earth, where towns were so small and such an unimportant aggregate, was nothing but a great reserve teeming with game. The rivers were full of fish, that twisted and jumped in their pools like springs of steel, the trees were boughs of birds, and all the woods and coverts were shields with deer hiding behind them.

It was in a southern part of this that the Greek Emperor hunted ; while its misty and frosted regions were threaded into these hunting tapestries.

The horns blow for ever, and the woods are haunted by a very different race of ghosts from that of the ilex and myrtle woods of Italy. The King and his ladies are shut away as a pack of cards in some close and secret grove of trees. There are castles all round to retire to and to come out from. At any moment, with a long and lingering blast, the diamonded and spaded court may ride out of the storm that has hidden them. Their flourishes

come out of the ferned valley, so deep in bracken that
the heads of men cannot be seen. So some, at least, of
these phantoms have become materialized into permanence, and here in these tapestries there are four
hunting scenes that have a never-ceasing truth, and are,
therefore, always in progress and have never stopped.

For a rest from them it is necessary to find some
tapestry with a quieter motive, and there could be no
choice more ideal than the Baillé des Roses. This is the
" verdure " tapestry in its most beautiful achievement.
The scene is neither room nor wood ; but is formed by
wide vertical strips of red, green, and white. It has been
cleverly pointed out by Mr. G. L. Hunter that this
scheme of decoration suggests the treatment of the walls
in Jean Fouquet's miniature, at Chantilly, of the trial
of Jean, Duc d'Alençon, in 1458, at which Charles VII
presided.* He also explains the ceremony that this
tapestry is meant to depict. The Baillé des Roses was
a homage paid by the peers of France to the French
Parliament. This homage consisted in the giving of
roses. The peer whose turn it was to make the gift had
all the chambers of the Parliament hung with flowers
and sweet-smelling herbs. He gave an elaborate breakfast to the officials of the Parliament and then went the
rounds of each chamber, having borne before him a
silver bowl full of roses, pinks, and other flowers, either
natural or made of silk, one for each official.

Such was the actual ceremony, but it is idle to pretend
that the French Parliament, or anything to do with
it, is represented on these three panels of tapestry. The
ladies who are so integral a part of the design are, in

* It may be noted, too, that red, green, and white were the colours of Charles
VII of France.

themselves, enough to contradict this assumption if it is taken literally. So, may it be presumed, is the presence of a tame monkey holding a cat in the lower left-hand corner of one of the panels. Nor can these scenes, though they may have some points in common with the fashion of decorating a room by hanging it with striped material, be taken as showing any interior typical of the period.

These tapestries are really a romantic and chivalrous homage. The ladies and gentlemen are in the finest costumes of their period, about the middle of the fifteenth century. Their dresses have been laced and belted to make them look as slender as possible, and they wear pointed shoes and large hats that accentuate this elegant slimness. It is a party in a rose-garden.

As the same authority on tapestry remarks, the figures and the rose bushes have been bent back into the plane of the ground, and then the whole ground has been tipped forward into perpendicular. The result is the elimination of one dimension, and this solves the most important problem in the designing of tapestry. Its solution is the result of a clever trick, and is not merely the result of knowing no better. In the finest Persian miniatures, the silvered pools so often portrayed in garden scenes are rendered absolutely flat as though drawn on a ground plan, so that a figure bathing in a pool is shown in horizontal perspective and appears to be floating on the surface of the water. Here, in the Baillé des Roses, there was skill enough in the weaver's hands to draw the whole rose garden fading into the distance and to place the knights and ladies in correctly diminishing perspective. But the necessary conventions of tapestry have been realized, and there has been no attempt to make this scene into a literal rendering of probability, into an enlarged miniature or book-illustration.

What little distance is necessary is shown in a curious fashion by a heightening or lowering of the position of each figure. Even then, they do not seem to have climbed any higher into the design, but a most peculiar effect is given, for a parallel to which it is only possible to think of the old Drury Lane pantomimes, where Jack climbing the beanstalk, or Aladdin looking for his cave, was portrayed by a figure moving slowly, or hardly moving at all, against continually changing scenery that gave the illusion of great distances traversed. In the Baillé des Roses, the knights and ladies seem to be dangled in exactly their correct positions. They cannot be moved ; but their background, the wide strips of red, green, and white, can be endlessly pulled past them. It has ceaseless and never-repeated variations, like a limitless stretch of wall-paper unwinding its rolls, and while this varies, and is yet never very different, the figures require no movement, for the leaves and branches lend them this illusion.

In all, there are three panels of this tapestry based on similar motives, but one of the panels shows figures more elaborately dressed than the others. In the middle stands the lady in a long, sweeping gown and high, divided headdress that falls in immense lappets over her ears. She has taken a briar of roses in her hand and has just given a spray from it to one of the gentlemen by her side, who holds his hat round with its inside showing, so that the blossoms can be seen where she has put them. He wears a kind of skull-cap under his hat, and has a short coat, patterned with flowers, pleated and divided like the shortest skirt to show his long, thin legs as far as the thigh. Fine rat-tailed shoes still further exaggerate

his length of limb. His companion, on the other side of
the lady, also holds a rose-tree in his hand ; his other
hand is thrust into his belt ; his heavy, coiled hat is on
his head, and he appears to be waiting till it is time for
the lady to pick a rose for him.

He stands behind some of the rose bushes and in front
of others. From the position of his feet there is a rose-
tree to either side of him. Another tree, he clasps, as I
have said, in his hand ; its roots are on a level with his
waist, and it is one of its upper branches that the lady holds
while she gives some of its flowers to the gentleman on the
other side of her. Then its branches trail away above
their heads. Far down below, at the feet of this other
man, is the tame monkey holding a cat, which I mentioned before as a contributory proof to the vague and
imaginary subject of this tapestry. It is down below,
and at the same time is shown small, and as though
distant from the figures of the lady and the two gentlemen.

In fact, the whole scene, with its curious arrangement
of striped and ribboned background, has the appearance
of figures seen on a mown lawn, where the machine has
pressed the grass in two directions by its passage, giving
it two tones, or colours, in this process. Figures
standing upright against this, and seen from a point on
the lawn itself, with a great expanse of grass framing
their bodies and continued high above their heads,
would be a true equivalent to the strange system by
which these effects have been evolved.

There is something exquisitely beautiful, in itself, in
the thought of so much work, and so great an amount
of ingenuity and obvious delight in its application, being
devoted to perpetuating anything as transitory as these
scenes of the Baillé des Roses. In itself it is but a couplet,

or a catch of words, with hardly space enough for an image to form.

It was the first leisure the world had known for a thousand years. But now we will turn away from this elegant vacuity, this afternoon in a rose garden. Sword and trumpet are still hung upon a tree ; but the pastoral poetry of the age blows its pipes, and builds a low fence of wattles for the lambs.

Their poets had never heard of the Sicilian meadows, of haunted groves with hollow words coming from the cave-mouth, of leaves that whispered subtle messages. Of the shores of Naples, where Virgil was buried like a god above the crackling sands, they were only told he was a wizard, had heard of the castle and the enchanted egg, but knew no more of him than this ; therefore, their pastoral scenes have a more true and less affected poetry about them.

We can take as instances two panels of tapestry ; one, the sheep-shearing in the Brussels Museum, and the second, the wood-cutters in the Musée des Arts Décoratifs at Paris.

The first is the most simple of ideas. A shepherdess and two shepherds are sitting in a wood of young trees by a wattle-fence, on the bank of a gentle stream. The sheep-dog, only sinister note in the whole afternoon, is gnawing a bone. A bulrush, and some tall flowers on the near bank, bridge over the water and break against the grass and the shepherdess's gown. The younger of the two shepherds holds a sheep close to his knee while he clips its fleece ; the elder of the two, probably meant to be his father, cuts a piece from a loaf of bread and hands it to the shepherdess, who is about to give crumbs from it to a lamb. Behind, under the trees, five or six sheep wander, cropping the grass, or feeding off the young, green shoots of the trees.

This is the most gentle of pastorals with hardly a mention of love in it, except, perhaps, a tacit, or even married, understanding between the younger of the two shepherds and the shepherdess. Had it been Greek or Roman, this poem or picture, however we like to consider it, would have taken full advantage of the occasion; and the posturings of the naked ephebi, supple, oiled gymnasts in a land of rocks and goats, would have twisted this whole scene into the kind of amorous opportunity that they loved.

Here, the whole conception of pastoral poetry differs from the ancient; in fact, it has begun all over again and is slowly working out its own scale of value and effect. The shepherds and shepherdess are symbols of industry; they are humble and hard-working, secure in their own family ties, and working, since lambs are a part of it, at a sentimental, even maternal, trade. To the people of the Low Countries wool was the great staple of life. They owed their wealth and security to it, and the highest order of chivalry, the Knights of the Golden Fleece, were instituted by Philippe le Bon as a romantic tribute to this source of their income. All the arts owed their flourishing condition to the wool trade; the Netherlands were crowded with cities; huge churches and prosperous private houses rose up because of it; while, as for England, where a great part of the wool came from, every beautiful mediaeval village in Gloucestershire or East Anglia was built from the proceeds of these clippings. Prosperity depended upon simplicity and dutifulness among the shepherds; we find them imbued with these qualities and far removed in spirit from those

Arcadian forms with whom the ancient gods came down
to play.

In the second tapestry, the labour of the wood-cutters
is shown on a much larger scale, with more accessories
and greater detail. At first sight, the subject and its
treatment are that of one of the roundels to be seen in
the calendar of an illuminated missal, where each month
has its typical employment and for November or
December peasants felling trees are often chosen. But
the wide spread of the design, beautifully balanced as to
its central group, and with subordinate figures filling
important positions in the extreme corners, means that
this was no slavish copy of someone else's inventions but
an entirely original conception.

There is the inevitable castle, built, this time, half
across a river and with a mill-house and mill-wheel not
far below. Another castle, or fort, lies on the horizon,
and the river valley has been given various signs of
population. But all the rest of the tapestry consists of
wood-cutting and nothing else.

A heavy cart and the loading of it with logs is the
centre of the whole scheme ; a man stands in the cart to
take them from the three or four foresters who lift and
give them to him. On the right and at the top, men are
sawing the trunks or trimming them with hatchets ;
half the wood has been cut down and this is how the castle
and the mill-sluice can be seen. On the left stand two
men. One of them is the overseer and holds a hatchet
with its blade on the ground, the other must be the owner
of the wood, or the timber merchant. He is well-dressed,
but far from aristocratic in appearance, for this tapestry
has put chivalry far into the background where the castle
lies, or else the dwellers in it are too proud to come

1

out and take an interest in the menial occupation of felling trees.

The visibility of this tapestry has been most admirably considered ; the figures are far less crowded than in almost any other tapestry of the age, less so, indeed, than was usual for a hundred years to come. The whole composition must have been the work of a very considerable artist ; indeed, this thing of a century before the time of Brueghel has much resemblance in spirit and style to the paintings of that master.

In direct contrast to this bustling autumn scene are such tapestries as the set of six panels of the Hunt of the Unicorn that came from the Château de Verteuil, between Poitiers and Angoulême. For many hundreds of years they hung in this castle and were the property of the La Rochefoucauld family. Four of the panels date from about 1480 and were woven at Tournai, or by weavers of Tournai training ; the other two were made later, in France, and show Renaissance influence.

The letters A and E, the latter reversed, tied together with a tasselled cord in the corners and centre of the tapestry, and on the collars of some of the dogs, must be the initials of the people for whom the tapestries were made. They have not been identified, but must, naturally, have been connected in some way with the La Rochefoucauld family.

The subjects of the panels are the start of the hunt, the fountain, crossing the Charente, the unicorn wounding a dog, the death of the unicorn, and the unicorn in captivity : and of these the first and the last are the two more modern in origin.

This fabulous animal of the hunt does not appear in the first piece of tapestry, where everything is preparation and the game has not been sighted, but in the second scene it is surprised in the act of drinking and pursued until its death, while in the last of all it has been resurrected and is shown as a prisoner. The choosing of this legend, and the whole circumstances in which it is set out, have for their object that security by inheritance which was the strongest part, and the cause, of chivalry. It would have a particular appeal to a great noble and his lady who wanted to symbolize the sanctity of their marriage.

The unicorn, in mediaeval tradition, runs to put its head only in the lap of a snow-white virgin, so that the animal in itself is symbolical of chastity. As for the fountain scene, where the unicorn is discovered drinking the water from a spring, its horn was supposed to possess wonderful powers of purification so that no beast of the forest would drink before the unicorn had plunged his horn into the pool. In the last panel of all, where the death of the unicorn has been reversed and it is seen alive again, the animal is shown as a captive, tied to a tree, inside a round fence. The tree is a pomegranate, the fruit of which is symbolical of life, and, from the numbers of its seeds, of the perpetuation of a family of numerous children.

It would be impossible to praise too highly the transcendent poetry and imagination of these scenes. Even in the reproductions given of them in an illustrated weekly paper at the time of their lamentable sale to another continent they emerged as clearly the most beautiful works of applied art of their epoch. And, like the Chatsworth Hunting Tapestries, they had remained hidden in the country for many hundreds of years, just as much concealed as though buried in a tomb. Now they are lost again—in the U.S.A.

They epitomize in every respect the qualities most typical of their period, and in this set of hangings are expressed those feelings and that sentiment which characterize feudality and all its heraldic clatter and appurtenance. The fabulous world that the men of the North made for themselves to live in by their legends, and by the unparalleled shapes that they gave to their doorways, their roofs, and their clothes, found a persistent echo in the Italian poetry of chivalry. For the Italian found here a more recent and a stronger collection of the high-sounding names that he loved. The Gothick North had the clanking armour, the spurred feet, and the clattering sword that made a louder, more active poetry for him than long intrigues closed with the dagger, or the poison-cup. This Gothick art, just dying out, had produced those stone leviathans whose uncouth, chaotic elegance the Italians could never master, and had sent forth the armadas and huge armies of the Crusades.

Even to-day the marionette theatres of the big Sicilian towns play an immense repertory chosen from this literature, and the names of Odoardo, Boiardo, Ruggiero, are ranted out ominously, while armoured puppets fight the Saracen knights and rescue their ladies from pagan castles. These plays, in their turn, form the subjects with which the carts of Palermo are painted (5); so that these same incessant campaigns can be seen carried on at every street corner in the lovely, but unlikely, corner of the world to which the ghostly Crusaders have repaired. They have become a part of the street mind, and even the stands of the lemonade-seller show some reminiscence of this favourite mode of passing an evening, while the mechanical organ grinds out a selection from *Carmen,* or from some opera written before the Fascisti had lifted their country out of the dust and by this effort spoilt its ancient melody.

The tall, yellow-haired paladins and their pale ladies had impressed the Italian mind that destroyed them, and in these tapestries of the Unicorn we find, as I have said, the late and decadent side of Gothick art at its most exquisite moment of flowering. This is the age of the delicate and the intricate, coming some two hundred years after the heroic epical period of castle and cathedral, when all energy was centred in the hands of the architect and sculptor, before the painter, the fine miniaturist, or the embroiderer, had leisure, or security, to practise his art.

Those warlike shapes remained, though, in a series of visions that were laboriously collected and set forth in needlework, just in time before all memory of them was lost. In the battle tapestries, all the elaborate ritual of mediæval warfare and its strange accoutrements are preserved ; they are so many true mirrors reflecting all armoured battles from the Crusades down to the invention of gunpowder. Memory was more acutely accurate where battles and their tangible results were concerned, and, as well as this, old pieces of armour belonging to famous knights were to be seen, from which some authentic historical reconstruction was possible. Where a set to illustrate some particular campaign was ordered, a kind of portraiture of everything except the actual visored face could be attempted ; and king, or prince, would not be satisfied unless his iron image, identified and sworn to by his own eyes, could be seen hewing down the enemy, or doing some feat of arms which had remained famous.

The legendary subjects, on the other hand, were

freqently most curious in their origin and pedigree. The great Gothick Alexander series, the most often chosen of all subjects for weaving into tapestry, was based, not upon the classical writers of Greece or Rome, but on the second-century, fabulous history of Alexander by the pseudo-Callisthenes, as developed by French poets out of bad translations from the Greek into Latin. The Gothick Trojan War tapestries derive, after the same fashion, not from Homer but from Benoit de Sainte Macere's twelfth-century "Roman de Troie," that claimed for its sources Dictys, the Cretan, and Dares, the Phrygian, the former a Greek, the latter a Trojan, eye-witness of the siege.

Authorities as involved and obscure as these will have been the sources for most tapestries, except for the more simple ones like the Shepherds and Shepherdesses, or the Baillé des Roses, for which a couplet from a poem, or merely a poetical idea, was enough material.

We find the full scope of the art, developed into its maturity, in a list of tapestries in the possession of Philippe le Bon, Duke of Burgundy in the year 1420. This inventory applies only to the hangings in his palace, and in the royal store at Dijon, one of the two capitals of the Duchy. The following are among the titles of the hangings, and in each set there may have been as many as six, or eight, separate panels.

The Twelve Peers of France, The Nine Knights and the Nine Amazons, The Seven Wise Men, The Battle of Roosebecque, The History of Lorens Guèrin who hunted the Wild Boar, Florence of Rome, The History of Youth and Sport called Hunting the Stag, The History of Helcanus who lost his Lady, Shepherds and Shepherdesses making Faggots, Young Men and Women playing Games, The Pride of the Land named Perceival the Gaul, Doone de la Roche, Shepherds in a Park.

Let us collect this stertorous, heraldic violence and its opposite of feminine, thin and tapering forms, into some open ground where a force, subtle or violent, can be used upon them. We can watch their ranks opening in pleasure or dismay, and the movement of this impact to one side or the other shows us the backs of those who had been coming towards us and the breast-plates of dead men who rode away long ago. After this manner, it is possible to read history backwards, starting at the index, as it were, and letting the past be influenced in its turn by the future that it led into.

Then history becomes, which is perhaps the truth, a level plain with all events lying side by side, next to each other, so that it is not possible to say one is behind, or in front of, the other. Such must be, in any case, the proportionate truth where the great stride of time is concerned, and results with their causes are trodden by the same step into the dead past.

But, before we try this, let us remember the silence and the isolation we have come to interrupt.

There had been nothing to disturb them. They had grown into their own fullness of shape, not contradicted by any influence from outside. But this was soon to come, and until it happens we can wander as we will in the world they had created for themselves.

Where, before this, were delicacy and fineness to be found ? In the lands of clove and saffron all beauty was spoilt by those cloying scents. No more than a breath of spice had come as far as this, and for the rest there was no hint of any other earth than theirs. Here, the exquisite and the fanciful held triumph, and in their dangerous pride never thought to be challenged. The trappings of poetry rattled in every wind and were consciously prominent and bold.

Tapestry filled and sank back along the wall. The rushes on the floor felt a footstep and crept up again when it had passed. But no ghost could be more immaterial than the live progenitor of such phantasies. Any breathing body was shaped and patterned as the figures in tapestry, and elegance turned them as tall and thin as this.

Their hands must be pale and tapering as though seen in water, and so must the hair be of long, straight gold drawn out and pressed back by the flow of the current. Different canons of admiration applied to the outside form and the inner figure ; for, if clothes were prolonged into compliance with an established code of lengthened folds, the nude body will have been admired for different points of beauty to those that governed this structure that it had to carry.

Thus, these mediaeval ladies lived in a double sphere of admiration and their beauty took two forms. Indeed, this reaches to something like the conditions of theatrical love, where a beautiful dancer has two distinct beings, on the stage and in life, and the contrast of these two, in which the other may amount almost to ugliness, is chief part of the attraction. This aspect of their exaggerated dress was sure of an appeal to the romantic and tired fancy of the aristocrat, and he, himself, had his other, or war, appearance, when armour so disguised him that he was only to be recognized by someone with a knowledge of that capricious steel form, for neither limb nor feature could be seen through the chased, inlaid husk in which he was living.

The romantic likings of the age dictated the capricious shaping of his armour, for each new invention was designed more for its effective appearance, a great parcel of its power, than as an intentional new protection against lance-thrust, or the striking of an arrow. It may be thought, even, that every fresh contrivance of the armourer made his patron's life more vulnerable, so that he contributed by his excess of zeal towards the effectual curbing, and final extinction, of the master he served.

These metal men can be studied, as nowhere else, in tapestry. They give the first, most salient character to the Gothick age, so that a man of intelligence from another continent would think of all these centuries as the time of armour. A knight's tomb in any little church may be, too, the first thing a child sees to turn his thoughts away and make him into the listless, dumb vessel into which poetry pours its fire. Heraldry, as bright and various as a pack of cards, lies at his feet, by the stone pillow where his head rests, or along every side of his tomb ; and the knight has used these inherited pawns to gain him others and to set him up safely above those who could never possess such instruments of fortune. He wore these devices upon his helmet in the tournament, and carried them into war on the trappings of his horse, on his banner, and upon his tent-clothes.*

* The delayed climax of the armoured man did not come until the early part of the seventeenth century. The Winged Hussars of Poland represent the final and most extreme point reached by Gothick fantasy. These horsemen, clad entirely in armour, wore a pair of wings some five feet long and made of grey eagle plumes, that were fastened to the shoulder and down the back, so that they spread open and fluttered menacingly in the charge. The armour of these Winged Hussars was illustrated in the *Times* during August, 1928. Two complete suits are still preserved in the museums of Warsaw and Cracow. It is a thousand pities that there is no tapestry of these paladins, whose character would have been so easily transferred into a woven campaign.

The battle-tapestries are the most enduring success of the Flemish looms. It is not possible to conceive of an experience more romantic in its strangeness, and in its revelation of a great series of masterpieces hidden away and inaccessible, than the impression, and no more than this can be obtained, of the battle-tapestries at Pastrana. This is a tiny hamlet of a few dozen houses, some thirty miles beyond Guadalajara, in New Castile. It has a small church, into which nobody who was not informed of its contents would take the trouble to gain entry. Indeed, except for these tapestries, it contains nothing of even the very slightest interest.

The set consists of some two dozen hangings. They represent the conquest of Arzila, in Morocco, by Alfonso V of Portugal, El Africano, in 1471. The tapestries were woven at Tournai, and were brought to Spain by Philip II, and in all probability given by him to one of his mistresses who became Duchess of Pastrana. In this way a tiny church was endowed with a patrimony of unimaginable beauty.

It is not possible to examine closely more than the one or two tapestries that hang from nails in the wall and trail their colours upon the dust of the floor. The rest are lying rolled up and piled one upon another, with no more care taken of them than would be given to rugs or mats. Their frayed edges catch the feet and tear at every step.

This little room seems loud and breathless from such an assembly of armoured men. Their heads spring up from the floor, while their bodies are distorted by the change of angle and are splayed into lifeless, inert corpses on the boards. As soon, in fact, as the tapestries are in their proper element, hung upon the walls, life and vigour come back into them, the armour rings out and the terrible clarions sound forth. The mouth of a trumpet, at one place, was in the air, while the lungs that blew life into it lay hidden under a heap of other dead tapestries.

The different forms of armour are beyond the power of any imagination to depict that has not a span of years in which nothing but their variety need be considered ; and such was, of course, the circumstance in which these tapestries were made. The jostling, jarring crowd have their helms touching each other, and it is only to be regretted that the probable cold morning of the battle's start did not allow of the steam of their breath to be seen coming from the hard, thin lips of metal. This would have made a fine parallel to the energy of the plumes upon many helmets.

Feathers branch out like jets of water from a coronet clamped dangerously upon the steel, or spring up out of a socket, wired like a stalk, and pushed into the head-piece. The proud curves of the plumes give a disdainful, stern pride to the wearers, whose horses are set about and thronged with the fighters on foot, some among whom, so humble is their comparative rank, even have their faces uncovered so that their slanting Gothick noses can be seen. The giants are in their ranks, lumbering through them on their armoured chargers, invincible in their steel dress, but too heavily laden to be a danger to anyone beyond the range of swung mace and trampling hoofs. The crests, lifted high above the crowd, balance with the head each time it leans back to gather strength for a blow, or drop forward with the force it has given and have to recover again, pulled up by the plated shoulders. Sometimes the horses are reared up and appear to be climbing into the hills.

Mottoes, like shouted words, are on the hems of

clothes, and upon banners.   There is, also, the trumpet's din.   But most of these heads must be silent, only muttering inside their helmets, speaking to themselves in despair, or exultation, in a voice as soft as through the curtains of a bed, or in a shaded alcove.   No sound can be heard from them, and they only lift their arms and move their bodies with every blow given or received. This enforced silence seems like part of their courage, and the inferior men below them shout and scream with a loudness that points again to the differences implicit in the wearing of armour.

As I have said, there is no attempt made to hang more than two or three of the tapestries, but a little of some of the others can be unrolled, though, in order to do this, it is necessary to tread upon the armoured warriors whom this wonderful art and the sad effects of time have reduced to the softness of spider's silk, still strong in its thinness, or to a strewing of rose-leaves beneath the feet, that give out a more piercing scent since they are weak and have lost the thorns that should protect them.   The hideous bestiality of modern clothes can nowhere be more appreciated than when, kneeling upon this brave chronicle, the legs and arms, of tweed or serge, are seen against the tapestry; the very contact sets up a shudder in the mind, as if the hairy hand of a gorilla had laid hold of a fair body, or had twisted its fingers into golden hair and was dragging away nymph or shepherd from the reeds.

All the heroes are powerless, and their armoured mass is brave, but ineffectual, having no more real force than would be the case if it was decided to defend a town with music.   The menace of drum and trumpet, and the heroic marches blaring from the battlements, could do no more than still the assault, and these airy screens built up with fist and lung would quickly collapse, surrendering their defences.

The Moroccan knights are by no means inappropriate to this Gothick maze. Their feudal castles in the Atlas, and the latticed windows and honeycomb vaults where they idled with their women, gave a form to their clothes which the conventions of this tapestry found no difficulty in expressing. Unfortunately, no more than this can be hoped for; it is the accidental coincidence of report that happened to tally with expectation, so that this partly confirmed guesswork has a general truth that it would be graceless to call into question. But this was a Morocco without an Africa behind it. There is no hint of the black warriors trained to fight in slave-gangs and to be killed as cover for their Moorish masters, or of the nubile shapes of the harem. Here, in the shallow swimming pool, or in the walled and fortified garden, an odalisque or dancing-boy of this ghostly midnight hue was their greatest pleasure, neglecting their own kindred for the gayer substance of the Niger-lands. In these tapestries no more than the coast of this secrecy is discovered, and the Andalusian of Granada has been the model for the more barbarous Moor who was the reality of this siege.

Most beautiful of those of the tapestries that it is possible to gain any idea of is the hanging that shows a naval battle in progress. The galleons of Portugal have come near into the harbour of Arzila and are beset by the Moorish vessels that are thin and rakish, of the traditional pirate character, coming in great part, it is probable, from Salé, the old pirate-town further down the coast. In this, the enemy are shown with a deeper degree of

exactness to truth, because the ships of the corsairs were
a tradition to which there were many witnesses.

But the combat is bent and doubled back by the floor.
Only the tops of the ship's masts can be seen, with men
climbing into those transparent towers, and oil and fire
being dropped upon them from the shaky balconies at
the top. These tossing minarets are near the forts of
the town, and have been lifted by the sea into a much
greater height than the true towers manned by the
Moors. The ships are but a few yards from the shore,
and the noise of the fight is terrific. The Portuguese
are shouting their sacred battle-cries, and the drums and
clarions are sounding their loudest. The Moors are
fighting within ear-shot of the holy voices calling from
the minarets, and are in a religious fury that makes them
gladly throw away their lives.

In fact, this is a belated Crusade, started merely from
a mercantile object, but converting itself, as soon as the
infidels were encountered, into a sacred duty. The
ferocity of a dog-fight burns in the blood of both sides,
and it is a maniacal, pointless slaughter. This savage
character gave the Portuguese escapade its importance,
and warranted such an expensive order from the Flemish
looms. A hundred years later, the ruin of Portugal
was brought about on a battlefield near Arzila ; the King,
Dom Sebastian, and the whole chivalry of Portugal
perishing in the last of such essentially Gothick adventures. So these tapestries, in their way, are a prophecy
of the final collapse and defeat of mediævalism.

With this prescient knowledge we can leave them,
taking a last look, as we go through the door, at the
rigging of the ships that rises in a web of ropes up the
mouldering wall. They have lasted here for centuries,

and their enemy is carelessness more than any actual destruction worked by time. This can only fade and hide their colour, but every person who climbs up the stairs to look at the tapestries takes away some threads of them on his shoes and upon his clothing.

The armoured figures are torn in a way that disgraces their war-like panoply to a far greater degree than would be shown by any honourable dent in breast-plate or buckler. It is easy to imagine what destruction there must be every year when the tapestries are taken down the narrow stair to be hung in the church ; when ladders, tied together to reach the necessary height, slant against the walls, and a man, groaning under the weight, climbs up with a corner of the tapestry in his hand ; when they hang in the wind flapping like the flags they image, and the rain blows in on them, and birds flying under the timbers let their droppings fall upon them ; and when they are taken back up the stairs once more by a mob of men and boys, hardly obeying the priest's rough orders for their care, and are pushed through the door, flung upon the boards, and untidily creased and rolled into the shapes that long confinement has inflicted on them.

If nothing can be done to repair the more decisive of these ravages, at any rate their colour can be restored to them, and this may be accomplished by a simple process, miraculous in its easiness and in its potent imagery. The tapestries are tied with ropes and stretched through the waters of a river. This must be specially chosen for its clearness and for certain properties, the force of the stream, the character of the source, and the nature of its bed, whether pebbled or earthy. A convenient tree, or a post driven into the ground on either side of the river, is bound about with ropes and serves to steady the

tapestry.   It must be secured on all its four sides so that
it is not carried away, or blown out like a long streamer
down the current.   The waters have to flow entirely
through it, passing into the web and out at the back.

What a sight such a set of tapestry as this would be,
stretched out and regularly spaced along the river as a
series of twenty-four booms, or defences, though their
only purpose, it would seem, was the building of a set
of images in the water, which daring experiment has
been achieved and the river is historied into its clear-
flowing depths !   The tapestries are hollowed forward
like filled sails, but only to a strength that does not bend
or destroy the figures upon them.   They are kept
perfectly still by the current so that the meaning of this
writing in the water can be clearly understood.

It would be the most beautiful experience imaginable
to float down the river and be brought by the stream
against one after another of the tapestries, to have to
pass down their histories, moving from end to end of
their length, to hear the water flowing through them,
pass by their paper thickness, look back to the ghostly
forms hardly discernible out of that voice of water
sounding from them, and to see plumes and then helmets
rising out of the next grave of heroes, for as they come
nearer they never move and are as dead as in the tomb.
The swords flashing in the water, the glint of the armour,
come up in their turn out of this passing of time through
their bones, and before the tapestry has been touched
by the boat even the little flowers of the ground can
be seen starring the meadows.   The field is powdered
with daisies, and with little blue flowers as small as the
blossom of the water-weeds that have been banked against
the tapestry by the force of the stream, and that cannot

pass through it with the water that carried them.   They
are piled up in a heap of trodden garlands, with twigs
of wood, blades of grass, and all the refuse of the stream,
and twine themselves upon the rope that supports all
this imagery in the river.   It can be lifted with an oar
and thrown over to the other side, when it drifts down
towards the next tapestry and lets in a still clearer light
to fall upon the space that it has freed.

The banks have become a thicket of ropes, every few
yards, and the whole river is pitched and divided with
this tent-like machinery set up in order to clean the
tapestries.   Further down, when this set has been passed,
come the other hangings that these pages have described.
The Hunting tapestries, the Shepherds and the Shepherdesses, the Wood-cutters, all these are in the river,
breaking that swift flow with their coloured nets.

The figures come out fresh and clear as new ; the
tongues of the hounds hang red from their mouths ; the
jewels upon the horse-trappings glitter in the false sunlight sifted to them through the water ; and the young
man whose sleeve and shoulder are worked with the
device of a cloud shedding drops of rain, or tears, is
young once more.   Blood runs in his veins, the hounds
tug at their leash, and the rain, or tears, upon his sleeve
shake with his breath and seem to dance like the motes
in a beam of light.   The Royal Hunt is in the shallow
woods, stirring the fallen leaves with their press of hoofs.
The horns wind and rumble in the distance ; the cranking
water-wheel lifts and falls, and the miller's daughter
comes out of the house again to talk to the fisherman.

The ghostly population of the tapestries, released from
their vaults and prisons, move in the river, throw their
reflections to right or left of them as they will, and may

J

be thought of as waiting in a state of disembodiment upon the banks until their doom sounds and they have to go back again into time which darkens and destroys them. Meanwhile, in this interval before their fate comes to fetch them, they have liberty to wander among the pastoral shadows set up by their ancient, faded beauty, that has been renewed and given back to them in this mysterious simplicity.

It is curious how of all these shapes seen so clearly in the water there is not one which is not clothed. Here, indeed, the painter, or the poet, must miss those naked bodies that are looked for in this element of crystal, and whose entirety has to be guessed from the grudging depths.

This expectation is only true of the tapestries from a later age when there is not a figure that could not step at once into the river. The nymphs are always naked, ready for cloud or water, and the genius of this latter time lavished every conceivable ingenuity of treatment upon them, with only this exception, that I know of no instance where the delicacies of the snow have been brought into use. The strange trees and flowers of the Indes Galantes ; the pavilions, the china vases, the nets hung upon the trees, the rococo fishermen of the Fêtes Chinoises ; the tinkling gourd-fed music of the sarabande danced under the flowering trees ; the wreathed columns and porticoes of the Fragments d'Opéra, and the Amours des Dieux, there is every device for their setting but this. (6) We may think of snow dying in its flakes upon the nude goddesses, but this crumbling of the clouds, and the shredded majesty of those chariots they rode in the wind, only cools them, for even the river runs hot in this faunal noon. The snow falls like manna to refresh the tired senses. Its flakes melt in little sighs

upon the water and their lips hardly reach to that flowing
fire, for the water is hot enough nearly to blister the
bodies in it; except where branches overhang and the
bathers can pattern themselves with leaves that make the
grace of their limbs difficult to follow.

Here there is nothing of the kind, and in the Gothick
tapestries the legs of a page in piebald hose are the only
indication that men and women have limbs beneath
their palisaded dress. The magpie youths with golden
locks reaching to their shoulders are allowed as safe
companions to the young ladies. These are permitted
to show their faces, but, perhaps, an equal importance
was attached to their hands. No work, for generations
out of memory, had been done by the tapering fingers
that were a birthright, and that had been bred specially to
be a party to the pale, combed hair, the bridged noses, the
arched doorways, and the fine, thin hounds for the chase.

But, if we mourn this lack of nudity, we have also to
lament that there was so primitive a music for them to
dance to. This other deficiency the Visit of the Gypsies
will remove, and the last tapestry to be described in
these pages may symbolize, at the same time, the breaking
of mediaeval isolation, and the stirring of the Gothick
age out of its blind energy into a knowledge of what was
on foot in other countries. They set forth in their
myriads for the holy lands of the East, discovered and
conquered new continents, and then suffered the inventions of Italy to alter the whole look of their lives, losing,
in the course of this, the individuality that their isolation
had given them. All these changes came first as a
rumour, a whisper hardly heard and not much heeded.
It came out of the East towards them; whether it was
a sacred trust to take back the holy places from the

infidel, a little noise of the Indies rustling in gold, or the arts of war and intrigue given a quick background of revived columns and shaded porticoes by secrets dug from the Roman soil.

The beginning of the symbol we have chosen was after the same manner. The gypsies, too, came out of this direction, though no one knew from whence ; and they would not say, nor, if persuaded to speak, could their words be believed.

They were the outlaws of the human race, driven by their own will from place to place, and never staying in one spot after the ashes of their first fire had grown cold. The contemptuous trickery of their thefts, and the ironic sport of the deceit they practised on all they met, bound them to this strange life they loved. Their wanderings took them away from the sunrise into the sunset, as if they were flying from a fate that threatened there.

No sooner did the rays of the rising sun shine on the dew, and fall in little fiery tongues upon their eyelids, than instinct made them strike camp and move away. All day they would journey, until the setting sun made the air to glow like a damp fire, burning the eyes while it chilled the body. The moon, like a disk of copper, hung behind them, and the plain seemed dead. All life had fled from it, and there was nothing but thick brushwood. It lay against the horizon like the back of a huge rhinoceros, or the hide of an elephant asleep. Here, almost touching that monstrous thing, they lit their fire, and the serpent with its cold and slimy coils climbed over their naked legs as they slept.

They stretched themselves to sleep upon low branches that made a hammock for their bodies, while every leaf seemed to have a nightingale's voice. The horizon was bounded by great sheets of water, and the rays of the early sun played and glittered upon these as though they were mirrors in which diamonds were reflected. Climbing down from the boughs, an elder-tree blossom, or a branch of briar or hawthorn, caught their fancy, if it was not the dropped feather of a bird that made a ready plume for a cap.

Their happiness lay apart from other men as they wandered. All their food they stole, raiding lonely farms, or robbing the woods. They shook the wild-growing trees and brought the fruit down like savoury hail-stones. When they came to the shrubs that strew the ground with trodden fragments till the grass seems tinted with blood, they gathered the sharp, red berries and ate them greedily straight away, for this was their bread, as was rain their water. But, even while eating, their instinct for mischievous destruction got the better of them, for seeing a young willow tree covered with frost, and looking like a huge bird in some sacred Indian vale, they shook the boughs and reduced it again, for nothing, to its native ugliness.

When night came they sat round their fires, and music sounded in the empty plain. In the very act of passing the bow across the violin-strings a natural inspiration suggested itself, and, without any search for them, there came forth rhythms, cadences, modulations, melodies, and tonal discourses. Their needy camp and patched garments learned in this way all the luxuries of the senses, and soon they moved to the music and ended with a frenzied dance in the forest glades.

But the slower moods were made use of to a different purpose. Having taken a young bear-cub from its lair in the mountains they put it every evening on an iron

sheet which had been heated, and played music to it of
a very slow, noisy, and accentuated, rhythm. The bear
at once lifted its front paws and stood upright, raising
one of its hind paws after the other in order to remove
it from the scorching surface, and timing its movements
to the sound of the music. When the cub had learned
how to make its dance agree with the tune, it had only
to hear it played in order to go through this clumsy waltz
of its own accord, knowing that should it be slow in this
the hot plate would be slipped at once beneath its paws.

All this time, the quicker tunes were playing with
wild varieties of rhythm. Sometimes like leaping
asclepiads, which progressing by unequal steps imitate
the slow reptation of the serpent, or throw themselves
forward in a bold curve quickly reaching to some distant
support. The path is strewn, as it were, with drops of
blood, to which certain notes in these gypsy rhythms
bear a definite metaphorical resemblance, and the best
players were those, who, having syncopated their theme
so as to give it a light swinging effect, restore it to the
normal measure as if preparing to lead a dance, after
which it appears, as it were, casting sparks in every
direction by clusters of small shakes.

Night after night, this only expression of their lives
was practised. Every day the gypsies came nearer to the
lands of sunset, and appeared, without warning or
explanation, on the outskirts of a town, or near the
ramparts of a castle. In fact, they have left the flat
Slavonic plain and are in this landscape of the knights
and ladies, within sight of the black-capped towers.
They have built their fire under a colonnade of ash-
trees and are sitting round it, violin in hand, on the
piled sheep-skins that are their only furniture. The

women are crashing their tambourines, and uttering little cries of mimicry while they dance. In the intervals of this there is the crepitous noise of the wooden axles of the wagons, creaking loudly as they are drawn back to make more room for the dancers.

Meat and wild honey are being eaten. The children cut capers, turn somersaults, and utter wild cries, while they fight over bags of peas, or crack nuts upon stones. The gypsy hags sit with inflamed eyes, warming themselves and listening to the music. The men resemble each other like sons of one mother. Some of them have profiles in which sarcasm seems to be actually sneering. Their tawny skins and faces are framed in locks of hair which fall like snakes of a bluish-black tint upon their necks, the colour of which is a lively orange. Their eyes shine like sparks which seem to be illuminated and extinguished by some interior contrivance.

They got up from the ground to look at some horses that had been given in exchange to them that day. This pleased them and they put on quite a heavenly smile, showing off their teeth, which were as white as snow. After this they started imitating castanets by cracking the joints of their fingers, which are always long and charged with electricity. Still uncertain, they began throwing their caps into the air, and followed this by strutting about like peacocks. Then, they looked at the horses again, and as if suddenly given the power to express their pleasure in the bargain, they flew to their violins and cymbals, and began playing in a fury of excitement. The Frischka, or quick gypsy dance, rose into a frenzy of delirium till the dancers were breathless and fell to the ground.

Next morning it was raining, and they rode off early to

the fair. Some of the gypsies were in long, narrow carts, holding about twenty of them standing upright. Those who rode on horseback wore their sheep-skin pelisses, with the wool outside, because of the damp. This made them look like as many bears mounted on wild horses, for they kept their spurs so much in play that the horses jumped at every moment. The drivers of the wagons went at full speed, cracking their whips above the clatter of the old ironwork of their carts. They bumped against heavy stones in the road, all the gypsies in the carts talked at the top of their voices and shrieked with laughter, and the children ran by the side begging from all they passed; while the young girls went up to every stranger, and even looked in through the doors of houses, to tell fortunes, blandishing and cursing their prey.

The fair was in the village just beyond the castle moat. These hovels held the serfs who worked in the fields, and the walls of the castle rose, to a height that took the breath away, above the mean roofs. But the sky came lower and grew dark and dreadful. Rain poured down in torrents; the fair was abandoned, the cattle were penned away, and the peasants, who had journeyed since the dawn to get here, collected in a great barn till business could begin again. The gypsies followed them into shelter and uncased their instruments, placing themselves in a semicircle.

In a few seconds came the distant roll of thunder, sounding like a deep organ-point, whilst the timbers of the roof, being very high, and the dilapidated walls of very thin wood, gave an echo which sent back every sound and produced a chaotic confusion of noise. The passionate passages, the ornamentations, the virtuosity and the feats of technique continued unaffected by this exterior clamour; all being rolled up together into a formidable total of sound. The roar went on increasing, being varied by noises more acute and piercing, as well as by lightning, flashing at brief intervals. Sometimes it threw a pale greenish light, and sometimes a transparent brilliancy, more red in tone, which showed the musicians in a real theatrical apotheosis, as Bengal fire shows up the demi-gods on the stage. During the tempestuous coda of this performance, it was as if every possible sound or tone was crashing down together like mountain-crests which fall with a frightful roaring in sheets of sand mixed with blocks of rock and stone.

To this succeeded the gentle and melancholy Lassan, the slow measure of the gypsies, expressive of a sombre and elegiac sadness. It was like a hero's death in mood, a lamentation over spent courage and exhausted strength. While it was in progress, no other sound was to be heard except the rain pouring off the roof, and the whisperings of the sorceresses who darted into the crowd and dragged their victims into dark corners to have their fortunes told. But the storm had stopped and the barn emptied, leaving the musicians nearly alone, who realized the change, slowed down their music till it died away, and went out into the freshened air to drive their bargains.

The winding of a horn came from far off, and another, and then another, from the forest's edge. It was the hunting party coming back to the castle, and now they rode out from the trees. They were the first of their race that the gypsies had seen, and these men and women in their tattered rags ran forth to watch the procession pass by and hear the flourishes and fanfares of the heralds. The leafed edges of the ladies' clothes had an appropriate beauty for the ragged women, whose eyes had never seen anything finer than the cutting of a leaf or the painted eglantine, for these Egyptians had passed their lives in a wilderness and were now arrived for the first time beneath the walls of a castle. The gypsy-men had never seen such permanence as that great height suggested, and they saw horses worth more than could be gained in a lifetime of craft.

Soon the horses were back in the stable again, the Knights and Ladies had changed from their hunting-dresses, and there was a little time still, before the sunset, to walk in the garden, or by the moat, watching the swans and their mirrored whiteness in the water. The repute and rumour of the Egyptians had gone before them and the Knights and Ladies had heard of their sorcery and the spell of their music. It was decided to put the powers of the Egyptians to the test, and they were summoned to come forward to the castle-walls.

It is this moment that was chosen by the tapestry-designer.* A gypsy-woman comes in front of her companions to tell the fortune of one of the ladies of the castle. The whole gypsy-caravan is just behind her, some on horseback and some on foot ; with nine children, five of whom are perfectly naked after the usual gypsy custom. The gypsy-king is in the midst of his followers, armed with club and sword. His queen sits on the ground near by, feeding a baby with a wooden spoon from a bowl held by another child, while the purse of a lady who is

---

* This tapestry of the Visit of the Gypsies, round which I have woven my narrative, is now in the collection of Mrs. Nicholas F. Brady, in the U.S.A. It used to hang in the Château d'Effiat, near Clermont-Ferrand, and was made at Tournai, about the end of the fifteenth century. The Effiat arms were attached to it by Antoine Coiffier de Ruzé, Marquis d'Effiat (1581-1632), who inherited the château from his maternal grandfather. He was ambassador to England under Louis XIII and arranged the marriage of Charles I and Henrietta Maria. His second son was the famous Cinq-Mars.

looking at her is being stolen by one of the gypsy-children.

A young knight is speaking to this unsuspecting victim, and at the back of them stand the lord and lady of the castle, dressed very richly, and talking to the head-huntsman, who shows them a quarter of deer, and to another young nobleman who holds up a rabbit for which a dog is reaching. A peacock with spread tail is perched on the wall of the castle, and, behind this, the background of the tapestry is filled with castles, with hills, and with hunting scenes, as though these latter were in perpetual activity. Just at random, letting the eyes range about, there are to be seen a deer, which is being seized from behind by a hound, a fox running across a field, another deer making for cover, and a hunts-man blowing a huge horn.

The visit of these gypsies was a sorcery come from the interminable vast, and its strangeness entered straight into the soul of all who saw it. No longer were the arts and beauties of life to be found only where diamonds glittered in a continual tremolo, where the hands touched gold where steel might have been, and where tapestry, such as this, put woven battles and spun pastorals upon the walls. Chivalry was called out of its own borders into the whole of the huge, hollow orbit lit by the sun's dying and reviving fire, and the apotheosis of the white man took him to the four quarters of the winds. His isolation was broken, the present was extended and the past came back again.

But, in a wider and yet unmeasured direction, because there are no tangible boundaries to its extent, the gypsies brought with them a magnification of the senses in music. Their appeal was, therefore, alike material and

immaterial in nature. Their tawny skins and suits of rags
were symbols of distance and adventure, while in music
there appeared an art, for the first time, that allowed
absolute licence of interpretation, so that any simile or
metaphor could be attached to its meaning. This
particular afternoon, not quite like any other there had
ever been, when the gypsies came under the castle-walls,
was chosen by the tapestry-artist as a particular instance
in the life of everyone. For the first sight of gypsies and
the first sound of their music had a definitely symbolical
or poetical importance in life, and no person who witnessed
such a scene would ever forget the first time it came
before his eyes. This is the significance of the tapestry,
but its import may be followed still further by a fulfilment of the movement set in motion by this scene.

The evening brazier lights up in the west, behind and
above the castle towers, so that it is difficult to see them
clearly out of the fiery mist. The waters of the moat
have an emanation of their own that clings closely to
the surface in rings and circles, as though these pale, still
wraiths were lily-clumps just folded below the water's
rim at this chill hour of death. Everything darkens, and
the Lords and Ladies go in.

The gypsies have arrived at the castle-yard and are
allowed as far as the banquet-hall. Bears, held by a
chain, look in this uncertain light like unfinished shapes
of wood, too soon deified and given movement. The
drum and fife, tapping out their measures, practise and
threaten these clumsy, sack-like giants. Soon a great door
opens, the butts of two spears ring upon the stone, and the
stairway crowds and jostles with the Egyptian strangers.

Silver clarions are sounding from the gallery as they
come into the hall, though this is not for their entrance,

but in order to announce the victims of the hunting-horn, wild boars and does of last week's frost, who are carried in and laid in sacrifice upon the trestles. And now a sadness, as of imminent change and imminent departure, hangs on the air. It stills the mind to a deeper notice of what is happening.

The steep hall of this banquet is solemn, and not unlike a chapel as to its walls and roof. So high does it rise above the tables where they sit that it is possible to feel silent and detached by thinking of this emptiness above that clamour. The gentle and melancholy music for the dance begins, as slow moving as that to which the bear treads his measure. Knights and Ladies are dancing to it, the Ladies managing the folds of their dresses with both hands, and the Knights with one hand on the hilts of their swords and the other playing with the ends of their blonde moustaches. But, suddenly, in the middle of this solemn dance, a man dressed entirely in rags walked past the tables and through the moving crowd of dancers. With flaming eyes and wild gestures of the hands, he threw himself towards the music, and, seizing the first instrument he could reach, played the part again as if inspired, while the dancers stood stupefied and not a person in the hall spoke a word.

When he had handed back the instrument seized so impetuously, the dancers surrounded him, the Knights and Ladies came up from their tables to see him, and the Lord of the castle sent soldiers to bring him forward. He had him at once reclothed in a magnificent garment, richly embroidered, and a coat of fur, in which he came back again into the banqueting-hall, walking in kingly and ineffable pride, but without his expression having undergone any change, for he seemed to look on the

Knights and Ladies with a disdainful indifference. He was given wine, after a few glasses of which he took up the violin again and began to play.

Then, the seals upon the senses were broken. This man who begged his bread from door to door played music of extraordinary fire but with a dull despair mixed in that quick, lofty pride. Nothing like this had ever been heard before, and in order to express its force and poetry those laborious conventions of angle and fold had to be broken and changed for others. Music had begun, and is symbolized in this little beginning that was to grow into the greatest of the arts.

So far, and up to this rhapsodic start, has tapestry arrived, but its subjective and woven treatment fails in this contingency and must be left here before the music has begun. It could picture that ragged caravan appearing before the castle, while the flourishes of the hunting-horns still held the air. Till now, the Egyptians had no more magic than is compatible with their tawny skins and raven, snake-like locks, though even this was potent to distract attention while pockets were pilfered and purses taken. But, beyond this point, no tapestry can go, and the unfolding of its beautiful imagery must give place to an art that allows any simile, and any individual interpretation to its meaning. It would be best, therefore, for the horns to wind again and the woods to be desperate and alive with peril. We see the Egyptians leave the castle and take once more to the wilderness of plain, while the Lords and Ladies vanish into the brown, autumn trees and a horn rumbles far away and another answers it.

NOTES

*These six notes refer to passages on pages
8, 11, 65, 83, 124, and 138, respectively.*

1. The Songhoi, a negroid tribe, inhabited both banks of the Middle Niger. They formed a distinct state from the eighth to the sixteenth century, were at one time the masters of Timbuktu, and formed the most powerful race of the Western Sudan. The Tarik es Sudan, a seventeenth-century history of the Sudan by Aberrahman Sadi of Timbuktu, gives the name of their first king as Diamen el Jemen, which signifies that he came from Yemen. Jenné, the chief city of the Songhoi, on a tributary a few miles from the Niger, was founded in A.D. 765, about a century and a half after the Hegira. It is 250 miles south-west of Timbuktu in a straight line, and is now in the French colony of Upper Senegal and Niger. This city is of marked architectural interest. Unfortunately, the great mosque was nearly destroyed by fire in 1830. In Jenné there is little trace of the Moorish or Arabian art, but, on the contrary, the architecture of many of its buildings bears a resemblance to the ancient Egyptian, the façades of the houses being adorned with great buttresses of pylonic form. They are mainly constructed of clay made into long, flat bricks. Massive clay walls surround the city. The inhabitants are great traders, and the principal merchants have representatives at Timbuktu and in all the chief places on the Niger, while the boats built at Jenné are famous throughout the Western Sudan. The great mud-built towns of Kano and Sokoto in British Nigeria represent this same Songhoi civilization; and it is in this district that warriors in armour, showing the influence of the Gothick Crusaders, can still be seen. This strange anomaly, with the peculiar architectural character of the towns, the dyed and striped dresses of the natives, and their prosperous and peaceful lives, make this into the only negro civilization, and it must be one of the best subjects now left in the world for the consideration of an ambitious writer or painter. An extravagance of dress and manner

151

comparable to the Gothick age, or to that of the periwig, still exists among the negro sultanates of this region. In Bornu, for instance, it is indispensable to a chief of any rank that he should possess a huge belly, and, when high feeding cannot produce this, padding gives the appearance of it. Notwithstanding the onerous heat of the climate, the body is enveloped in successive robes worn over each other, the number of which signifies the rank of the wearer. The head, likewise, is enclosed in numerous turbans. Such figures can scarcely stand up, or move, without the support of their slaves, and an assembly of this nature must be the most curious spectacle. The lumbering armour of their cavalry is in keeping with this. (Cf. articles in the " Encyclopædia Britannica," Barth's Travels in Africa, 1850, and P. Dubois, " Tombouktou la mystérieuse," Paris, 1897.)

2. Engelbrecht Kaempfer, the son of a Lutheran pastor, was born at Lippe-Detmold in Westphalia in 1651. He studied medicine, went in that capacity to Sweden, and accompanied the mission sent through Russia to Persia by Charles XI in 1683. From Ispahan he proceeded to the Persian Gulf, and reached Batavia, in Java, in 1689. The following year he set forth for Japan, where he resided for two years, being back at Amsterdam in 1693, and returning thence to his native city, where he passed the remainder of his life, dying in 1716. The manuscript of his travels in Japan was brought over to England, translated, and published in 1726. It has never been printed in its original German, but only from a German translation of the English version. For at least a century and a half Kaempfer was the only authority upon Japan, and, save in this instance, its isolation from the remainder of the world was unbroken till the middle of last century.

I put the following details of feudality into a note, for they would impede and delay the text. Their derivation is in the fourth volume of Captain F. Brinkley's " Japan." Buddhism was established in A.D. 552, and from that date the whole feudal system of Japan came into operation, centring round the Mikado, who quickly receded into sacred and secure retirement, while the whole power of the State was exercised in turn, until only sixty years ago, by four great clans who had married continually into the Mikado's family, or were descended from the younger sons of Emperors. In 1192 the Shogunate was established, and various dynasties of Shoguns ruled the country over the Mikado's head until the abdication of the fifteenth, and last, Tokugawa Shogun in 1867. Between these two dates the Daimyo and the Samurai appeared, and suffered no diminishment of their power. But, four years after 1867, feudalism was abolished and the whole of this peculiar world of pride vanished into smoke. Too proud to work at any trade, they were left starving in their thousands, while their daughters were thrown on the streets to seek a living. Thus the whole nation renewed itself by pressing what we may call its middle-class out of existence, though this middle-class was a minor nobility of hereditary soldiers, the fiercer and much multiplied county-families of Japan. After this vigorous kind of pruning, the whole civilization rolled itself over like a ball into the trappings of Europe, the railways, the trains, the black hats, the newspapers.

During the thousand years before this happened there were four princely families next to the Imperial throne, the Fushimi, Arisugawa, Katsura, and Kwan-In, whose function was to supply an heir to the throne in the event of failure in the direct line of succession. Then came the Kuge, Court nobles, headed by five families in which the great offices of state were hereditary— Konoye, Kujō, Nijō, Ichigō, and Takatsukasa. Next to these were nine families—Sanjō, Saionji, Tokudaiji, Kazan-In, Oi-no-Mikado, Kuga, Kikutei, Hirohata, and Daigo—who served exclusively as ministers of state. In many families of the Court nobility certain accomplishments were hereditary ; calligraphy in the houses of Shimizutani and Jimyoin, floral arrangement in the Sono, football in the Nambu and Asukai, poetry in the Raisi and Karasumaru, sword-making in the Shijo, heraldry in the Yamashina and Takakura, wrestling in the Gojo, and divination in the Yoshida.*

---

* The grands-veneurs, grands-chambellans, grands-hussiers, grands-échansons, grands-écuyers of the old Courts of Europe, form a parallel to this. These hereditary posts still survive in at least eight European countries.

K

It is interesting to notice the low financial status of the Mikado and his Court compared with that of the Shogun. The annual revenue of the Mikado was only £30,000, to which the Shogun added £35,000 to £45,000, and an occasional special grant. The incomes of the Court nobles only totalled £70,000, the wealthiest of them, the Konoye, having but £2,800. Many of them increased their incomes by the practice of some domestic industry, the making of pictorial playing-cards, umbrellas, toothpicks, or chopsticks.

We now come to the Shogun himself. He copied accurately the traditions of the Imperial Court, appointing three families —Owari, Kii, and Mito—and subsequently three more—Tayasu, Hitotsubashi, and Shimizu—for the privilege of supplying an heir, should his own direct line fail. Below these were two groups of five and seven families, corresponding in position and privilege with the similar families attached to the Mikado. But the Shogun's position was one of absolute financial control over the Emperor and the whole country. No one of his barons had an income of less than £6,000 a year, while the richest of them— Mayeda of Kaga—had half a million pounds sterling. Two hundred and fifty-five of his feudatories had incomes of from £100,000 to £200,000, and fifteen reached to figures varying between £200,000 and £600,000. The total revenues of the Shogun's feudatories was twelve millions sterling, so that the average income of the two hundred and eighty-seven families exceeded £40,000, whereas the Court nobles, who numbered one hundred and forty-three families, had a total allowance of £45,000, being an average of only £314.

The income of the Shogun himself was returned by the commissioners of finance in 1847 as one and a quarter million pounds sterling in coin, and half a million sterling in kind. But these returns are supposed to be much below the truth, and it is said that the income of the last Tokugawa Shogun was two millions sterling annually. When the western wing of the Shogun's castle at Yedo was burnt down in 1838, one million and a half pounds were appropriated towards rebuilding it, while the present Emperor of Japan's palace in Tokyo cost not more than one-third of the sum necessary to restore this one destroyed wing of the Shogun's palace.

Finally, it should be said that the feudal responsibilities of the nobles were extremely onerous, so that their large incomes entailed more public responsibility than might be imagined. The humblest of them had to equip and maintain a force of twenty-three swordsmen, two spearmen, one archer, and one musketeer, while a fief with an income of £60,000 must be able to put seven hundred and fifty men into the field at any moment. Altogether six hundred thousand Samurai families had to be supported out of these revenues, and a muster of all military men between the ages of twenty and forty-five would have produced a force nearly a million strong.

3. Conrad Witz, a painter from Swabia, on the Upper Rhine, came to Basel in 1433, probably in order to decorate the churches and buildings for the great Council held there in that year. In 1444 he painted this triptych for Francis de Mies, Bishop of Geneva, and till the Calvinist outbreak in that city it adorned the chapel of the Macchabees in the Cathedral, which chapel had been founded by the uncle of the donor, Cardinal Jean de Brogny. Only the upper and lower right shutters of this triptych are now in existence; and on the one of them not referred to in this passage St. Peter is shown sinking in the water and stretching out his arms towards Christ. The lake is the Lake of Geneva, and the banks, with Mont Blanc and the great Alps above them, are clearly shown from a position that can, even now, be identified with certainty. The year of the painter's death is uncertain.

4. The abbey of Vézelay was founded in the middle of the ninth century. Its great glory is the triple doorway of the nave, elaborately sculptured, and standing inside a covered porch. This, and the choir, date from 1161-1175. St. Bernard proclaimed the Second Crusade here on 31st March, 1146; and, in 1190, Philip Augustus and Richard Cœur-de-Lion met in this church before their start for the East. Works by the same school of sculptors are the church of St. Pierre, below Vézelay, and the churches of Saulieu and Autun, not far distant from Vézelay.

5. The painted carts of Palermo are made chiefly at Bagheria, a small town full of villas of the Palermitan nobility, built in the wildest rococo to be seen anywhere in the world. Their subjects, as I have said, are taken from the Marionette repertory, which is principally made up of scenes from the poetry of Ariosto and Tasso. Otherwise they portray saints, ballet dancers, or scenes from the war. In no other town in Sicily do they attain to the perfection of Palermo, though there is another variety to be met with in Trapani, and it is said that Messina, before the earthquake, had its own school of artists. The only other parallel to this strange product is the decoration upon the fishing-boats at Leixões, a little harbour near Oporto.

6. This passage refers to the tapestries that Boucher designed for the Beauvais manufactory. His connection, later on, with the Gobelins produced nothing of comparable importance to these. The four Beauvais sets more especially in mind are Les Fêtes Italiennes, Les Fêtes Chinoises, the Fragments d'Opéra and the Amours des Dieux. The first of these comprised fourteen subjects and was a development of Watteau's material of figures promenading in parks decorated with fountains, statues, vases, and classical ruins; the Fêtes Chinoises was a set of nine panels; the Fragments d'Opéra had four subjects, and the Amours des Dieux was a series of ten. These are the masterpieces of their kind, and it is to be regretted that painters greater than Boucher,—Fragonard, or Tiepolo—were never given their opportunity in this medium.

BOOK II
THESE SAD RUINS

I

DIALOGUE IN THE APPLE-WOOD

THE evening was still quite young when I came out from the hotel and started forth in search of a café. There were several just down the slope of the hill, and choosing the cleanest among them I walked inside, for the air was rather chill, and sat on the comfortable settee before a marble-topped table. The waiter brought my coffee and liqueur and I could see the night lying undisturbed before me for some little time.

Mr. and Miss Corder had certainly arrived at a most opportune moment in my own history, for their profession and their actual physical appearance were, towards myself, like as many tests upon my speed and endurance. Not only this, but they pricked against what I may term the balloon of my thoughts, damaged it not inconsiderably, and very nearly brought down the whole affair. The heavy weight of sentiment that clung to them made their drag upon me yet more dangerous, until I determined to add them to this part of the book that I was writing and to use their personalities as so much ballast towards the greater security of my own voyage. For I was about to add the concluding chapters to this book when my chance meeting with the brother and sister made me recast the whole shape of the thing

157

in my mind and it emerged in its final form strengthened by the addition of their two characters.

They walked into the café when I was half-way through a cigarette and sat down at a table just opposite. While they were taking off their coats they saw me, and Corder, without any more hesitation, came over to me.

C. C.: I knew it was you. We felt pretty sure at the Château, and then at Vézelay we had no more doubt about it. Are you alone ? May I bring my sister across ?

S. S.: Yes ! do !

C. C.: Well, Hilda, you see we were right !

H. C.: Yes, Carl, and it's a compliment to his old teachers that he hasn't forgotten us. We haven't set eyes on each other for fifteen years. You haven't changed so much, though.

C. C.: Well, what are you doing here ? We're on our annual holiday, come here to sketch, as you know, but somehow this isn't the sort of place I should ever have expected to find you in.

H. C.: I taught for ten years at St. Asaph's and it was the unhappiest time of my life. Then father died, and we had enough money left us to buy a cottage in Cornwall, where we have lived ever since.

C. C.: You can tell him all about that later, Hilda, but first let him explain his presence.

S. S.: I have been writing a book for a year or more, and it has entailed my travelling to these parts, though I am much more at home in Spain or Italy.

H. C.: We know that : I bought " Southern Baroque Art " and Carl read it after me.

C. C.: There's some fine stuff in it. I always say you were our only pupil of talent. But there's

Matthewson. Have you seen his water-colours ? He's had more than one exhibition.

H. C.: They wouldn't interest him, dear. If he has seen them he has probably tried to forget them by now.

S. S.: That isn't true. I remember him perfectly. He went on drawing at Eton with Sidney Evans. They sell tremendously, I believe, and he must be quite a rich man. A hundred, even two hundred guineas, a water-colour.

H. C.: Yes. A year's salary for a morning's work. But I envy no one.

C. C.: You won't mind my saying this, but I knew you'd never make a painter.

S. S.: So did I, but anything was worth it that got one off games.

C. C.: Well, you've quite made your name in another direction—as a poet. I could never have taught you that.

S. S.: Neither could anyone else. But perhaps you and Miss Corder got as near to it as anybody could.

H. C.: How compliments are flying ! But we must come to ground. How long have you been in these parts ?

S. S.: I came from Le Mans three days ago. We've been motoring a hundred and fifty miles a day, and the roads have been none too good. It's terrible between Le Mans and Tours.

C. C.: Le Mans ? I've always longed to get there. But surely you don't like it ? Of course I don't know the part of the world you've written about, but I realize there are fine things from your book. How were you brought into contact with them ?

S. S.: I don't know. I lived in Italy a lot as a child,

in Florence chiefly, but I never went to Naples and Sicily till the year after the war ended. That awful word " Baroque " has haunted my footsteps ever since. It's not my fault ; but people like labels, and then they think they've got you safely into a pigeon-hole and needn't worry about you again.

H. C. : Then, why did you write the book ? I thought if you liked the Baroque you'd never care for the things here.

S. S. : If anything, I prefer them. But I wanted a subject that hundreds of other writers hadn't sullied, and that I could treat freely in my own manner. They're cheap things down there, perhaps, but in effect they are like popular tunes. When I first got to Naples, and went afterwards down to Apulia, or found towns like Noto and Ragusa in Sicily, I felt like a composer who has suddenly discovered a whole world of new folk-tunes. I could not help writing something round them, and giving them a big symphonic treatment which very likely their merits don't deserve. But they were my own discovery, I was very young then, and so I look back on the whole thing in a romantic spirit, and feel at home there. I have never believed that the only form of good prose is a novel. They are all so many academy pictures now, and there is no good in a poet trying to enter the lists against the hundreds of young female geniuses who are declared every year.

H. C. : But " The Constant Nymph " and " Dusty Answer."

S. S. : Oh, never mind ! You'd hate to have to read them in three years' time. Let's leave our contemporaries alone ; let their voices be heard now, since they'll never be heard of again. We'll talk about permanencies.

I'm sorry not to have seen Mont St. Michel this time; I remember the drawing of it we used to copy so well, and shall always associate it with you both, on preferably a windy Friday night when I used to wonder how you ever got home across the common.

C. C.: But what are you writing now? What is this book that made it necessary for you to come here?

S. S.: Well, it may seem to you an odd idea, but it's a history of the fair-haired races in Art. One hears so much about the decline of the West, and certainly all our American progeny will produce nothing for centuries to come. It took five hundred years for the Romans to produce an artist, so how long do you think it will be before the Americans can do that?

C. C.: I should think ten thousand.

S. S.: Yes. There you are, you see we agree about that. I think it is time white men asserted themselves again, and by this I don't mean the Italians, and hardly the Spaniards either. They are dark Europeans, and what I am trying to get at is the true fair-haired race and its achievement. But, even out of that, I shall only choose what interests me, and what is useful to my purpose. I can, and shall, leave out all sorts of things. Their cathedrals are the biggest things they did, but what's the use of my writing about Rouen or Amiens? They have become almost sham Gothick from adulation and familiarity. No, the only thing is to find, again in this second instance, some work of theirs that has not been altogether sullied and spoiled. As for that, you're a pretty good danger, both of you, with your sketches.

H. C.: What? Aren't we to be allowed to have our holidays any longer? We must motor round, must we,

K

with cameras, instead of going slowly, like we do, and appreciating every detail ?

C. C. : Well, he must buy us the motor, Hilda, or we shall be worse off than we were before, walking and taking snapshots. I suppose sketching is awfully antiquated, isn't it ? But no amount of postcards are going to stop me.

S. S. : Oh, I wouldn't have you prevented for anything. You're a much more alive audience to the buildings you sketch than are the people in a concert-hall to the music they are supposed to be hearing. Still, it's a ghoul's work creeping in and out of those old churches.

H. C. : But we are dead ourselves. Are you sure you saw Carl and myself to-day ? You're really sitting alone at your table, thinking of us, because you saw a man and a woman sketching who brought us back into your mind.

S. S. : Draw me something, then, on the marble-table and rub it out with this piece of bread. Bread and charcoal are the sacramental symbols of the studio, and how seldom they're substantiated !

Carl drew a great stag. Its antlers were like a dead tree in an old park, and it had gone again in a moment with the crumbled bread. Miss Corder took the charcoal from him and sketched an upturned boat which was scarcely building before a glass of mineral water was thrown over it by my elbow. The waiter took it away with a damp cloth.

H. C. : If only I was young again, and had my youth before me, unwasted ! I was getting near forty when you last saw me, now I'm fifty-five and more. Carl, who always seemed so young to me, is over fifty. Think of the paradise we might live in. We might travel about for weeks together, the three of us.

C. C.: We'd go to Spain; it's not much more than a day in the train from here.

S. S.: Yes. I'd lead you round and rub your noses against the old, worn stones.

C. C.: We'd arrive back in our London studio with armfuls, taxi-loads of sketches. When we were young the amateurs were still in their drawing-rooms; in those days it was possible to hire a studio for other purposes than jazz on a gramophone. Well, let's think we had a future in the past. I can't promise anything in the present. And yet it must be a present with all to-day's conveniences. We must be allowed to motor, and not have to ride on mule or donkey-back.

S. S.: What about the char-à-banc I saw you in this evening! Isn't that nearly as bad?

H. C.: It's no worse than third-class on the railway. Now it's a world of omnibuses, third-class carriages, cinemas, Virginia cigarettes; let's get out of it as quickly as we can!

S. S.: Don't worry. You'll be back there the moment I stop thinking of you.

C. C.: Then where are we? Are we here in this café, or aren't we?

S. S.: Didn't I see you this morning at the Château d'O, and this afternoon at Vézelay? Do you deny that?

C. C.: You're the best judge. Didn't I draw a stag for you on the table?

S. S.: Yes. And where is it now? Be careful!

I was alone again, and I had been right in thinking that the night lay undisturbed before me. It had been a lovely and wonderful day; a castle, a ruined abbey, and an orchard of apple-trees to walk in while their beauty made a loom for all the poetry the mind could conjure out of their loaded boughs. We were under the same roof and if they were not there in their flesh they were certainly with me none the less. There had been an indestructible romance about every leaf and every sip of air in the whole day. It made me remember the first things I had ever seen that possessed beauty, but were I to write down their names I might nearly cry. I had come back very near to them.

So I went into the apple-trees and saw the dim ground starred with a myriad flowers. They clogged the feet and broke like a spring-tide against the stems. It was a young, a very young cabinet that lay locked and hidden there, ready for its doors to open. When this arrived, the whole world was still and obedient for them. The hermits in the wood found the key to this secret, and for a long time they, and they only, had the use of this knowledge. Yet it was no stored wisdom of the past, but a comb of present and vital honey pressed out of these flowers and with no scent or sweetness that did not come from them.

There has never been so vast and anonymous a beauty. In its violence of birth it could afford to throw away great efforts and great pangs of labour. Many of its supreme struggles have been vain. It may be doubted whether one single cathedral has proved an unmitigated success. Such undertakings were so enormous that their completion required the life-work of several generations, and the skill and fire have diminished down these degrees to a patient and uninspired close. Also, the centre of a town is never so safe a soil for experiment as some monastic oasis in a smiling wilderness. There, no hindrance has come to these long, deep breaths of intoxication and the clear air and clean winds have added another strength to their potency.

The whole movement may be compared to an inspired outburst of free-formed poetry ; where it has fallen into good moulds the molten metal has run into pure and unbroken shapes, in other places a cracked and too emphatic failure has been the result. It is not necessary for admiration to be indiscriminate where there are so many things to choose among. There is no need to stoop for fruit that has been fanged by the wasp, a symbol for the public in its stinging and destructive waste. We may let them burrow where they will, blind to the good.

They knew no past save that of their own memories. The heroes and the gods of Greece and Rome, in ignorance of their nakedness, they were not able to clothe in anything save their own similitude. A suit of old armour was as a Pharaoh's tomb to them ; its little differences to their own were the ripples and the rilled shells of time, a great and unknown sea with no gods upon its glaucous fields and nothing but a wintry terror to its name. Nowhere to the north of Provence was there an antiquity or its monuments, and so they filled the hills and valleys with a race of legends, making themselves into the progeny of these giants and excusing their few relics by crediting them with an overabundant energy and a life of chivalry that left no time for anything beyond its own punctilious observance.

In the centuries when a river could not be forded, or a bridge ridden across, by any knight who would not accept the challenge of the champion on the other side, it is impossible not to feel a more sincere admiration for the priest or monk who could cross with impunity, thanks to the credulity that he served. The church was the only sanctuary for those not prepared to give, and to receive, hard knocks. Its activities had thus a double energy behind them, for they both believed in the superstition they were extolling, and tried to dramatize its supernatural quality so as to build themselves a more secure shelter in its shade.

Let us try to examine their satisfaction and the manner in which they achieved it.

We have seen their castles, bundles of towers, at any strategic position and have described the armoured castellans and the flat-sided women who lived in that dark and windowless confinement. We must live for a little time longer like parasites upon their vitality and try to analyse the pleasures and distastes in their blood. For a woman to possess great beauty in their eyes she must bear the true warrants of her birth in pale skin and aquiline prominence of nose and cheek-bones. " Cuteness " and " sex-appeal " as now practised in the United States over the counter and in the chorus, would have advanced her no further at that time than the dairy-door. Very long legs, straight sides, and a perpetual pregnancy had to go with this fair skin and straight hair. In clothes, they aimed at producing shapes beautiful in themselves, for it is difficult to believe that there was any sex-stimulus in the fantastic heights of fashion that they reached.

These points of physical admiration are important because their fulfilment was a guarantee of heredity, and owing to the risk of death in battle, tournament, or crusade, the hereditary principle had to be vehemently insisted upon. The barons had to accentuate and sanctify their caste, and this was made easier for them by their difference in appearance and in speech from their serfs, or from the citizens in the towns. Court French was an international language that they shared with the peers in foreign countries, and it was as useful to them as Latin to the mediaeval church. Their pride was kept at a perpetual state of alertness by the world of heraldry in which they moved, and by the bardic records of violence and fidelity that were read to them and had been composed about their forbears. It was an age that bristled with opportunity and coincidence, for an excuse could be made, or a parallel be found, to the wildest feat that these intoxications might inspire. Women played a large share in such incitements to danger, and without their support half the achievement of the age would have been left undone. Strength and bravery they admired in men more than good looks, manners, or learning; and from this they took their delight.

Terror and exaltation were the two poles of their emotion, and they give a very different diameter of feeling to the clogged or sprightly interplay of fine eating, fine talking, and ironic or delicate music. In the eighteenth century mountains and forests were horrid; Mozart would faint at the sound of a trumpet; there were no moustaches except with cavalry officers and Jews; drawing-room editions were printed; few beauties of the mediaeval age would have found a husband, and, conversely, not one of the fops or wits have gained a wife. Between their states of terror and exaltation there were but a few degrees of happy boredom and contented dullness; and, on either side of these, exaltation and terror approached each other so nearly as to be indistinguishable. To get their effects, architecture and sculpture had worked themselves into the most perfect instruments of panic and rhapsody. But these were qualities that men and women never sought for in their own homes, where embroidery and tapestries were the only decoration; and so they associated these two ends of passion with nothing else except religion.

A huge race of celibates lived in their midst to pander to these two emotions. All that side of life which they imprisoned in themselves flooded up within them and broke into these new channels. Their austerity and privation reinforced its strength, and where the more fervent and primitive emotions failed a kind of spiritual as well as physical onanism contorted the imagination into strange flowerings of art. The men and women celibates were two more sexes over and above the procreative and accustomed pair, and the world of human beings doubled its own forms and was richer by this multiplication. There is a similar and even wider process going on in the big cities of the world at this present age, and it is possible to conceive that if their growth of population goes on unhampered for some century or more into the future there will be many more than just the two established sexes. No doctor could deny that these changes are already taking place in the great German cities, and what may be true now of Hamburg, or Berlin, had its parallel in the classical world with the later Alexandria, or with the Rome of Nero and Petronius.

The velocity implicit in such changes of direction can be wasted in a vulgar dissipation, or else it can flow into such extraordinary shapes as those by which all Western Europeans are surrounded. The bleakest Scotch moorland, the blackest and foulest slum in Sheffield, the most chic French watering-place, the bloodiest bullring in Spain, none of these can hide themselves many miles away from such evidences of the past. Whether lying in ruins, or still in use and smelling of incense, or of hymn books, this is our past before we gave birth to the new world of America.

In a sense, there are almost no other buildings. No one with trained eyes can see much more than the poetry of desolation in the dead temples of Girgenti, or Paestum. When new, they were dolls' houses, built by children, and brightly and badly painted by children. Roman remains are worse because they lack any naïveté that the Greeks possessed and because they had become brutalized by conquest. The dying gladiators vitiated an audience which had become urban far too quickly. After this we arrive at Byzantium, and the false enthusiasms of the dilettante have exaggerated the beautiful mosaics of Ravenna and Cefalu, and their one splendid church, St. Sofia, until the Byzantine age has been established as the greatest time of European art.

Outside and beyond this there is nothing, or nearly nothing. The filigree courts of the Alhambra have the beauty of fringed tents, or of coffered chests, but they have no more pretence than this to architecture. The pavilions of Japan and China are a diminishment even of this Arabian profession. So there is nothing but a mosque or two in Cairo, and the Taj Mahal, that Italian bastard born to the Indian lotus-pools. This has a poetry of situation and colour which hides its full-blown shape and the tired and expensive finish to its detail. The deserted city of Fatehpur-sikri, not far from Agra, and its mosques and palaces of red sandstone, may be more beautiful and finer work than this, but it is all;

and, indeed, if Cairo is allowed to be in a Mediterranean land and not in Africa, it may be said that the Moghul buildings are the only things out of Europe and the Mediterranean basin. They are far away and pleasant, lying in opaque tides of moonlight, or under a copper sun that beats down any eyes that are raised towards their domes. In fact, the Moghul palaces and mosques are loud in their excuses, and their delicacy has won them a considerate treatment that will not allow too close an inquiry to be made of their condition.(1)

Half their loveliness was a harem secret, only seen by the women, by one man, and by a crowd of eunuchs. It was of a much more selfish variety, then, than that of a cathedral; and even a little more selfish than that of some great monastery, where at least the church and cloister could be seen. As well as this, the fact that all carved detail had to be abstract, and that painting or carving the figures of men or animals was forbidden, made their world of beauty into a blind pattern, and turned their thoughts and their poetry into extolling nothing but the things they were forbidden to touch in the other arts. Poetry became an aphrodisiac, occupied merely with the limbs and the machinery of love; it could never advance out of this into being a literature. Their buildings were sporadic in origin and in life; what one Emperor, or Shah, built, his son and successor pulled down, or more certainly neglected. Their mosques had no service, no ritual, and no music. There were no vestments, and no priests to wear them; no splendid sacristies and chapter-halls; no sculptured tombs of knights or ladies; no carved stalls, glass windows, or tales of heraldry.

In the Eastern kingdoms there was never anyone but

the ruler ; there were no nobles, and even a rich merchant was forced to hide and conceal his wealth as much as possible, while that part of it which he dared to spend went on the most temporary forms of decoration and did not proceed to further lengths than embroidered shifts, or silks shot with gold. The thousand years of Musulman power that began with the conquests of Mahomet's generals and ended with the gradual decline of the Turks produced, indeed, a beauty of stuffs, and little more than that. Its other aspects have benefited by a wild exaggeration produced from the external magnificence of royal processions, and from the romantically shuttered palaces into which no foreigner could penetrate. In literature, and in architecture, neither Persia, Egypt, nor the Moghul Empire are of greater importance than so small a country as Portugal. The art, as well as the wealth and the wisdom of this particular East, are a historical delusion.

Instead of this one vicarious East, Europe has had a number of permanent Wests, whose romantic value, being ourselves Europeans, we are unable to appreciate. England, France, Spain, Portugal, Germany, Flanders, Holland, Florence, Rome, Venice, Naples, these are the most easily identified of this constellation in whose path we are still following. In all this, there have been two main agencies : the Italian, and the tall fair-haired man whom this book has been written to extol. The older sort of European, responsible for the classical world of antiquity, for the Roman church, for the Renaissance, and for the cultural developments which came out of the Renaissance, we can see thousands of times over in the flesh, and in pictures, but this type has been best portrayed and fixed ethnographically in the portraits of El Greco, and in, for instance, the crowd of Spanish nobles who stand at the " Burial of Count Orgaz."

A particular trait of race in them is the eloquence of their hands, they speak as much with their fingers as with their tongues. They are small in stature and eloquent of speech, their impetuosity carries them far, but they have no retreat and little stamina. They flew with a strange fury, out of the Gothick that they never understood and could not practise with any conviction, into the Renaissance, building this theatre where they staged their own past in an incredibly short space of time, as though it was meant to be of scarcely greater permanence than a painted scenery. By the time laborious execution, which comes behind inspiration, had caught up with them, their conception had changed its form and flowed into broken and hysterical shapes that sought to frighten, to astonish, or to amuse.

The twelfth century left its monuments in every country of Europe, while the High Renaissance before it died in Tuscany and came into a heavier and more gaudy life in Venice, produced few buildings, but each of them was a masterpiece. The palaces at Urbino and Mantua, the Temple of the Malatesta at Rimini, later on the library of Sansovino and the villas of Palladio, these are the achievements of the revival and they were inhabited by the highest type of European and probably the finest human type there has yet been. None of those Eastern races who live in an architecture of pavilions and have not yet learnt to use a chair* can afford even the weakest and most humble comparison with an Italian of the sixteenth century. But this is not the place to attempt an investigation into the paradise where the

---

* This is surely an important criterion by which to judge the human race.

mind of this man liked to walk. We must leave him here as one of the two instruments of the West until the moment comes to approach him again when we discuss the influence of the fair-haired race upon his conceptions of poetry and beauty.

We are back again in those two states of terror and exaltation, of panic and of rhapsody, which we described as being the poles of emotion for the Northern race. But behind these powers of superstition there were the secular and military emotions. These had a kind of genealogical sanctity, being a series of affirmations that it was unwise and dangerous to contradict.

The man sitting on the outside of the bus reading the football news in his evening paper sees the whole country in terms of the different teams. Each big town is not much more in his mind than factory smoke, a noisy street, and the footballers paid, or unpaid, champions of the crowd. The armoured figure of the knight saw the world in rather similar terms through his raised visor. He may have seen with his own eyes as many castles as there are mushrooms in a field ; further on, just out of sight as it were, there were numberless others, of which he knew the names and no more. In certain definite directions he may have travelled great distances in a crusade or on pilgrimage, but everything out of sight lay in a thick mist of improbability, and all he knew was that just the same institutions of religious and secular power held sway as far as the shores of the sea, on the further side of which, with the Saracens, or in Africa, something very different might be reasonably expected. The football-lover's world of sport is closely paralleled in the ring of chivalry and elaborate fair-play by which the knight knew that he was surrounded. If on his travels, his presence would be made welcome at any tournament held near his path, and the superstition and credulity of those centuries are well illustrated when it is realized that sudden advents of this nature were the only kind of arrival possible since it was not practicable to send messages more than a very few hours in advance of your coming.

If there was a tournament in the green meadows below the castle the news might be brought that an English knight and his retinue were but an hour's ride away, making for the lists. There was no other criterion upon his importance than the value of his armour, but these elaborate and dangerous games of chivalry could give a quick estimate of his other qualities and this mimic battlefield was a veritable drawing-room of deportment and demeanour. They were quick judges of his faults and strengths, and the horse he rode they considered almost as part of himself, putting down its faults as much to his disadvantage as they allowed its good points to his credit.

After it was over he would be entertained in the castle for a few days, and then rode away never to hear of his friends again. He could not write and had soon forgotten the correct pronunciation of their name, but he knew that their exact copies in hospitality, in situation, and even in physical appearance, were to be found over half the known world, keeping the peasants in subjection, or perhaps guarding some fanciful battlements against the Moors. The only change was in the landscape where these castles stood, and in the different peasantries who were their serfs.

Some of the castles were on cliffs above the sea, others in a border-land of marshes, on a rock at the bend of a river, in the clearing of a forest, on a small hill rising from the middle of a village, at the most difficult curve of a mountain-pass, anywhere that profit and defence could be made from their position.

Different schools of military engineers designed their capricious forms. The divisions of this military archi-tecture include the castles of the Welsh marshes; the Spanish castles, of marked and peculiar style, built as a defence against the Moorish cavalry; the castles of the Teutonic Order in the Polish marshes built to keep off the Tartars and convert the Lithuanians, the last pagan race in Europe; the Norman castles of Sicily and Southern Italy; the castles in the Peloponnese; and the fortresses that the Crusaders erected in the Holy Land, and in the Latin Principalities that they set up in Asia Minor.

All these are garrison castles, held by a permanent force of soldiers, and they are the supreme expression of a violent age, with below them the countless feudal towers and private family fortresses of each country. But the race who inhabited the castles in these different lands was the same, and they were as much strangers to their environment as are the English in India. If all the countries of Europe in which they established them-selves are thought of as a whole the general situation is much like that of India, where the differences of in-numerable languages and the hatred of one peasantry for another have achieved the permanent establishment of the white man, though his number compared to theirs is about one in six hundred.

There are half a million English, men and women, among over three hundred million Indians; and the ratio of the Normans to the populations that they conquered can have been no greater than this.

Their alert and martial architecture adapted and gave strength to the elegancies of the Ile de France, while to the other side of this was the equally strong and massive Burgundian style which came from Cluny and Cîteaux and directed great monastic building activities all over Europe. In this way a most extraordinary body of energy was assembled and put into operation, and within two or three generations, before it came into its own decadence, the Norman race and the other races into which it had bred, all of whom constituted the fair-haired man, had nearly achieved a unity of Europe which has existed at no other time save under the Caesars. They even took Constantinople, and nothing save their quarrellings could have made their conquests impermanent. But too many of these proud champions had separate ambitions of their own, and this brought the collapse of the whole movement and turned it into the smaller European history of two or three kingdoms. The developments of the imagination and of art were lost to the Northern races and became the property of some two or three Italian mercantile states ; while that great building activity lost its strength in continual wars and expended its last energies on a few separate technical masterpieces where delicacy of detail and fineness of invention were the object.

The strong emotional power that the mediaeval builders put into their works can be easily understood when it is taken into consideration that there were so few drags upon their inspiration, and that the necessary concentration of mind was not continually wasted upon needless excitements. News was something entirely lacking in their lives. There were no newspapers, and nearly no books ; there being about as many people in the country who could read as there are persons who can understand Russian in this kingdom at the present day.

" News," books, music, the theatre, any sight of things drawn, except in the rude frescoes of a church and an inn, or in the finer and microscopic ornaments of an illuminated book, all of these were things wanting in their lives. These intoxicants and drugs were lacking in their sedative as well as their excitant properties, so that their state of mind and nerves was of a more perfect normality than it has been easy to attain since these various inventions have come into an universal practice. It was an early morning of the senses with a cold and energetic freshness, clear and brilliant light, and no need to go further than the wild-flowers in the fields for images of poetry or motives of ornament.

Red campion and blue Canterbury-bell, fox-glove and gold-flecked strawberry, these became the properties of an age which had never heard of acanthus, myrtle, or asphodel. The campion was an alert sentinel on the path to the nettle-bed; the Canterbury-bell blew its faint scent like a far sound from the holy towers; the fox-glove let fall his painted gloves for fairy hands to try and hoped to hold them prisoner in this pomander that was more stern than any fetter; the strawberry had baited his sweet, red flesh with some golden straws to catch the birds, and he trusted his propagation to their quick beaks under the strawberry net and their safe flight home to the thick boughs.

The stone-wall of the garden had a steep and ridged coping heavy with lichen, its slanted depth was meant as an awning to the fruit trees catching the sun below. There were more fruit trees standing by themselves in the ground and hung as heavily with fruit or blossom,

L

according to the month, as the great candlestick in the cathedral has lights to its branches, or smoke of incense hiding its lit boughs. A pair of magpies perched on the cloud of blossom and then were gone, leaving an image on the eyes of their raven heads, white shifts, and tails like a crinoline or a parachute, carefully arranged to steady their low and deliberate flight through the trees and over the wall's sharp edge.

Flowers were like little faces to look into. Pansies had downy cheeks and soft eyes; periwinkles were no more than blue eyes in themselves and of the sort that go with a pretty innocence and a protection of straw hair easily kindled into love; violets had no beauty in themselves but only with their sisters when the appeal they made was that of a town on a holiday, or a wood live with sunbeams. There were snapdragons guarding these lowly things with their sleepy fires, and their jaws were old traps closed tight in the heat; near by were the rose bushes, holding back their beauty with the pathetic spears that are their only protection against the hand. All of these flowers were single, and they were thin and fine to focus, strengthening the impression that this was an early morning of cold and energetic freshness, clear and brilliant light.

All the while, something was going on, the flowers were nearly audible. Smoke climbed straight into the sky at several points over the wall. There were doves crooning in some tall elms, and then with a sudden break, and after that into eternity, a cuckoo sounded quite near out of some secret window in the trees. The cuckoo and the turtle-dove were the soft and strange discords in this place where everything else was related and but a unit in a great entirety. They were foreign to this little perfection and gave the only hint of any other world than this. They breathed jasmine and clove upon these simpler scents.

Far off, and so distant as to be in another world, shapes of jasmine and of clove walked in other gardens by a rill of water from the hills, or lay in a pavilion where their jasmine skin made the marbles cool. They swam in deep water and made two worlds of poetry with their lotus curves and petal limbs, climbing out of that glass matrix into two strange and pagan antiquities. A naked and double mythology built itself out of their beauty and resolved itself into these new scents, strange and strong above the violet and the rose. The eyes had burnt themselves out of their blue purity into black and velvet coals of fire ; the golden hair of the north had turned to gloss like the raven's wing ; the limbs and body, while they kept their thinness, had lost their pale tone and gone into dark and spiced smoothness, or into the lacquered gold of the jasmine. The mouth had a hotter fire out of these spices and this burnished smoothness, and the shoulders were rounded into two arches, two pavilions. The sharp mornings had changed into long afternoons dawdled in these shades of marble. But the turtle-dove and the cuckoo had settled on the trees, and their notes sounded just the same message of strangeness and difference to the languor below.

They were out of sight, hidden in the branches, but the warm contentment of the one, and that double-note of warning of the other, gave the alarm of something far away and alien to these slow courts of shade.

Clove and jasmine died before the eyes, and the voices of these birds snuffed out their scent as quickly as a candle-flame. They went into the darkness of which they were part, lying at the back of night so far into its depth that they were near the day at the other side of that wood of flowering trees, and they lived in a twilight made from its blossom that powdered the whole air with lit, but faint, boughs.

Instead, long twists of smoke rose into the sky, and the dove and the cuckoo were in the elms. At one point, a great grey back like a whale showed high above the wall and towered right up, dwarfing the tall trees. It was held in position, tied down as it were, by a fiery pattern of stays and ropes that had settled themselves into a fine and delicate beauty of strength. Far even above its pinnacles the thin, tented roof sloped up into a knife-edge that flowered perilously with what might be the weeds and sea-fronds gathered by that sharp keel. It was nearly impossible that this huge thing should for ever hold to its moorings, and even on such a calm day as this there might be no wind if you stood right in its shadow, or moved entirely away from it into the fields, but if you moved out of the safety of its sides just a step beyond its shade so as to be free of those giant walls, immediately a violent wind blew round its edges, of the buffeting sort that a harbour-wall has to fight against.

The front of the whole thing was recessed and worked like the poop of an immense galleon as though designed for swiftness and safe balance, and high up in the centre of it was something which changed from a wide-open rose into a huge and ominous wheel, and then altered again into a series of sails, furled and rolled, but ready to open at the wind's provocation. Later on in the evening this wind blowing out of the sunset would increase in force. The western fire caught the spaces between the spokes of the wheel, so that the petals of that huge rose had burnished leaves to protect them, and the sails, not yet stretched to their full height, strained and raced at their ropes. All was ready, and as the low clouds coming down for the night began to close round, some among them passed quite close and low above its roof, and this huge stone thing in its stillness, just about to move, contrasted with their steady speed as they went to their posts in the darkness, and began, itself, to move out into the night.

But this was not yet ; just now it lay at anchor tied down by the stays and ropes that we described and showing its grey, whale back above the wall. Everything in this new world was strange ; things had begun their fresh formations under no hint of what there had been before. The castle, standing out of its moat, showed again in that brackish water ; and there were two castles, joined together in their foundations, and riding on an even keel in that choked river where water only stood and never flowed. The garden was walled on three sides, on the fourth it was open to the moat and edged by it so that the castle in its new chalk whiteness climbed straight out of the pansies and violets into the high air. A wooden bridge, looking like a ship's gangway, or part of the castle's fortifications in its new and grained material, crossed over the moat and led into the garden. Looking up at the castle walls there seemed something bare and blind about their surface, and this was due to the windows which had no glass, so that they were either wide open, or closed and sealed with wooden shutters. There were no panes for the light to catch, and none of those shields to throw back the sun. The windows had lintels like old and worn eyebrows above them, and there was no decoration anywhere until the eyes got as high as the roof, where pinnacles and turrets made the bravest show possible, and there was a riot of unnecessary elongation and capricious crocketing. Up there it was supposed to be safe, and it was the part of the castle which had the most permanent value for decoration as it could be seen furthest away. Indeed, down the sloping cornfields, the black caps to the towers rose straight out of the harvest and suggested that a band of witches was hidden in the corn.

Higher in the fields, the towers rose very tall, and now their huge white mass, or bundle, stood inexplicably against the cloudless sky, giving a peculiar sense of power and force, for there seemed to be nothing strong enough for their weight to stand upon and they, again, must climb out of the trodden barley. Then, at last, upon the brow of the hill the moat could be seen, and the towers floated lily-like on its green surface.

Everything within sight had this clean, new appearance. The flowers were sharp and delicate enough in colour to make the most lasting dyes, and indeed gold might have been extracted from a bed of tall sun-flowers that were growing in an exposed place where they could get all the heat and light possible. These must be the colours in which the castle-dwellers made their clothes.

It was a reign of hyperbolic fashion. Rich young men wore their cloaks and sleeves cut like the sharp edging of a leaf or a fish's transparent fin. They were proud of their legs, and liked to illustrate their pride by showing each leg in different coloured hose as though offering a choice to the cloister-skirted maidens. Hats were of fur or of cloth with some news of a turban in their folds. The hats of the women were by contrast of a much greater elaboration, as though atoning in this for the uncompetitive simplicity of their skirts and bodices, which avoided any comparison with the fantastic clothing of the men. No prophecy of the aeroplane was too unlikely for the forms of their headwear, and in extreme instances it compromised between the aeroplane and the fullest rigged sailing-vessel. This mass of white planes and contours was designed to show off the rounded elongation of the face and the tinted cheeks that they admired, and often its folds were continued below the chin so as to draw the fullest profit from this framing for the face. Consciously, or without this guile, the domestic animals that walked with them were calculated still further to enhance those peculiarities of appearance. Small, curled dogs, not much bigger than a Pekinese, contrasted their inextricable confusion of curls with the straight lines of dress; and, on the other hand, fine greyhounds drew attention by slight parody to the physical and fashionable angularity of their owners. Gerhawks and falcons riding on the wrist were as aquiline as anything could be, and the slender ankles of the horses gave a further reinforcement to these ideals. For the battle, or in the lists, the knights rode a heavy horse, the ancestor of the present cart-horse, and its stamping clumsiness added another contrast to their plated armour, beaked helmets, and the thin, small men who climbed out of these husks as soon as opportunity would allow.

The vertical was an obsession of their minds, for they believed every blessing came straight from heaven and every trouble climbed directly out of hell. Where it was necessary to refine, or excuse, this dogmatic direction they at any rate made the steepest approximation possible. What they admired was height, in human beings as in everything else; the height of a castle or church was their preoccupation and they would only embark upon construction over a large area when they knew that this was necessary to support the thrust of immensely high walls. Other dimensional values were of much minor importance in their minds; and for largeness in its vulgar and plutocratic display they had little feeling, and have left few examples.

Fair hair was an inalienable prerogative of their caste, and it had an almost hieratic importance in their art. It was dwelt upon with insistence at every opportunity. Fair-haired men and women are as much a part of tapestry as are skins of saffron and of jasmine of Chinese painting; for until the Latin reconquest of the imagination their achievement in tapestry far excelled anything that they accomplished in painting. It was the true art of the North and none but Flemings or Northern French have ever understood it, while its extreme costliness of production destined it only for the castles of the very richest nobles who were sure, in themselves, to be possessed of this attribute. It added yet another genealogical flattery to their pride, for they saw themselves strictly echoed in every attack upon the ideal.

They passed their lives in a dense forest of legend where the antiquity was all contemporary, indeed it may be suspected that " old clothes " were hateful, and indeed haunted, to their minds, and that the placing of legendary figures in contemporary dress was not only a necessity from ignorance but the result, as well, of a refusal on their part to see beauty in anything but the height of fashion. The utmost degree of prolixity and elaboration was practised, and indeed expected, so that the figures on the wall might well be guests staying in the castle for some great event like a wedding, and they could have joined their hosts at the table without any difficulties of convention. Besides this, the eyes were not trained, as they have been in the last two present generations, to an ordinary commercial drawing of the figure as seen in posters and advertisements, and still less to the comfortable and suburban-home ideals of the Royal Academy; so that elongations of the figure, overcrowding of the composition, improbable richness of dress, and the fact that often a story is told in successive stages going on within an inch of each other, none of these things disturbed their appreciation, or let them think they were in a position to dictate their ideas to the artist.

The ever present poetry of sunny days, blossoming trees, indeed the ordinary lyrical properties that are eternal and unchangeable, were reinforced by the materials of the epic. They had fought to establish themselves in their new lands, and now, having mingled their blood with that of the earlier Northern wave of invasion which had built up its dominion, they tacked on its ancestry to their own and added Charlemagne and his paladins to their roll of heroes. Every invasion of fair-haired men from the North was made use of, and they armed themselves as widely as possible out of that uncertain past. King Arthur and his Knights, Charlemagne and his Twelve Paladins, the Visigothick heroes of Spain, the old Teutonic legends, this was their Trojan age of romance. Later on, such was the inspiration of this poetry, they put its ideals into a practical experiment and embarked upon two centuries of dangerous but sanctified romance. The gods and heroes of Greece and Rome were scarcely present in their cosmogony, for its extent was almost overstocked with their own property.

Perhaps the Franks, and its adjective Frankish, are the

truest and most accurate terms to apply to this civilization of the fair-haired races, for it applies to all their
different branches and covers their Eastern as well as
their Western activities.   French was its language, Paris
its centre of learning and fashion, and the district round
Paris the experimental soil of its peculiar architectural
style ; but all its ideals were carried out and propagated
chiefly by the Normans, and secondly by the Angevins.
They were the instruments of its inventions and
discoveries.

If we called a great parliament, or a council for a
crusade, these knights, between whose races and language
there would be so little difference, would discuss and
complain among themselves of their serfs in a polite
and fashionably refined French. Their appearance,
their dress, and not only their language, would tally ;
and the illusion given would be that of an united and
unanimous race of conquerors who had imposed themselves upon a hundred subordinate types of men.

The barons from England could instance the sandy-
haired Scots, with their bare knees, Roman kilts, and
broadswords ; the dark, guttural Welsh ; the gabbling,
barefoot Irish in their blue cloaks.   All these were
lands of mountains and lakes.   The great castles of the
Welsh marshes were built for Edward I by the architect,
Henry de Elreton.   Their purpose was to keep the Welsh
in check and to hold the coasts for his armies embarking
for Ireland.   Beaumaris, Carnarvon and Conway are all
works of this one engineer, and they were outposts of
the Normans into a wild and barbaric race that produced
a huge output of poetry and preserved a prouder genealogical roll of their chiefs and petty princes than any other
European country can show.

It was especially Ireland which was a difficulty. The red-haired men, but many of them were dark and Milesian in their origin, had an unheard-of vitality. Their monks wore habits of tweed that were dyed with seaweed and the sea-shells of the bare coast, and they chose the most inaccessible rocks of the Atlantic for their hermitages. The unreal greenland flowered into a myriad white tents, and the minstrels and poets gathered at Tara, each with the sept he belonged to. From the blue hills of morning till the blue hills of night there was a perpetual challenge of poetry, and warlike or lyrical measures were sung to the appropriate harp, chronicling a beauty which is lost and forgotten to us. There was a Spanish pride attaching to these ceremonies, and the poorest beggar bore the proud name of his chief and claimed relationship with him. These were inflammatory occasions, and the mail-clad Normans would raid down upon them and interrupt the dangerous poetics, getting back as quickly as they could to their stone forts.

There was the same trouble with the Bretons, whose rocky corner of the earth was the cradle of the Arthurian cycle. Their language was uncouth and hard to understand; they were not yet properly cured of their Druidical worship and were in dangerous communion with their Celtic relations in the English west. But they were fanatic in what they had assumed of Christianity, and were already building sombre and exuberant churches of a greenish granitic stone that spoke of the iron-bound Atlantic coast and the long, roaring waves that broke their lives upon it.

Far to the east of this there were worse dangers with a still pagan population, and the Tartar hordes riding nearer and nearer over the horizon. Against these

perils the very strongest defences were necessary, and at
Marienburg, on the Vistula, the Teutonic Knights had
built themselves a fortress using every resource of
mediaeval art to make it impregnable. It was constructed
of red bricks in the peculiar style only met with along
the shores of the Baltic, and had three vaulted storeys,
the cellar, the ground-floor, and the dwelling of the
Master of the Order, above. The Chapter-house, a
huge hall with a fan-vaulted roof, was supported on a
single giant pillar of granite, and every detail to do with
this militant abbey was of stern and martial simplicity.
The church looked as though it was in a state of siege,
and the bastions and ramparts of the fortifications
outside gave an impression that there was no peace, and
never any prospect of a day not passed in armour. These
jangling martinets, with their beards flowing out over
their robes, had a campaign of more than fifty years in
front of them before they could subdue the pagan and
Slavonic Prussians; and, at last, after nearly a century
and a half of continual warfare, they were forced to
surrender their monastery to the shaven-headed, long-
moustached Poles. The Teutonic Knights form one
of the strangest and most uncouth chapters in Gothick
history, and their distance from France was such as to
make it a safe statement that not one of their number
could have understood that language of civilization, but,
none the less, they represent a part of this universal
chivalry, and so they cannot be omitted from any account
of its different facets.

There were French Knights in Hungary who had
gone there in the train of the Angevin, King Robert of
Anjou. Fifty years earlier, in 1266, Charles I of Anjou,
his grandfather, had gained possession of Naples and

Sicily. These three countries had their complement of Frenchmen, and in the case of Hungary it has already been mentioned in the course of this book that two famous French architects Martin Ragevy and Villard de Honnecourt built cathedrals at Kaschau on the slope of the Tokay mountains, and in the most distant parts of that country. It is the second of these two architects, whose sketch-book, a unique architectural document and the only one of its period in existence, is preserved in the Louvre. The most competent among contemporary minds were at work in that corner of Europe, but Hungary was a country of immense wealth able to employ the most expensive craftsmen of the time. The Angevin King Louis of Hungary ruled over Poland as well, and, for a time, Naples, after the murder of his brother, Robert the Wise, by Queen Joanna.

There was an even greater building activity at Naples under the Angevin Kings. That magnificently bastioned fortress, the Castel Nuovo, was begun by Charles I of Anjou from the designs of Pierre d'Agincourt, and the churches of San Giovanni a Carbonara and Santa Chiara contain the magnificent tombs of the Angevin family. In the church of San Lorenzo there is a picture by Simone Martini of the coronation of King Robert the Wise by St. Louis of Toulouse, and the King is shown with the red hair and beard that two centuries of Hohenstaufen rule, followed by this fresh invasion of Angevins from the North, must have made part of the inherited physique of the ruling class in Southern Italy and Sicily. Indeed, their perpetual ascendancy was nearly established ; and if it has died out in Naples, and if one half of it has been diminished in Sicily by the massacre of the French Angevin Knights in the Sicilian Vespers, the taint of their Norman conquest is still most visible in the blood of that island. The Normans had wide feudal powers and great possessions, and their castles round the slopes of Mount Etna have never yet been studied with the detail that their importance demands, while the cathedrals of Messina, Monreale, and Cefalu are, as regards their exteriors, of undeniable if peculiar Norman architecture.

We can deduce, then, from these last two paragraphs three more types of the Norman, or French, pioneer. One of them would bring rumour of the Tartars, and of a still more dangerous foe, the Turk; both the others had their castles near to an active volcano, a symbol that they had arrived in landscapes very different from the green meadows and chalk cliffs whence they had sailed. At Naples, they were in the only city of Europe, save Constantinople, where a great population had continually existed since classical times; and in those alleys of beggars and cripples, painters and sculptors from Florence and Northern Italy worked for them in an appropriate French style that they could not really understand, but which was the nearest approximation possible to the fashionable Gothick of the time. In Sicily, the Normans came into contact with a strange maze of races composed of Italian, Greek, Byzantine, African, and Arab, and the weakness inherent in this mixture made the most pliable material for their rule. Out of all these, their preference, if it was a case for employing craftsmen, was undoubtedly for the Arabs, and there is, consequently, a breath of the honeycomb and the stalactite hanging about the Sicilian vaults and arches. The coronation robes of the Holy Roman Empire, now to be seen in Vienna, and in reality Sicilian work of the twelfth century made for the Norman Kings, will give an idea of the extent to which Arabian motives invaded this new colony of the North. On their arrival in Sicily their number must have been extremely small, and it may be considered doubtful if anything like a hundred families of Normans achieved the conquest. But their administrative as well as their military genius led to the instant arrangement into order of this new dominion, and where there had been no organization for so long the skeleton dispositions that a few Normans could accomplish established peace in the island for some centuries to come.

Lastly, Syria and Palestine were the classic land of fortification and castle building. The energies of the whole of Western Europe were engaged here over two or three generations and the purest air of romance lay over everything concerned with these incessant campaigns. The castles were called by names taken from the Arthurian cycle and from the whole literature of chivalry. The walls of Mirabel, Beauvoir, Belfort, Nigraguarda, and Blanchgarde rose up in their strength near castles with such names as Toron and Scandalion.(2) This choice of titles may give some idea of the spirit in which the Crusaders left their homes and established themselves in the Holy East.

The purpose in pointing to all these differences has been to try and establish the essentially cosmopolitan nature of the various regimes set up by these invaders from the North. For some six or seven centuries there had been nothing of the kind, and since the last Roman Emperors fled into the marshes of Ravenna there had been no civilization like this one, equipped as had been the Roman, with a governmental as well as a military

genius. We will move for a time in that hot land near
the castles with those names of romance. We have to
think of them, not only in their actuality, but also in the
ideal landscape that their name suggests. There has
never been, before or since in history, anything at all
like the physical and mental atmosphere of that age.
It represented concrete and realized ambition on a scale
that has no precedent. Life had turned into poetry,
and poetry of the most martial and alert beauty. It
had changed into a vigorous paradise that made it worth
while to run its dangers as well as enjoy its pleasures.
The scenes of chivalry that were the background of
their minds sprang into life, and it was as miraculous
and incredible as if the wildest theatrical ideals of music
and scenery had become a permanent existence affecting
everyone who had ever suffered such dreams. The risks
and hardships attached to it were no greater or more
serious than would be the contrast between that amazing
fulfilment of possibility and its hours off-duty; just,
indeed, the moving away from that heaven to the eyes
and ears into the rainy streets and cheap meals stretching
between the last lights of that paradise and the kindling
of its lamps again next day.

Beauvoir may have been a stony crag above a salt and
waste land, but there is no need to insist upon its realism
when the brackish river, hardly running in its bed of
stones, could make silver and perpetual music. The reeds,
with no river god and his urn to symbolize their green
plenty, sang of the tawny or gypsy end to these blond and
fair-haired vapourings, and its voice raised up a hundred
mirages to deceive them and cheat their fancies. The
conquered Saracens and their struck pavilions would
surrender the sloe-eyed beauties that the mind could

conjecture out of those far-off Indian and Caucasian
vales. The heroic trumpets had an apostolic fervour
behind their frightening din ; armour shone as bright
as feathers ; the phalanxes of spears were thick woods
and each tree had been dipped in a cold and deathless
light that never left it ; the hard, sharp cliffs beyond
the burnt plain looked at dawn and sunset as though
some strong and terrible liquid had been thrown at
them, they became ribbed and took on the shape of
shadows, till these bony, thin ghosts would rise up and
walk away from their posts, following, it would seem,
the retreating clouds that went down to the horizon so
as to leave a bare and empty night above, a night deep
and appalling in its staring, eyeless depth, and made even
more sinister by the starlight. The battlements were of
burnt clay and the sentinels dreaded an iron footfall and
a giant, metal man upon the ramparts ; but this phantom
might be there for their protection as much as to destroy
them, for they thought the Apocalypse was near, and it
must be allowed its shadows to throw before it.

Mirabel was less cynical in its interpretation of the
name given to it. But part of the safety that it suggested
lay in its impregnable defences so that in its shelter there
was room for a good many contradictions of the desert's
stony soil. The hillside sloping down to the little lake
was terraced out with vineyards, but they were young
and scarcely gave wine. The villagers in the valley had
sufficient water to make their gardens fruitful, and the
harvest of yellow plums was rich enough to make the
Knights give the castle this name. They were hard,
dry fruit compared with their golden parallels upon the
stone walls of the North, having lost all the lusciousness
of the plum and taken on little but a mockery of its taste

M

and colour. Those few stunted trees below the castle
looked poor and insignificant from above ; when in
blossom they were little better than linen thrown on
the brambles to dry, and after the half-hearted flowers
had turned into fruit the hot sun became an iron frost
to them and took all the life out of their flesh. But the
castle was called Mirabel from this faint reminder, and
an orchard sprang into life at the name ; a wood of
such thickness and depth, by contrast to this, that the
women of the castle who could never have much freedom
from the walls, found themselves perfectly lost and
hidden in its heart. There were birds singing in every
direction, and it was just as difficult to listen to any
particular song, not knowing where it lay through the
boughs, as to catch sight of the castle-walls through
leaves parted by glossy wings and shining throat.
In that sudden opening a spray of yellow plums would
look as though ready to drop into the mouth and melt
there, and then change just before that window closed
into a cluster of little parhelions burning by the tower's
black caps and hung there by the eyes, that had looked
up too intently at the sun before dozing into the hot gulf
of afternoon. It was too late, the towers had disappeared ; and the hours lulled themselves asleep until
the castellan and his knights came back and their voices
broke like a mystery into this evening that had lost all
sense of direction. There was dead silence at sunset ;
the stone well in the middle of the orchard was like a
drum to catch any sound. But out of that centre of
everything their voices were soon heard and the ladies
climbed out of the trampled grass to join them.

Blanchgarde was the greatest contradiction of reality,
and the only truth that it had was the grove of cypresses.

These had, at any rate, something of the thinness and delicacy belonging to the name, and they were the home of innumerable owls who called out in their abrupt tones all through the night as though to summon the sleepless to their windows. From these, some semblance of truth lay in front of the eyes. Moonlight was flooding the whole landscape, and it had become a winter of the purest and deepest snow, untrodden and unchallenged. It was still and quiet as this, but for the owls, until the suspicious warmth of its light told the mind that there were no trees to be seen anywhere, and now the whole point of that particular castle, guarding some princess in the winter woods who held a whole dynastic future of tragedy or triumph in her labours that were due before the frost died, faded and vanished out of the air. The sentinels on the ramparts saw their castle turned by this pallor into some other situation befitting its romantic name, and Blanchgarde seemed to lie by a silent and wan sea that stretched out in every direction so that the castle and the cypress-grove were the only incidents on its point of rock. The waters sparkled with salt and the waves were dead, heaped into mounds that could roll no further. One of these glittering masses moved a little and the alarm was sounded.

Their trumpets were of a more primitive nature than those that sound in concert-hall or on parade-ground, and the sound beat on the air like a flail. The one raucous, metal word they uttered clanged forth again and again, faster and more insistent than the owls hooting in the cypresses. Men poured out of doors and down each flight of steps ; but they had been wakened by a false rumour and the hindermost among them could turn on his steps and go back to the straw before he had

got more than a few paces into the night-air. So those
tides were unbroken and unstemmed. It was a peaceful
sea, indeed softer and more calm than any ocean can ever
be, and the sleepy and lilied air became a lake with the
castle of Blanchgarde climbing from a wrist in its waters.

Nigraguarda was to the south, in a most leaden and
burning land. The black clouds rolling up for a storm
meant an avalanche of rain, or a blight of locusts ; while
thunder, when it came, was a loud and terrible drumming
above the battlements, and lightning lit up the hosts
fighting in the sky. It was decidedly a land of tempests,
and it faced towards a mystery, for the shelving slopes
were the first advances of the desert and no one knew
what lay beyond, at the far side of its unknown breadth.
Africa lay in the direct, if uncertain, distance, and the
caravans of negro slaves passed on their way from the
coast not so very far into the hidden waste that they
could not be intercepted and the woolly-haired, basalt
prisoners be made to change masters. So the knights
of this castle found they had a negro tribe to work the
arid lands for them, and the giant stature and huge
physique of these serfs made them a little afraid of their
force. One day, perhaps, the teeming millions out of
these swamps would invade this land to revenge the
cruelties that had been practised upon them. They
would come to this point on the quickest road to the
slave-markets, and, not knowing the Arabs from the
Franks, would drown this whole castle in the flood of
their black numbers. Nigraguarda had, for this reason,
more romantic possibilities than just the one conventional trust against the Saracens, for anything might ride
up with the hot winds from the desert. Therefore, the
bastions were kept in an exaggerated repair and the

horizon was scanned with more than ordinary attention, for on just one day in perhaps a century all these cares would be rewarded and find their justification. It was an outpost directed against a new kind of foe with whom the knights had never been engaged in battle; and out of this strangeness they may have dreamed of an empire over the mirages of the desert into their true fulfilment of crystal water and golden sand at the far side of its dead waste.

As for Toron and Scandalion, they were in the thick of the battles. The first had a stubborn, bull-like strength and impregnability, with treacherous ramparts advancing like horns to entice the enemy into ambush. The second was built of the thickest and most armoured material to be found. It had deep wells of water, great granaries of food, and could stand a long siege. Missiles bounded back like hail off its towers; and even the deadly slings, stronger and much more dangerous than any arrows from a bow, simply twanged and throbbed out their force against its strength. It lay, stretched out like a lion across the plain, and its garrison would spring out on any force retreating from the siege and destroy them before they reached the hills. These two castles were the most dreaded by the Saracens, and they gave the greatest pride to the Crusaders; their defence yielding a more legendary and romantic pleasure even than that of the two great fastnesses of Kerak and Iblin, though both of them had an incontestable security.

In fact, there were castles in every direction, and no stretch of sky was true to the eyes unless towers rose up at some point of its horizon. Many of its opportunities have already been described. Where two peasants are to be seen felling trees for firewood there are castle walls shining white as any lighthouse above their bowed heads.

Further on, the vines are being trimmed down close to the ground and not one, but two, castles climb into the distance as a tribute to the blue clusters that will soon hang upon those gnarled stems. A shepherd plays his pipe to a dog who dances on his hind feet, behind them the sheep are cropping a smooth field and a castle climbs up at their back into the cooler air of summer; the peasants are hoeing in an enclosure fenced with wattles that are gilded with sun, and the castle makes a painful comparison of its luxury with their ceaseless labours. If summer is burning towards its greatest heat, the village boys are bathing in a stream with a castle high above the banks and a still and exquisite pool for bathing hidden, to all probability, in its walled garden; and now, at last, the harvest comes and a man and woman are reaping the corn with method, for its yellow and clearly cut comb stands stiffly where their sickles have worked, while the red poppies and blue cornflowers grow here and there in its borders. It is a hot September afternoon, the gold lightning breaks out of a cloud that hangs ominous above the labour in front of them, and the castle stands on a little hill in the other direction quite safe from the storm that would seem only to threaten the peasant and his crops and never to menace the castle-dwellers.

I arrived back from this searching out of towers and found myself in the apple-wood again. The lit mullions of the inn burned out, still, through the branches and I tried to make out which were the blind eyes of my own room. Nearly half of the inn must be occupied. The servants lived in damp, old-fashioned closets under the roof, then came a couple of ordinary floors, and under that, some rooms, half drawing-room and half bedroom, of which the doors were always left open so that their magnificence could be seen by anyone going upstairs. I should like to have placed Mr. and Miss Corder in imagination in an elaborate suite of this sort, rich in gilding and mirrors, but I knew that their good fortune had left them careful, so that their rooms were probably not far under the roof, while optimism would make them pretend that they always chose rooms on the top-floor because of the view. They were probably quite near to me, and it was more than likely I should hear them calling to each other, particularly, I thought, early the next morning before I was properly awake, myself. They would be exclaiming at the beauty of the light and promising themselves a prompt breakfast so as to take the best advantage of its doubtful, autumn life. Later on, I should hear their voices on the staircase.

But I came out from under a tree on to the footpath and there they both were. He had his arm round her waist, and they were talking so busily that they did not hear me come up to them.

S. S. : So you've not gone to bed, yet !

H. C. : No. The evening is so lovely. I should like to sit up all night. Come and talk to us, for we shall never all meet again like this.

C. C. : Let's drag these two seats together ! Oh ! I'm sorry ; have I soaked your shoulders with dew ? Everything is wet with it. Mind, if you sit down, that your feet are on the asphalt. Luckily we have all got coats and can't catch cold ; besides, who could, on a night like this, so long as one's feet are dry, that is to say ?

S. S. : Who could, indeed ? Well, what have you done to-day ?

C. C. : Another wonderful day of it, but this can't go on. It's too good to last.

S. S. : Well, what exactly was it, this time ?

H. C. : We have both been young again. We started off early, so early, in fact, that everything was mist. It was like an August morning and I thought we were back once more by the blackberries. We used to love them so, but, of course, at the time I'm thinking of, we weren't children any longer. Oh, it was years and years before you knew us ! We weren't children, but we'd only just begun sketching. To-night we can remember everything we've ever seen. We were going to be artists once, but I had to teach instead, and so had Carl. Never mind, we've had enough money the last ten years to go everywhere we used to want to be. Everything is so clear and fresh to-night that we are just imagining to ourselves that we had got to such places before it was too late. In fact, we are going anywhere we like and have reached there just in time to be inspired. I'm so happy in this make-belief that I regret nothing. All the hardships of travel are gone, and there's nothing one need do except drink in the poetry before one's eyes, and try to remember it.

S. S. : Well, give it me in more detail. Where did it begin ?

H. C. : You tell him, Carl. I should take too much time, and there is such a lot to say.

C. C. : Hilda began the story quite right. It was very misty when we left the inn, so much so, in fact, that we hardly knew which way to go, but I heard the sea from one end of the valley, and so we walked away from it, as near as we could judge, and soon found the beginning of the stone steps. When you go up the middle of the village you will remember there is a mountain stream pouring down to work the mills, and you walk straight up the path by its side until you reach a couple of steps and a bridge. You cross this, go down the other side, walk about twenty yards, and then you reach the real beginning of the stairs ; and it's better to go very slow, because there's an hour's climb before you.

The cobbles are all wet and glistening. For a bit there are high walls on either side, till you get above the houses and the wall gives up trying to keep pace with the steps. Then they go up the sheer side of the cliff, held up on little stone brackets. Presently you have climbed above the top of the cliff, and this is where the real valley—the Valle del Diavolo—begins. The bed of the valley is on a steep slope, and by this point the top of the cliff is practically the bed of the valley. There is a big boulder here to mark the best place for the echo. It's at one side of the road, and the cab drivers stop by it and shout through their hands. All the way up the valley you can hear this being done. But we didn't wait long there, we crossed the road and took the steps again at the other side, soon leaving the road far down below puffing laboriously up its curves.

S. S. : I know, already, where it is. The echo gave it away to me. I've had "Servizio, signore" and "buon giorno per tutti" bellowed at me many a time by that boulder. Go on !

C. C. : At this point there are a certain number of trees, not tall ones, though, because there's too much shade and the air's damp. The rocks are dripping with maiden-hair fern, like you see in conservatories ; but soon it becomes less rocky, the path is no longer stone steps but beaten earth, and there's actually quite a lot of soil on the ground. The path climbs round a dark corner into the light, and this is the top of a second cliff.

When we reached to it the mist had cleared a little and we rested there, looking down at the sea. While we waited the fog lifted like anything.

S. S. : Yes. The clouds go up the hillside like pulling up a blind. In ten minutes they can be gone.

C. C. : They were moving so quickly we decided to go straight on so as to get the view the moment it appeared. The path is now a steep incline with a stone step at regular intervals of a few paces, and a whole flight of them whenever there is an awkward corner. Down below, the road has climbed up much nearer and is almost on a level with us at the end of the valley. It is banked up round that corner and then comes back to our side of the hill ready for its last climb. Soon our path joins it and we have to go on past the timber carts and the struggling mules.

A few houses come into sight, and there are great piles of firewood at the side of the road shining in the sun like sticks of chocolate, and so distinct that you can see every separate twig. Here the carts are loading and the air is noisy with shouts. Just past this, the road is suddenly level for the first time and the walls of the town arch across it and cover it with shade.

H. C. : The walls are Moorish.

S. S. : That's right. I never see them without thinking of a scimitar and a white burnous—a soldier-monk, in fact. Did you stop to see the Moorish cloister ?

C. C. : No, we decided to eat our lunch on the hillside above the town. We were told which path to take and went on straight ahead without stopping. It's another path just like the one we came up by.

H. C. : But we must see the town. We must stop on our way back.

C. C.: We needn't climb too far. We just want to go up this valley above the roofs of the town so that we can see right over the spur of hills on which it's built.

H. C.: Then we're nearly high enough, now!

C. C.: Just a few steps further. Not even the top of this flight; no, the next will do, I am sure. Now we'll leave the path and climb a little into the grass, in fact we can change from place to place round about here and stay some time. There are different views every way you turn.

H. C.: This is the most lovely valley in the world. Look at the vines all terraced out. And what is all the shouting down there?

S. S.: Giuseppe, the old cabman, is one of the voices. The others are children playing with the echo, and women working in the vines. But they stop singing the moment a foreigner comes near them. It's a traditional song, heaven knows how old! Isn't it extraordinary to think that these sounds so far away are really just a few yards as the crow flies? All the little villages in the valley shout their news across to each other and carry on conversations. There's a festa up in that one, Pogerola, once a year, and you've no idea what the brass band sounds like echoing back from the rocks all over this vertical landscape going in the opposite direction to the ordinary; the villages in the valley are some of them half-an-hour apart and yet they may be only two hundred yards away through the air. You speak of the vines, but they're just beginning to cover them in for the winter. It's done with thin straw mattresses, and they do the same with the orange and lemon groves. It looks as if you could walk along them, they're laid so close together.

C. C.: There seems to me to be something of every kind of beauty in the world here at our feet. Look at those limestone rocks, they're worn into the shapes Leonardo loved to draw!

S. S.: Come a little nearer the edge. We must try and climb in front of that corner on the right; I should like you to see something beyond it.

Down below, the sea was a floor of lapis flecked with the most violent gold straws; and in the middle of it an immense golden bridge led straight into the fiery furnace that burnt with hardly a cloud to shield it. The rocks were hot under the feet and almost burnt the fingers.

S. S.: Come right out into the sun, here, so long as you're not frightened of the drop. But don't look at it, watch the sea, instead. It's too far below for you to be frightened of it. Come and stand beside me here, one by one; there's only room for one of you at a time. Those are the isles of the sirens, and that's Capri.

Following the line of coast the horizon, just off the land, was marked with a lovely pattern of blue strokes, like ink from a brush, but put there by a genius in calligraphy. The beauty of arrangement was such that it was impossible to believe they were simply some rocks and an island; indeed, one of the rocks was a great natural arch rising out of the sea, and even at this distance the light could be seen through its centre.

C. C.: It's unbelievable. Who can blame Tiberius for shutting himself up there?

S. S.: It must be twenty miles, or more, from here. Think what it must have been like till a hundred years ago; you know Murat brought it into history again. He captured it from the English. There are two pictures of his attack on the island in the Museum of

San Martino at Naples; most curious things, in themselves, because of the landscape and the strange uniforms of Murat's troops. His son Achille wears either nothing at all, or else a salmon-pink pair of trousers and a tall, plumed shako.(3) The island was remembered again after that and people began building villas and spoiling it. Before that, there was no life there except fishermen and goats, and one solitary Carthusian monastery.

You are right. There's every kind of beauty in the world somewhere here at our feet. This is a sort of cosmogony or universe, and so far as one can see there's nothing left out of it. Do you see that mountain over there above the town and beyond the next bay? The stone building you see at the top is a ruined monastery, the Camaldoli dell' Avvocata; it looks small from here, but it's quite a big place when you get up to it. In front of the gate you can sit at a stone table and watch the very top of Vesuvius coming out of the hills at the back here. The smoke rises up as if from a chimney. I have always thought that would be the place to climb to if there was an eruption.

H. C. : What is the other side of Vesuvius like? We have all driven along by Portici and Pompeii.

S. S. : It's a huge plain of vineyards right along to Caserta, only they're grown much higher than any other vines I have ever seen, and form really big trellises; but nothing can hide the mountain; it's always there if you turn your head. I need hardly mention Caserta. I know you've read about its garden with three miles of cascades and about its marble staircase. Then there's the aqueduct that brings water to the garden. It crosses valleys like Roman work, five tiers of arches one above another. There are great ilex-woods in the park;

every single leaf shines and glitters, but you'll have seen a wood of that kind at Portici.

The real plain of Vesuvius is like nothing else in the world. Pulcinella came from down there at Aversa. Even in Roman times those towns were famous for impromptu comedies. The white clothes of Pulcinella were taken from the peasant's dress; they worked like that in the vines. The dog-days of the grape-harvest were a naked saturnalia with sunburnt bodies jostled by bloated and aquiline masks; every incident of the day became a comedy and these scenes were playing all the time in the blacksmith's and the butcher's as well as in market-place and vineyard. Think of the tarantellas! Think of the tenor voices singing in the night; read the President de Brosses or Doctor Burney's " Musical Tour " if you want to know what both trained and untrained music was like in Naples.(4) The city had as great a population as London, and its churches and palaces were as fine as any to be found in Europe. It had fresco painters who floated a whole population on clouds if a wall or ceiling was allowed them. There were four or five monasteries as big as walled villages, full of majolica cloisters and painted halls; each had a parlatorio, a concert-hall where the choir sang, and a pharmacy to sell its particular sweetmeats and perfumes. Just a little later, after Murat's Hussar-kingdom had collapsed, a new kind of music appeared and Bellini's airs were sung all over the town.

But we are getting far away from this bucolic lunch we are eating. What have you brought with you ?

H. C. : Only some sandwiches. We were told we could pay a few coppers and pick ourselves some fruit.

S. S. : Then shake some of those apples off that tree.

They taste of lemons, and are a special kind grown on these hills and on the slopes of Vesuvius.

C. C.: Look at that boat down there, Hilda. It's like the skeleton of an insect from up here, and when the men in it are rowing it walks over the sea on two pairs of legs. It's like a skeleton slowly moving in liquid blue amber.

H. C.: At one time it would have been enough for us, by itself. Just drawn up somewhere with a few nets on a cold shore, and we'd have sat in the wind drawing it.

C. C.: A couple of nights ago the fishing-boats were better than anything I have ever seen. They came sailing in at sunset, each with a wonderful arched sail as curved as a swallow's wing. Then the night fell and I could hear them getting out their tackle and putting things ready. Soon each of them had a light burning and they started to move. All through the night these lights were perpetually arranging themselves into fresh formations.

S. S.: They're like a flight of birds in slow motion. They are all the time wheeling into line, dropping into place. The windows of the hotel, terraced high above the sea, make a wonderful place to watch from. You might be leaning over the edge of a cloud, and the whole night through little waves are breaking. Their sound is like thin glass rods being dropped and broken, or a handful of coins thrown into the air and fallen jangling back again. As they go along, a man in the prow of each boat knocks against the timbers and this is done to attract the inquisitive fish, over and above the entice-ment that the lamp has to their curiosity. There is so much hammering that it is difficult to sleep and you feel some enormous ship is building through the night.

C. C.: You are better at describing things than I

am. Next morning, when I looked out of window, all the boats had gone, and there were only a couple of little things, quite square in shape but hardly bigger than canoes. In each of them there was a man sitting with his coat over his head because of the cold mist. They were off the end of the pier. Because of these cowls the men looked like monks; but although they moved they were not rowing, and when I looked to see how it was done I saw each of them had his hands, but only just his hands, in the water. This turned them for me from monks into water-beetles, and they became still more inexplicable until one of them, without turning the boat or even looking round, began to move backwards and I realized that they were patrolling their nets, hauling themselves, hand to hand, along the strings. We ate some of their fish for dinner. Aulli they're called; they have beaks like swordfish, and green backbones. I can't say I liked them!

S. S.: The fishing-boats will have gone back to where they came from, across there in Calabria, at the far side of the bay. It's an almost unknown land. I went not long ago to the Certosa di Padula, a huge ruined monastery where, so far as I know, only one Englishman beside myself has been. It has the biggest cloister I have ever seen, and beautiful majolica floors. Paestum is only on the edge of that country. You'll have to go there to see the three temples! But do you see that enormous knife-edged mountain? It's at the back of Paestum, twenty miles from there and sixty miles from here. It is the mountain that Virgil loved, and he wrote about the green oak woods on its slopes.

H. C.: Yes. And what about Ravello here, just in front of us. It has a Moorish cloister?

S. S. : A Moorish cloister and a great deal besides. It has a Cosmatesque pulpit carried on a pack of lions, each with his tail curved in a fresh direction ; it has a Moorish fountain, Moorish walls, and one or two other churches with smaller pulpits supported on less numerous families of lions.

C. C. : Let's climb a little higher. I should like to see right over Ravello into the valley beyond. We'll go further up the back of this hill.

We started to walk up the slope and soon came into quite a thick wood of chestnuts. A little mountain stream ran through it in quick and headlong leaps down the side of some great masses of dark rock, which I was surprised to find were of lava, so that this molten mass must have been thrown right over the shoulder of the hill at some time. The grass banks were slippery and polished with heat, so we left the water and climbed up the hill, which had now left any kind of cultivation behind. The chestnuts, with an oak tree here and there, were used as feeding grounds by herds of pigs, and some children looking after them sat high up on the rocks so that they could see their charges.

S. S. : Let's stop here ; we can see everything, everything, that is to say, except Vesuvius, and that we could see if we toiled uphill for another quarter of an hour. We have got almost every conceivable thing to interest us here at our feet. We could live up here ; and, if we wanted to learn, just go down the hill. Greek, Roman, Byzantine, Saracen, Norman, the Gothick and the Renaissance, anything and everything down to the time of Murat lie below us.

C. C. : I'd sooner stay up here ; I can't be bothered with them. What do I care for styles ?

N

H. C. : That's quite a new sentiment with you, Carl.
You'd have never said it before!

C. C. : I could live in a hermit's cave on apples and
chestnuts, and never want anything richer than a little
honey. Even that I can imagine tasting of asphodels,
or thyme. Why did you bring us up here; you've
spoilt everything on the way ?

S. S. : I thought we came up, on purpose, in order to
get the view.

C. C. : So we did, but now it's nothing more to me
than the glass of my spectacles. It's only the cool air
and the peace that I like, and I don't want to look off the
hillside; it only makes me sad.

H. C. : It's all over now, all over, and we've only got
to do down-hill for dinner and for a few minutes' talk
in that smoky sitting-room before we go to bed.

S. S. : And it's " all over " in a much more serious
sense than that. Look at all this below us, and then
consider that for the last hundred years there have been
only two forms of art : music and the novel. Apart
from this there has been no painter or writer who has
been given proper opportunities. Architecture, the
greatest of all the arts, and all the minor arts at the other
end of the scale, are dead ; they don't exist any more—
unless you call faking a minor art, which I don't. Worse
than this, there is now nothing between Academism
amd the idiocies of the American poets, of Le Corbusier,
of " Les Six." They're no better than the men of
the academy ; they've tumbled over the edge and can't
climb back. But the cruellest thing of all is that because
we have produced nothing of our own we are to have
centuries of Americanization. Anything, anything, anything, except America ! ! ! Wouldn't you sooner be

a beggar in the dust ; or live up here, as you say, on chestnuts and apples ? Their nerveless, senseless vitality and their vulgarity ; when can there ever be anything to come out of that ? They will have ruined the whole world before they produce anything themselves.

The English are always a little way behind ; can't they catch up with the present and make it their own ? They have done this before. They were a century later with the Renaissance than Italy, Spain, or France ; they adapted the principles of Palladio two generations after his death and worked them out to their logical finish ; they produced their first good painters when every other country had stopped ; and after the Napoleonic wars, when Europe was nearly as dead as it is now, their poets and their painters were the first to search out the material on which the French genius fed itself till the new discoveries made by Cézanne. Can't we apologize to history in some such manner as this for our offspring across the Atlantic ?

Do you know what is one of the greatest evils of our time ? The railway fare to Paris is too cheap. It is a fatal thing to copy with the object immediately under the eyes. That is what is wrong with the painters to-day. How many of the Englishmen who made our Renaissance and formed our classical architecture had ever been to Italy ? Only the one or two of them who had enough individuality to cope with what they saw, and to keep their talent as an interpretation and not an imitation. There were enough ideas left begun, but not finished, by the Italians in their fever of construction to last us for a century and a half ; till too much classical antiquity was unearthed and we began copying again instead of interpreting.

Naturally, a proper documentation is necessary, but, once that is secured, it is not essential for any advance to be along lines parallel to the thing studied. It is a radiation from a centre, and not two lines like a double railway track locked close to each other and moving through the landscape in unalterable relation to each other.

Men of third-rate talent could produce a lifetime of good work in those days. There was little genius but much accomplishment ; in fact, the trophies of good manners and good education, the results of being taught things that were useful and that pointed towards practicable directions. Fashions changed slowly and there was not too much hurry. Above all things, their output was continuous and not in the least degree shy or constipated. There was no occasion to be nervous of criticism if your new work did not show such a radical difference from your last work that it was difficult to give it credit as the work of the same person. These things apply, as I said, to third-rate talent, not even to marked ability, and still less to the real, and ever rare, inspiration of the day.

It is time for some new and tremendous energy to be put into action. One man could do it. It needs an Inigo Jones, even a Wordsworth ; and if such a person were to arrive, there might be a safe future of fifty years following after him. Why should all our pleasure come out of the past ? We want to look at the past with a different focus of the eyes so that it does not simply stay on the retina, but soaks into, and then out of, our bodies ; leaving some kind of life-principle behind it and not merely its dead shadow that gets in our way and trips us up at every turn. The action of the past upon us

should be like that of a fine day, when the sun's rays go
entirely through one, and their warmth and vitalization
can be felt the whole time at work within the body.
Indeed, it should be just the same sensation as we are
getting now, sitting upon this hillside.

C. C.: That is all very well, but what use is it our
trying to pretend we are Moors, or Sicilian Greeks, or
Angevins landed at Naples ? We can never be anything
but ourselves. I was born like you were on the North
coast of England. Trams, trawlers, perhaps a bit of a
castle in ruins or an old abbey, these are the things at
the back of our minds, the only ingredients and material
that really come natural to us. Objects outside that
are an artifice that no amount of imagination can support
for more than a few moments. The longer you meddle
with these things the more dangerous your situation
becomes.

S. S.: Do you realize what things you are denying by
this ? Plato wished to banish poets from the perfected
state because of their incessant grumbling and their
strivings after spiritual and physical preferment ; there
was hardly what we should admit to be music in his time,
but musicians are a still more dangerous gang of con-
spirators, and they would be banished by Plato to the
bleakest and coldest Siberia. How much better it is to be
surrounded by grumbling than by placidity and blandness!
I suppose you prefer a state of easy contentment ?

H. C.: Carl didn't feel like that when he was poor.
He used to hate any kind of boundary, or finality, but
now he would like a wall built round the five hundred a
year that father left him.

S. S.: I am a great believer in walls, but I want them
built round quite other things than an income.

C. C.: Think of those dead bodies below. It isn't even our own cemetery : it's an alien burial-ground.

S. S.: You must admit, though, what a degree of pathos there is attaching to them. There is nothing left for them except time-wasting. They are choking and clogging time, trying to delay him. The more developed one's senses, the more dangerous and potent is their command upon one's time and attention. But it seems to me to be a most welcome usurpation.

C. C.: You are younger than I am. I have spent three-quarters of my life puzzling over them and asking them questions. Of course they never answer. They can't.

S. S.: That's exactly where you fail. You should both ask the question yourself, and answer it yourself. Sometimes you should be ready with your answer before you have decided what the question is. We were talking of the weight of pathos that there is hanging upon these old, shattered ruins. They are so old, so dreadfully old, and some of them have become almost impossible to believe in. The dead Caesars have nothing left now except their physical likeness to certain newspaper peers ; and as for the mediaeval age, it is impossible to be too careful about it. In the book I am writing I have tried to steer absolutely away from its known and conventional scenes. Magna Carta, Westminster Abbey, the battle of Crécy, what use is there in breathing upon those dead and hollow bones ?

But I think an attempted resuscitation to be of the very greatest importance, for unless some strong effort is made, we shall lose half of our greatness as a nation and may soon be thrown back upon our old and original continental situation, and in order to prevent this, or, at any rate, to deal with it when the situation arises, we must discover what our origins have been and what has been their early and natural direction. In doing this, we find our destinies were in the hands of a small minority, who also moulded the future for several other races besides our own, so that the inquiry has to be directed upon more general lines than just the particularities of our one half-island, for I am thinking only of England.

In thinking of all that Europe has produced, and there are five or six different dregs of this production in the valleys at our feet, it is no use to us to think of ourselves in terms of what the ordinary, dark Mediterranean man has accomplished, because he is as far removed from us as the African or Asiatic who may be our rival in the centuries to come. But our own type has broken into this identical landscape, and even carried his activities much further, up to the most distant corners of the Mediterranean, and it is as the alternative to the Latin that we have to consider him.

All we have to show for our contribution towards a general culture of the white man over the last three hundred years has been a steady succession of good poets, and this misty and rather intangible pre-eminence is, perhaps, enough to justify an attempt to bring out some further poetical material in our past achievement. But, besides this, there are two other facets to our task : the amount of this energy in Northern Europe that was not influenced by Italy and that, at the same time, has not become too familiar and spoilt from over-familiarity ; and, secondly, the sort of spiritual conquest of the Italian by the fair-haired race who fixed so often upon this physical type to convey his most convinced messages in painting. In fact, the question is resolved into that

amount of the Gothick which the Renaissance did not
conquer, and that amount of the Renaissance which was
conquered by the Gothick; so that we are feeling both
edges of our subject, and thinking of it only in victory
and not in defeat.

Don't, for the moment, let us delay any longer over
those dark, sallow townsmen, for we have the immense
bulk of our own achievement to discuss and it is a far
more profitable soil to ponder over for our own future.
We must come down from this hillside into greener valleys
and more gentle slopes.

H. C.: Do you notice how much lighter it is up here?
The valleys are getting quite dark.

S. S.: The Camaldoli, that ruined monastery up on the
mountain, has the sun shining on it for some ten minutes,
or quarter of an hour, after it is dark everywhere else.
The top of the mountain is like a little cropped field and
where it slopes out of sight is the actual summit. There
are a quantity of goats up there, and the sunset must have
the most intense pastoral beauty under this particularized
sun-burst thrown up over a cloud-top from far below
on the horizon. Everything round is a dark sea of
unknown depth with enormous rocks coming up nearly
to the surface.

As we spoke, the beams slowly slid over the highest of
the mountains' rocks on to the green plateau at the top.
But this evening it was only for the duration of a moment;
a cloud quenched these rays at their source and the
darkness engulfed that far-off hermitage. The mountain
was half-hidden in clouds, all the colour went out of every
object and the twilight had begun. All the same, there
was enough light to pick one's way quite carefully between
the stones, and in and out among the tree-stems. They

were oak trees, or chestnuts, with here and there a few of
the apple trees that grow only on these hills and on the
slopes of Vesuvius. Their yellow-green fruit has a lemon
taste and almost a lemon shape, and it was their boughs
that we had shaken to help out our midday meal.

It began to be extremely cold; but in a curious
manner as though it was some bitter sentiment and not
simply the chill evening that made it difficult to linger
on the way. I should have liked to go slowly, stopping
at anything which drew my attention, and I allowed my
two friends to walk some distance in front of me down the
cobbles, indeed we were a turn of the path apart from
each other, and they would be going for this reason in
one direction while my way was set in another.

This landscape had a popular emotional importance
for me, because my own spasmodic and frustrated
attempts had so often taken place within its orbit and
under its direct inspiration. Each year I spent several
months of the winter here and it had become for me,
since Venice, which was my true predilection, was too
crowded, too urban, and too cold, the very epitome of
that most desired contact with the heights of poetry, and
prose, to which I hoped to climb. It was associated in
my mind with an alternate fever and depression of the
nerves; typified by the incredible beauty of the landscape
contrasted with the poverty and squalor of Amalfi, that
little dead fishing-town; and the most copious springs
of inspiration in contrast to what could be the appalling
and deathly dullness of many months spent in that unique
and extraordinary hotel.

Near by is Naples, where I used to wander rediscovering
for myself a whole tribe of forgotten architects and fresco-
painters. The volcano is in every view, alike from a

window or from the belvedere of a monastery; and to
and fro from the town it is necessary to pass the opera
where Rossini won many of his triumphs, and the con-
servatory of music where the composers from Jomelli
and Leonardo Leo down to Bellini had studied. The
Neapolitan air is alive with its own lyrical or comic
melodies. The beggars and the slums are worthy of
Benares and the crowded cities of China. Nothing is
spoilt by too much being known about it, or by the false
enthusiasm of the foreigner.

As for the country place to which we retired, enough
has been said about its steep and ecstatic wonders.
Little villages are perched as if on solid clouds of rock to
which it takes many hours to climb. They are inaccessible as the monasteries of Meteora and Athos. The
Valle del Diavolo is designed like a Chinese landscape
as a decoration against the sky and not a design upon the
flat earth. It unrolls itself vertically. On a clear day,
if you stand in the valley and look at its two highest
ridges, the sea like a solid blue wall towers up visibly above
them, and loses, altogether, its appearance of a plain.
A thin line of golden sand, that the Greeks called the belt
of Venus, runs round the bay into the distance towards
Monte Alburno and the temples of Paestum. The
whole direction of its curve seems to be designed to lead
the imagination towards those fabled, but crumbling
beauties of pillar and architrave ; while above them, but
far away, even in their distance, stands that legendary
mountain with its terrifying and jagged knife-edge of
rock. Beyond that, the land seems to be of rocks, of
goats, and of eagles, until the Val di Diano is reached with
the Certosa di Padula like a floriated Escurial in its midst.
This building, until I managed to reach to it, lay on the

furthest borders of ambition, and I was led to hazard its splendours on a scale which, luckily for my contentment of mind, the actual sight of its majolica halls could quickly confirm.

Such was the scenery of my ambition for several of the most impressionable years of life, and I found far more in it than would ever have reached me among the spires of Oxford or the cafés of Montparnasse.

So far as I was concerned there was an indescribable romance about every bough, every rock, and every sip of air in that whole day. They represented the first things I had ever found for myself, and their mere enumeration has the strongest effect upon my emotions. I felt that the first phase of their activity upon me was over and that when I came back to them again, for better or for worse, they would find me at a later stage of development. The arrogant blossom now gave place to the fruit it had been masking, and who could tell how long this process might lie fallow and dormant before it happened again ? But my two friends with whom I had spent what seemed to be long hours of travel and experience, had been my first introduction into even the possibility of such things, and, in thinking of the distance between the first hints they had given me and the realization of their effects, I could see a range of immeasurable heights before me to be reached by energy and courage.

The new subject in front of me broke into a coda, or final fantasia upon its themes and trappings. The different orders of monks were so many uniform and drably communistic tribes of insects, vowed for a greater patience in their labours to perpetual celibacy, and spurred by this privation into more glorious feats of construction. The legalized magic that they served kept them safe, and their carefully preserved strength had continual reinforcements of fresh blood, the same type being perpetually drafted into its body as though they had, themselves, the power of procreation and the faculty of determining the look and the disposition of their offspring.

The horizon trembled with towers, and the air shook with bells. The northern woods that up till now had held nothing more lively than wolf or bear flowered into the strangest blossoms of romance. A universal desire for beauty passed itself over even the smallest details of life, so that nothing was left untouched by it and even the scratchings on the walls of a prison, drawn in damp darkness with perhaps nothing more serviceable than the nail of the finger, possess exactly the same characteristics and ingredients of style as the highest masterpieces that the age could accomplish. The fair-haired races had come into their powers of creation, and before they abandoned these for commerce and for the more practical sciences of life, and before they established the often unwilling colonies of their blood in other continents, they worked upon larger if less accurate images of heaven than the Mediterranean man, who was slower to abandon his superstition, and, if he did so, changed quickly from it into the newer rumours of mythology. The small septs of this fair-haired race working on the leaven of Celt or Teuton over whom they had secured dominion arrived at a feverish and precipitate fermentation of their ideas ; and they carried their principles all over the known world where the only barren soil for them was Rome, and even Naples and Florence broke into some fulfilment of this alien style.

The Dominicans, the " dogs of the Lord," were

habited like black and white mongrels; they matched the magpies in the fields. Carthusians were nothing more nor less than Moors of Atlas; the Cistercians more faded and less full in their line; the friars rusty and travel-stained in their drab brown. They were all at work upon their hives and were busily storing them for the centuries of winters that lay in front. The façades of the Latins had but a flat eloquence compared with the more nervous and troubled architecture of the North, which wore as much protection and made as many thrusts into the air as any armed warrior in his mail. The rigours of rain and wind had been taken into consideration instead of the summer shade and moonlight of the South. Roofs were buttressed and strung into position; the glass walls of churches were held up as perilously as any dancer by the corps de ballet.

Villages with more geese than men lay along the green lanes that led from town to town. The villages were empty because the peasants were working the fields. And all the time a gang of white cranes stood mutely like overseers in the distance and came up whenever the peasants moved to see if any grain or any roots had been left behind. Their nests were on the chimney-stacks and among the roofs. The strange, almost oriental elaboration that these birds gave to the landscape was supported by the dress of the peasants, who celebrated a feast-day of the Church every week and were, therefore, seldom for any stretch of time out of their best clothes.

The armies of the day, however small, made an extreme and unparalleled effect, for, once again, like the insects, certain ranks out of their number, and those the most potential and dangerous to the enemy, were considered to be of so little importance that no attempt was made at their protection, and they were left without armour. Once the bow and arrow, their weapon of offence, had become useless from too close quarter, they had no shield, no helmet, and nothing better than a sharp knife, or spiked club, with which to defend themselves. No quarter was offered them ; for they were not thought of sufficient importance to be taken prisoner. For this reason it is difficult to find their record, and artist or sculptor passed them over rapidly, if even delaying at all, in order to arrive at his patron, the Knight.

There is a bend on the path and a clump of these steel men are seen pointing beakedly, and creaking with a suspicious noisiness, towards where the artist has thought fit to station himself. We may add a frostiness to the early air which the artist lacked the faculty to portray, and so we can equip the knights and even their horses with the appropriate smoke of breath. If their beavors were down, ready for a surprise attack, they had no wider range of vision than the horse in his blinkers, or the bull who charges wildly ahead with his eyes on the ground. In order to see anything to either side of them both knight and horse had to veer round, and their slow, noisily rattling progress and the caution with which they had so often to turn their whole direction, has removed their semblance to human beings. They are the warrior-insects, flanked and backed by the harmful but defenceless varieties that are only meant to kill and be killed, and not to kill and be saved, whether defeated or victorious. Once he had been knocked from his horse the knight could not rise to his feet, much less mount his horse without help, and this left him safely on the ground, where he knew that honourable quarter would be offered to him. His code of manners let him accept this without shame ; unless he was killed outright in battle he would survive.

The cloister was the only alternative to this life of risks, and the making of cloisters is an art which the climate of Spain and Portugal favoured more particularly, with their extremes of heat to be shaded from and the windy draughts of winter to be kept away, so that no fair specimen of this range of invention can be found in Italy, or in any other country, and these walks of latticed stone must be seen in their finest examples in Catalonia or in Portugal. There they seem essentially to be the necessity of an invading race, to whom the new climate was either enervating, if they came from the North, or vigorous, if their land of origin was Africa.

However that may be, the mind prefers to think of them in the summer heat, or before its true fullness, while the garden walled in by the cloister was lit by low and humble flowers. The fruit-boughs lifted their loads of snow into the upper air making a delicate and fragile tracery against that soft and pigeon-throated blue. Below this, the cloister windows were sharp cut and nerved like leaves to these flowers above, which murmured, not with the crooning of the appropriate dove, but with the loud wings of the bees gathering honey. For thinness and fineness it was like living among the frost-flowers on the glass. It was very early in the morning, and in a moment the first footfalls would sound down the stone corridors. Then the boughs would turn from their blossom into fruit, for in the imagination we need not time our moods to the season's clock.

But that footfall never came, nor did the blossom lie for longer than a thought upon the bough. The leaves had been jewelled into this image by the moonlight, and when I looked round there was nobody in sight and not even a lit window among the mullions in the high wall. So they had gone, too, and I wondered if they had ever been with me, under the ridged roofs, and in this world of transmuted orchards. They were back in the pathos out of which they had been drawn, and into which they were put away each fresh time they were considered.

There was nothing to disturb this tranquil mood, and even the branches held themselves still as though unwilling to break it. The wood was little more than a tapestry in this faded calm, so that it had a tenuous but indestructible strength that nothing but its own changes could alter. This would hold until the dying out of the feminine and thoughtless moonlight, which only adds its own ghosts to the world. Just now it had not even this promise, and the two figures who had been with me must have wandered far away into its depths and would not, or could not, come back. So I walked between the apple-hung phantoms into the dead house, and kindled one of its sleeping eyes with a light that poured my own image into a misty glass, where I looked, and, even then, found no one beside me. Nor was there any sound in the house; and they must have been sketching far away, at such a distance that this very darkness had become light and had lent itself generously to them for their unwilling mockery of the detail that they loved. There I should have liked to follow them, and did so in some measure as I lay trying to sleep.

THESE SAD RUINS

THE autumn air in the early morning outside the train had all the qualities of taste proper to its season ; it was the time for yellow and green plums, for partridges heaped by the red berries they live among, and even, in the not distant future, for venison. The spotless villages that the train flew past seemed just to keep their foothold, and no more, in the sandy plain, among the bracken, or in a clearing of the fir-trees. In spite of the sharp winds that blew round every corner the streets of Berlin had not a particle of dust in them ; the motors were noisier and more determined than those of London or Paris, and there were no beggars or street-vendors loitering on the pavement.

This is the town to repair to for a true and clear focus of the present. It has a modernity which is really omnipresent and has not been arrived at by the mere showing of a few freak pictures in a dealer's maws. It has no Latin Quarter, no slums, and there is a decidedly barbarian strength about its newness.

Now the writing of this book has been a slow and interrupted process. It has entailed many months of digging and delving in museum and library and many days in railway and motor car. In its happy moments it has moved at a sure and headlong speed that, if the

o

book has any merit to it, must have shown its fast and fiery track to the reader and blown him along in the same wind of poetry that helped me to my ends. I have said that there were many interruptions, and it is only fair to add that some of these were at my own instigation, for, however hard I may be working, I must be the master and not the slave of my method. My actual reason for coming to Germany was in order to revise and complete a long delayed book on the architecture that is a parallel in building to the age of Bach, of Mozart, and of Haydn. Here, in Berlin, and there is no need for us to go further, I found new states of mind and new conditions of life that made this particular past I searched for, seem even deader than the stones and plaster out of which it was composed. This trip that I was making was an interlude in the bigger work that lay behind and in front of me, and of which this book is the outcome, but here I found myself assisting at a scene within a scene, and discovered a great impetus in its contrast to the two tasks I had set myself and in its difference from every other culture of the present.

After living in two dead pasts and a drab present, compared with what the present might be, were one to think of it in terms of the ideal, certainly this city led one, whatever its shortcomings, into a new and stimulating perspective, even if its details were crude or repulsive. The conditions of life were undoubtedly moving, and not either drifting or slowing down into a paralysed mockery of their own dead days of activity. Ugliness and rawness gave something to the mind which the brick villas and trim gardens of our own country can never supply. The war of sexes and the war of machines were at their height of strength; there was no pity and no quarter allowed. Because of this, all the combatants had the air of tried veterans, and the fruits of their experience showed in remote and curious corners of the spirit.

This city of " night-life " had a very different air to the *dîners fleuris* of the Riviera, as though the cost of flowers and the short life that is all they have, had banished these ornaments of dissipation in favour of the more material satisfactions of food, wine, and music. Money spent had to buy its full weight of these three things, and, in comparison with that elegant and vacuous coast of villas the food had to be heavier, the wine stronger, and the music louder and more brassy-breathed. These novices in pleasure had a younger zest and a bigger appetite for their task. They were more seriously inclined to it. The promptness of servants and waiters was no part of elegance and fashion but had been enforced by the business-man's standards of efficiency. It had a military insistence that no time should be wasted, a very different disposition from that of all other haunts of this kind where the only aim and purpose is to spend time. Even the hotels and their inmates were interesting. This was true of so unlikely a place as the hotel-lounge, and the strange horror inspired by gross appetites hung heavily in the smoke-laden air and distilled itself from cigars, from leather chairs, from the women waiting there, and even somehow from the lift.

The continual journeys of this comfortably padded cage were the moves and countermoves of a game. Someone noticed long before would now come out from that metal door and associate himself with one of the girls waiting there to be taken out to dinner. He was a young, but largely built man of commerce travelling, probably, in some minutiæ of machinery, the name and use of which would be unknown to a layman like myself, and before they went out of the swing-door into their taxi they would have a moment's talk with a whole group exactly similar to themselves, and to whom they were obviously well known.

Even the lift that shook up and threw down these changing dice had about it some details that gave clues to many of the lesser mysteries.   Inside, there was a large paper rack full of the *Chicago Tribune*, and with a generous assortment of German illustrated papers. These were a study in themselves. A cohort of Tiller and Jackson girls dwindled along into more native beauties, and they were certainly as far removed in type from the big-heads popularized in North America by cinema necessities as they were unlike the revue-stars of England, or the plumed spectres admired by the French. But a moment's glance along them led the eyes to a placard with the words Claude and Cordelia D'Ors from the Ambassadeurs, Paris, upon it, and then the lift came to a stop and it was time to step out from that familiar door with overcoat held carefully so as not to catch on the steel trellis.

Sitting in the hall this time were three or four young negresses, the property, as I knew, of the jazz-band players from the night club on the roof of the hotel; and then, on its return journey, the doors clanged open and Claude and Cordelia made their appearance. They were dancing every night for a week in the roof-garden on top of the hotel. They were a remarkable pair. To begin with, it was evidently their intention to give an impression that they were brother and sister ; behind this were several other fixed ideas. Both Claude and

Cordelia had fair hair, Cordelia wore her hair long and
Claude had a fair moustache. These were two items
on whose distinction they much prided themselves, and,
as well as this, Cordelia wore long skirts that all but
trailed upon the ground. Even among themselves they
spoke French, but French of a significant, strained kind
that roused suspicion as to whether they may not have
been French-Canadian, instead of French, by origin.
It is difficult to know under what aspect they visualized
themselves, but there was something vaguely Chopinesque
in sentiment about their appearance, and its effects were
too carefully calculated to allow of this impression being
fortuitous. Upon this background there was super-
imposed, somehow, the suggestion that the tango was
the natural measure to which they moved, so that fox-
trot or one-step they would provide so as to oblige their
audience, and it would be beautifully executed of necessity, but without their allowing it to be supposed that
it really interested them, or that they were doing it for
any other reason than simply to please their friends.

They looked quite unruffled and entirely sure of themselves. I wondered if they ever quarrelled. Now and
again, I felt sure, Cordelia must feel irritated by these
long, straight lines imposed upon her conduct and
appearance, and must rise in revolt against Claude.
" I'm longing to stop this nonsense of yours. It gets
on my nerves. I'm tired of it." " Do as you like,
Cordelia, but you'll lose your contract with the Blue
Room, and they'll never have you back at the Ambassadeurs. Isn't it much better to be quiet like this
and keep to the floor ? Give it up by all means, but
then you must learn to throw yourself from the balcony,
or twirl round with one foot in someone else's collar.

But I don't care, you can do what you like!" "But just tell me, Claude, must I wear this hat all the afternoon? After all, we are only going shopping!" "Do whatever you like, I tell you. But I am going to keep to the poster, or my living's gone."

In fact, in this poster, their heads were put so close together as to be almost embarrassing, and they looked like a brother and sister of supreme and unenviable social distinction reverted, by some act of witchcraft, into their days of childhood; for who has ever seen a grown-up brother and sister behave like this? Such wistful tenderness of blue eyes and fair moustache, such an answer of blue eyes and fair hair to that masculine pretence. This was all very well, but the nursery was the place for it, and how should a moustache be in a nursery?

That very afternoon there had been trouble, I think, for when they came downstairs to start off on their shopping, Claude in his grey sombrero and Cordelia in sober and trailing black, they went towards the cashier's desk with a pride that had a little protest and a little resentment about it. There was ever an air of mystery about the few words they exchanged at the desk, though these were really some whispered confidences about the day's luncheon and the amount that should be deducted from their week's account. But there was a bigger treat in store this evening.

They came out from the lift in full evening dress and began to walk through the lounge towards the dining-room. Their duties in the roof-garden did not begin till midnight, but every evening they dined in the restaurant and by special arrangement were given a table where they were easily seen but not conspicuous. Indeed, to the ingenuous-minded it might seem that this tender romance was smiled upon by the management, so that they were placed not too near the band where they could talk to their heart's content. Then, but only for about one tune out of every two, they got up from the table and danced together. People dining in the restaurant for the first time would wonder who this idyllic pair come among them could be, and would make conjectures as to whether they were brother and sister, or a pair of lovers. But Claude and Cordelia were absorbed in the music, and they seemed to look on the other diners, if they happened even to notice them, as the merest canaille. It was difficult to think of them as having any lives apart from their dances. They were a prince and princess from a fairy-story, that was the idea ; and only the grossest of mortals would have known this was their livelihood and that they were not dancing here purely from light-heartedness.

But I should be creating a false impression if I ascribed more than a passing importance to Claude and Cordelia, for they were only incidents and not by any means the chief ingredients in the atmosphere that I am trying to recreate. They were alien to it themselves, thrown among what they thought of as canaille compared with the lacquered and chattering shapes they would have liked to dance for.

An extraordinary background of noise and glitter builds itself behind them and begins to hide their forms, so that they are seen through it with just the elegance and reticence they would have liked. The mouths of these dancing-halls roar out their music into the street and are as noisily melodious as the hell for which Offenbach wrote his music. This particular hell had several twists to its corridor so that the music dinned upon first one ear and then the other, and altogether its approach was like a passage in a tube-station. There were many arrivals, and the time that these took in giving up their coats gave an opportunity to notice the jaded and listless air of the cloak-room attendants which spoke of how little they had to expect, and of what heights and extremes were necessary to wake them out of their impassivity.

Once this barrier had been passed a new and peculiar world was reached, and it left one strong and prevailing impression upon the mind. This was a limitless extension of all the bounds of fiction, as though the possibilities of this art had become suddenly multiplied into infinity. But the fatigue and inertness of the guardians to this new world acted as the hardest criticism upon it. Nevertheless it lay here to be explored, but with a terrible horror at the end of all its corridors, however comic or burlesque might be the passages leading to that finality. All the needful dramatis personæ were here assembled, for the newness of these discoveries had not yet worn off sufficiently for them to be dispersed in a general manner over all quarters of the city, and like the proselytes to a new religion they still collected nightly in the catacombs.

There would appear to have been a regular staff attached to the establishment, rather in the manner of the Italian actors of impromptu comedy, who, we may suppose, signed on with their manager, the general lines of their masks being known and understood, but its details left to be developed by them as occasion and opportunity arose. There would be Harlequin, Pantaloon, the soubrette, and a number of others ; and here we find a company of the same kind engaged and practising their vocation, but occupied, at our moment of entrance, at the bar, where they were drinking with the management, receiving instructions, and discussing things of the night before. One of their number was going round from table to table selling signed postcards of the company so that it was easy to learn their names and memorize their appearances.

If the word " respectable " may yet be used in this connexion, we might call this the respectable side of the German criminal world that rose up and thrived from the warm ashes of the war. It signalized itself in extreme instances by a series of crimes of unprecedented and haunting frightfulness, which can be collected and exemplified under one head by the mention of Hartmann, the butcher of Hanover. The persons concerned in this case, and in all the others of the series that have occurred in Germany, have been extremely young in years, and it is probably safe to think that these equivocal and heterogeneous figures here gathered together, spent their daytime behind the counters of shops, and in surroundings where their nocturnal activities can hardly have been suspected. I suppose they hurried home through the twilight, and changed in cheap rooms into the travesties that they wore for this second and leading half of their lives.

It was possible to turn these histories back into themselves and to imagine the strangest tragedies, beginning, as no sense of humour could deny, from a comical, if distorted and bloated, start. Everything concerned with them had something of that feeling with which the acts of insects must be regarded, there being the strongest tinge of horror and disgust about each prompting of their senses. It was conceivable, for instance, that someone falling in love with one of these unreal ghosts, and who did not realize the deception of which he was the victim, for the most sincere tributes are due to their skilfulness in disguise, might find himself the next day wanting to buy a pair of gloves or a hat. He would walk down the street till the right shop was reached, and enter it to find himself being served by the sinister, but changed, spectre whose embodiment he had been admiring but a few hours before. Following upon this there would be a lapse of days spent in visiting alternately the two, earthly and ethereal, contacts with this phantom, days occupied with this extraordinary and sordid myth of the present, and in a set of situations that only a minor deity could be expected to surmount.

This was among the most simple of all those possibilities, and behind it was a Rabelaisian world augmented, to speak of these different tones and chords as though they were an orchestra, by limitless travesties and masks, till fiction at that far end of its orbit ceased to be concerned with life, and returned into the mythology out of which it has begun. Here, most certainly, was fiction lifted out of the drawing-room where it has been confined, and its likeness to an Academy picture has gone together with the grand piano and shaded lamp that are the symbols for both. The scenes and characters are too crude and large for any ordinary treatment at the hands of a phalanx of young women-novelists, and the future is troubled and broken into a hundred uneven surfaces.

The most ordinary vistas of life become complicated and obscure. What should have been a straight street leading to a happy ending is here darkened and made ghostly with the shadows of a number of statues that cannot be painted in the picture. They throw these shadows in order to trip the feet, and where closer inquiry has been made it is seen that these are really authentic, dead worlds come to life.

There can have been but few times when so copious a material has lain ready for treatment, though, to do justice to its strangeness, the novelists' forces would need to be increased, as I have suggested, by some qualities of the entomologist. These two talents, working together, would have the whole of this new world thrown open to them and I could think of no better beginning than to start the whole series at the first cold month of the year. The winter was, even then, not more than a few weeks in front with its frightful menace of fireless rooms and foodless days. This dancing-hall was, by contrast with nearly every home in Berlin, of a suffocating heat, and the first wave of influenza would affect almost a daily decimation, for no one of these people assembled here could have the very slightest sum of vitality left over from the strength they had to employ in keeping such perpetual late hours. The stories could begin, then, as though with siege and famine, and I was still thinking of their possibilities and envying the writer who had the gift to give them life long after I had left the place.

Some of the more salient of the characters stayed in the mind and nothing could drive them away. A small dark woman in black with hair brushed straight, a man's collar and tie and the kind of armoured bulkiness suited to an essentially masculine black-beetle, but who had allied this to an onerously hearty and cheerful manner, and who danced all the evening with a young girl—but was it a girl?—whose dark eyes and eyebrows to a bell-shaped head of flaxen hair made this seem a wig, worn for a minor deception where so much was travesty.

A horrible and Satanic Algerian; a young girl in a
German dress and hat which seemed more strange still
from their odd conventionality in such surroundings;
and finally those two extraordinary brothers. These
were dressed in well-cut suits of a nearly similar pattern
as though both had been selected together, and their
waisted figures gave them the air of male impersonators,
though, when this was investigated, their sex was quite
impossible to determine and they may have been equally
two sisters masquerading as brothers, or not brothers
and sisters at all but merely two persons—whether men
or women none could tell from such evidence to the
eyes—grown like each other as might two chameleons
always associated with the same rotting leaves and rank
decay. Now and again they would be called upon for
an exhibition dance, and we can take our leave of them
as they walk into the middle of the floor and start to
the music, while we notice their peculiar and fixed smiles,
part pride, part defence, seeming to express their mutual
and inalienable love for each other and the kind of comic
secret that was theirs.

So we get back to the hotel just in time to see another
and less perplexing progress. This was the transition of
Claude and Cordelia from the dining-room to the night-
club on the roof of the hotel. It was midnight and their
engagement was about to begin. By now their identity
was known to all the diners in the restaurant, and as they
walked out they were stared at with a different kind
of attention to that they had drawn to themselves in
the earlier evening. Now, it was less kind and more
critical; and as they went out, people stopped talking
to watch them, for their secret was known and there
was little left to be said about them. The fairy-story

was broken, and the prince and princess had become
public entertainers.

There, for the duration of life's realities, we must
leave them, though, later on, their symbolical importance
may be stressed. I never saw them again; I never
watched them dance except in those wilfully unpro-
fessional moments during dinner; and I left Berlin the
next morning feeling that Claude and Cordelia were
witness, more than evidence, to the strange and new
lives that I have hinted at, so that, indeed, they could
be used to tell their experiences in some future dialogue.
I went away from Berlin, and I never got to Hamburg,
where my instinct told me I should go in order to see
these things in their new and authentic setting against
the sharp, emphatic architecture of that city. In
Hamburg the eyes are not distracted by so many signs
of Imperial Germany, and the unstable and trembling
plutocracy has put its messages of no pity and no com-
promise into the very shells in which it moves. Not
having seen them, my interpretation of their meaning
must lose half its strength, but its general accuracy
cannot be questioned; and I felt that Claude and
Cordelia were my emissaries into this fresh experience.

Having sent them out upon this errand we need not
think of them again until they have returned from it;
and we leave them in the fast darkening autumn days.
Rain and snow are near, and every evening the lit lamps
have come a little closer to the flat noon of this declining
year.

For this, and for the usual reasons, it was not a gay
journey back to London. The streets were full of new
faces and queer voices; the National Gallery and the
British Museum were thronged with Americans, deriving,

it may be feared, but little benefit from these guys left
over from so many dead and vanished cultures. The
fact that these two institutions were visited on one and
the same day should in itself be a proof of how little else
there was to do. The afternoon was spent in wandering
about after this fashion, and even the familiar figures
in any shop entered were reported by apparent strangers
as being away on holiday at some seaside town, or in
Devonshire. But walking home, on my way down
King's Road, as I passed an artists' colourman, there
emerged from the shop-door, the sombreroed shade of
Mr. Carl Corder, and I found myself being taken just
round the corner to his studio.

C. C.: So you're back from Berlin. This time I'm
afraid there's no chance of our meeting abroad, because
you've come back and we're just off. No! It's under
the archway and down this long passage.

S. S.: I don't think I know these studios.

C. C.: This is the one I've always had, and though
we live in Cornwall I keep it on as a *pied à terre* in London.
Put your things down on that chair. Now let me offer
you a drink. Some vermouth ? I'd suggest tea, but
that depends on Hilda, and she's only coming up from
the cottage to-night with our luggage. Well, how's that
book getting on ?

S. S.: It's well over half done, thanks very much.
But it's taken me two years and it's sad work living so
much in the past, though I can't tell you how much I
prefer it to this present world of money beetles and
newspaper peers, holiday-snaps, young lady novelists and,
as the highest possible achievement, since it is so little
use hoping for a good picture or fine building, some
business man's prose—a particularly British invention,

this, since we are the first and only race to produce good writers who are never artists : Dickens, to begin with ; but I won't mention any more names.

C. C. : These are a poet's grumblings.

S. S. : Of course they are, and that's what a poet's for. Thank God, I've always been outside life, and it's too late to drag me into it now ! I know I should pull the piano into the corner and turn on the shaded lamp, but I'm not going to do it. Everyone can be their own Galsworthy, but I won't be conscripted for it.

C. C. : Of course you like everything screwed into the kind of perspective that suits your imagery, don't you ? You wouldn't like any subject that stood flat and square before you.

S. S. : What nonsense ! I like either a good photograph or a good portrait, and I find neither of these in the books we mean. What I hate and abominate is any attempt at an average. A lot of writers seem to imagine that realistic treatment means the selection of a boring subject and then the choice of the most uninteresting method in which to portray it. An interesting or beautiful subject paints or writes itself ; and, for its opposite, why were men born poets or painters ? But I mustn't be snared into aesthetics, for I know next to nothing about them ; you wouldn't want a pianist to make a musical critic, would you ? In fact you'd feel suspicious of him if he were.

C. C. : Yes. I see the point of that. But you know it's very bad for you to live entirely on artifice. Your own life can't be either so happy, or so unhappy, that you have nothing to say about it.

S. S. : All right. I'll tell you what I'll do. You're away for a fortnight, aren't you ? I'll see what I can do with the next two weeks, and I'll show you what I've done when you come back.   Where do you go, this time ?

C. C. : Oh! Amboise, Brantôme, Chinon, a few little places of the kind.   I shall be sketching away all the time you are writing.   But don't get up and go now. What are you doing this evening ?   Can't you have some dinner with me ?   Hilda will be back soon after it's over, and then we can all three have a long talk.

S. S. : I'm sorry to say I'm already engaged.   I'm seeing my only other friend left in London, beside yourself.

C. C. : So this is good-bye—until those two weeks are over.   Well, try and do your best for me, and we'll often be thinking and talking of you as we sit at our easels.

In a few minutes I was back at home.

III

SIESTA

A LITTLE wind, riding with the sunlight, beat the blind to and fro, and this rattling just served to prevent me from falling alseep as I lay on my bed whiling away the last spare moments after my bath.

That rattling blind acted also as a shuttle, weaving remembered facts in and out of my dreams. In the long spaces that these made out of a few seconds each tap was a shutter flung open or closed. I saw things lying in ribbed and spined light, or hidden almost in their alternation of thick and mute darkness. All kinds of emotions played between these two extremes, and every one of them seemed to have for its aim the epitomizing of that dead summer, hardly flung aside yet so near were its last hours.

Yes, the middle of September had come. It swept up the summer as the tidal bar thunders up some great river. London was flooded with new faces and queer voices. The British Museum and the National Gallery were thronged with Americans.

Certainly this feeling of lassitude was most lovely. I was carried forward on each little wave of sleep till it broke and my thoughts were troubled in the foam. Indeed, this kind of dangerless surf lay just in front of sleep, but I never quite reached to it, and was only lifted up and cooled by the spent fever in trying to reach to that quiet.

The emotions played a gentle music, trying to lull me in this way over the barrier into sleep, but that same wind outside, with its rattling of the blind against the window, prevented this, and I lay without strength enough to get up and settle that noise, unable to do anything but listen to my sentiments, which became embodied by this conspiracy to soothe me into sleep.

There, once it was reached, I should have enjoyed the sort of freedom that no one has ever known, awake, for the boundaries of fact are completely arbitrary in this condition and there can be a stableful of clouds to ride away upon with anyone whom your fancy chooses out from the mythology of daily life. There they are bedded upon this white and drifting snow, or the same quick machinery that gave them possibility invents some other background for this fruition, and a maze of green lanes will spring up in an instant to hide the sunburnt and gypsy shadows that are waiting there.

But this paradise was cut short and cancelled by time, which woke me and was censor to all I might have seen there. The hour was getting late, and this sense, like a kind of conscience, kept me awake and eventually pulled me right out of any association with these twilight figures.

I woke up and tumbled on to my feet, falling into the sleeves and legs of any clothes that lay near to hand, for my evening clothes had been lying on the bed ready for me to inflate them with my breath and body. Since I am the Mercury or Harlequin of these pages, designed, that is to say, to run into the world with the messages of my own feelings or, on the other hand, to mock and parody their sentiment, I must set myself, here and now, against a mirror, in order to frame in my substance. And what could be an easier place for this than my bedroom? I like to emphasize, or excuse, any good luck that is mine by a play of discomfort; so, besides a bed, two or three chairs, and a mirror, there is not much else to notice about my room. I have, at times, a genuine small melancholy which is elaborately fostered by my histrionic feeling. I am worried, though this eunuch age need not really make me jealous, at what seems to me the small amount of work that I produce; or I feel lonely and try to palliate this with a friendship that has a suspicion of purchase about its fast and easy build.

But I am half-dressed now and fully awake. Yet all the time I was dressing, the easy machinery that prompted my imaginings, the tapping drum that was all the music to my puppet-show, kept up its insistent beat upon the window, and it was difficult for phantoms not to move to that live monotony. Its insistence, made from so many breaths of wind, brought everything fresh and cool into my mind, and I saw the fair hair and heard the cold voice that had shaped and moulded my last few weeks.

There was no doubt that Joaquina was cold—very cold—indeed chilly. Nothing pleasant or unpleasant had the slightest power to ruffle her, and she was able to pass, unscathed, through the most severe family storms and the most poignant stresses of affection. Nor could it be said exactly that she did not take her share in any of these troubles, for she certainly answered her mother with sufficient sharpness, and in my dealings with her I could not complain of her not being interested in our situation; but, all the same, she seemed to lead

a life of her own with which she would allow no interference. What she meant this life to be, and what her
aims were in trying to keep it separate from so many of
the things out of which it was really composed, it was
difficult to conjecture.

As I opened my bedroom door there was a rush of
wind, and the blind blew still louder upon the window.
Its violence made me realize that this would go on all
the time I was out and for the remaining two hours of
daylight ; and wherever I might happen to be during
this time the thought of it would carry me back to the
memories it had evoked while I lay trying to sleep, for
in their efforts to lull me and drown that insistent noise
my senses had conjured up all the most pleasant things
lying within their reach in order to carry me over that
barrier into their grasp.

Even to think of them now meant a complete break
with any other thing occupying my mind at the moment,
and while other matters held my attention this would
still be here.

The same wind would blow the dying sunlight into
my room with a noise like the sea sounding in the intervals
between the rappings of its fitful heart. Just at this
same hour, the most beautiful time of the whole day,
the sea is still fluttering and smiling, though everyone
at the seaside is indoors at his evening meal. Its huge,
blue plain wants ships more than ever, then, and there
is an indescribable poignant calm in which nothing else
is of any moment except the vibrant and chiming surges.
By the time the world is abroad again it is all over ; and,
in the same way, eating and the other people eating with
me would destroy my mood of sensibility, and the only
thing that could be endured after it was the theatre.

There, at any rate, artifice has managed a successful parody, and I could see as many hints at Joaquina as I pleased, placing her, as she had been that day in the swing, along a chain of images under the boughs, or masquerading, even among these stage people, in a travesty that put their ineffectiveness to shame.

IV

AT THE PLAY

MUCH to my surprise, and contrary to all her own rules, Joaquina was actually waiting for me in the lobby of the theatre when I arrived. It was unprecedented, and could only be because she was going away next morning for two months. But the piece had already begun ; loud music came down the draught from a swing-door, and we hurried into our places.

In the theatre of to-day anything is better than words, and in order to avoid them as far as possible I had gone to the opposite extreme and chosen a musical comedy, preferring music, however bad, to those verbal settings of an Academy picture which the genius of our young dramatists produces every time it sets to work. There were more words even in this piece than I had expected, but at least their horror seared itself into the flesh in a new fashion, and the raw crudity of the American mind seemed better than our own native inanity.

I felt tortured by an unusually bad joke.

" I hope you don't mind this, Joaquina ? "

" I can forgive it when the music begins again. But they're not acting at all to-night. They're just playing tricks on each other."

Owing to the season, the actors were suffering under a

246

peculiar emotion, for the old year ends emphatically and categorically at the end of July, and nothing is ever the same again afterwards.

The new year begins and a whole new atmosphere distils itself, but for a few weeks it has not sufficient strength to carry things along with its own velocity, and so August is a calm where one wind dies away and another has not yet begun. Actors are more subject to this feeling than any other class of people, for their plays begin either in the very mouth of this Sargasso, or else they have just fairly started before it sets in, and they are left floundering in uncertainty between two particular and definite horizons, neither of which is within reach. In this case the latter alternative had happened ; the play was by now some six weeks old, and already I had been forced by fate into watching it twice.

The theatre was still crowded, as they often are through September, but filled with a mass of people who composed an entirely different audience from the ordinary. When I came here before it had been the conventional house at its most typical moment of complacency and self-satisfaction, using this piece as a kind of mirror to their own ambitions for themselves ; fancying themselves if humorous, handsome, or pretty, as filling their own rôles and being their own selves upon the stage, or, if more modest in their self-valuation, as seeing so many examples there, behind the footlights, of how to develop and fortify their own personality without exaggeration or affectation into a definite improvement upon its present state.

To-night it was not at all the same kind of person sitting in the theatre. They were from the provinces, or the more distant suburbs, and they had come here in order to drink in the ways they had read of in the social columns of the newspapers. They were, therefore, more attentively silent and more demonstratively pleased. But their applause held little satisfaction for the actors. By now, for lack of other interests, they had begun to find the virtues in themselves.

So different was the audience from that to which they were accustomed that it was like acting in a foreign country, and this feeling gave them licence to carry over some meaning into their words above that amount of it which they expected the audience to understand. This knowledge made their antics of double importance to anyone who knew what was going on behind that façade of words. Besides being in each other's company the whole evening at the theatre, they would spend the whole day together and have supper after the performance at the same table in a restaurant. This state of affairs never came at any other time, for even when on tour in some provincial town there was always too much to see to, and they were never long enough in any one place for the whole machinery of life to be running so smoothly as to require no attention.

The comedy was lavishly produced, and one of the Harkers' very best scenes held the attention with a strength that was only the just tribute to its extreme realistic brilliance.(5) It was a Mormon house in the State of Utah; the building formed the left side of the stage, and the whole space that the boards took up was given over to the garden. This had a low wall running round it, over which there was a view of the mountains with a green Alpine lake in the foreground, edged on its far side with a wood of fir trees that ran up their thinning spears into the sides of the hills. The actual garden was completely full of flowers, bedded out apparently for the occasion ; and rather to the right of the stage stood a beautiful fruit tree in full bloom, looking exactly like one of the flowering trees from a Persian illuminated manuscript.

The open space between the flowers and the fruit tree held five or six girls in it, and they were prettier than ever Mormon or Persian can have attained to, while their dress emphasized this with a fine abandon that deserved a better master than either of these voluptuaries.

The music to which they were dancing had a bastard virtuosity about it which derives from the excellence of the piano-playing. It is born out of Rubinstein and out of the more meretricious Liszt. In order to be true to the first of these suggested parents it must be Jewish, and without that blood this kind of invention fades and withers from its own weakness. But so long as there is really this strain in its paternity nothing can exceed the power that it has of interpreting the dangerous banality of such an existence as that hinted at among these flowers. It holds all the bridge-heads leading from the impossible into the realization of such scenes, and once it has started you can walk along into their full scope.

It has, also, this peculiar property, that these essential strains of modernity coming out of a new social system and a recent emigration and transfusion of races that has never been exceeded at any period of history, have the power to catch up and turn anything that they touch away from its natural atmosphere into a complete parallel, a true accompaniment to themselves. So this scenery of an extinct realism, changes into the ideal setting, the adept background, and these girls who would have been pretty in any dairy from any fairy-story, appear, suddenly, in spite of their English type, as the select interpreters of this Jewish, or Negroid-Russian dream.

On this occasion there were no less than three pianos placed side by side in the orchestra, and they sustained a steady and decisive masculine din above the noisy flowers and the garish words; in fact, they disposed everything into their own arbitrary patterns and were definitely in control of the whole affair.

This was one of the moments in life when the modern, far from lagging behind, ran by the side of, and really overtook, the past. Indeed, these conventional prettinesses had not only life in them, beside which anything dead and beautiful must look cold, but, also, in their easy acceptance, they achieved something far simpler and finer than the ugly obscurity which passes for modern in so much of the music and painting of our day. When every piece of music and every picture which has not this contortion of style is genuinely and really hopeless, this sudden revelation of something that is good without any of these drawbacks, and that has a kind of easy and fluent poetry about it, induces a feeling of comfort and relief. Of course this was all spoilt and shattered in a moment by a bad joke, only to be restored again when the music had started once more.

It was the sort of harmony for which I was searching, and it is its absence that makes life forced and bitter in nearly all its moments. I wanted this sort of thing transferred out of what I could only see with my own eyes and hear with my own ears; I would like it to be carried beyond these long-distance senses into some nearer contact with myself, where I could touch it and feel its movements. In fact, I wanted it living beside me, whatever it might be, and perhaps I was prepared to be disappointed in the end so long as it had been by my side long enough for me to understand and study some of its secrets.

Meanwhile it was a sad relief for me to place my own strivings after this ideal as near as possible to the natural achievement of it that I saw going on before my eyes. I sat and watched it, while I mingled my own phantoms with those real things that lay in front of me.

Joaquina seemed to move among these other girls in a freedom and intimacy that changed their whole aspect and made them into school-children; but they were pupils of a convent school, and I felt myself looking on at their studied innocence from the safe shelter of this wall that kept them out of reach and out of harm. It was one of those cases, so often lighted upon by the French artists of two centuries ago, where guilelessness is the secret of seduction. But the whole of this scene changed before more could be made of its opportunities.

The new one portrayed a room in, presumably, a yacht club, for out of some five bow-windows in the semi-circular back of the set the sea could be seen, and the centre window, which was really a door and led in from the balcony outside, showed a great expanse of the blue and heaving main with several yachts tacking at a dangerous angle across it.

A cold and salt breeze seemed to blow through that door, and it had its origin from the band. The tune they were playing summed up the whole situation as quickly as a caption. The girls who had been dancing only a moment before by that Alpine pasture had now arrived at this very different venue, and Joaquina took her place

as easily among them this second time, for her golden
hair and Northern skin suited the waves just as well;
indeed, her hair was a tidy and gleaming casque protect-
ing her against the wind.

It guarded her, too, against the full, insidious meaning
of the music so that she was now a little apart from the
others, but she faded out from the scene, which took on
a deeper note of realism with her disappearance.

There was a great amount of over-acting and over-
emphasis that evening, for reasons that have already been
suggested. This had a most peculiar effect upon the
inanities of the piece, for behind their futile and shallow
meaning it built up something that can only be described
as a series of mirrors in which I could see the backs of
the actors, their necks and heads straining more than I
would have imagined to be possible from the false gentility
of their manner when seen from the ordinary angle.

Here, in that double or second world in which I
watched them, they were acting for a different audience
from that among which I was numbered and with an
extravagant energy that showed they were competing,
not with the absurd persons they were supposed to be
portraying, but with their own true selves armed with
each other's guile and knowing each other's secrets.
This gave them an earnestness of purpose that they
never attained to on ordinary evenings.

They had got back into the garden. It was lit with
as many lamps as it had flowers; the same house made its
appearance once more, but seen this time from the right
instead of the left; in fact, it was another side of the
garden, and the whole scene was nearly roofed in by a
great bough of a cedar tree that gave almost as much shade
as a tent.

All the familiar figures came on that in their short life of two hours had become such a part of existence. It was just the same sort of evening as that lying outside the theatre, and this scene gave a miniature of its feeling and at the same time showed the best way of dealing with its rigours. If only this small thing could be projected into the great void that lay beyond it, what a paradise of a summer evening this would make!

But no effects in life could ever be so rehearsed as these, and, if they were, that very sense would destroy their quality so that only people looking on and not taking a part in them could find any pleasure in the spectacle; indeed, the proof of this was the feverish over-emphasis of the performance we were watching. So close was my attention that I had become involved, myself, as something more than a mere spectator, and their feelings were communicated to me so that I shared in their ennui and could appreciate their frantic efforts to find an interest in the banal words and the conventional scenes in which they were doomed to pass their evening.

I liked the distortion and emphasis of their mood because it overlapped from the play into their own lives, and I could see things in them that were beyond and above the amount of acting for which they had been engaged. My very interest in these scenes brings out, perhaps, certain points in my own character; for I would not be in search of such easy and vapid amusement if my own life was altogether charged and brimming with those qualities that I lacked and had come here to search for; and my keen scrutiny betrayed an anxiety to become involved in some adventure.

I wanted to arrive at some attitude where I could imitate the apparent carelessness of what I saw before me, and carry it into terms of ordinary life. Until such an adventure started, I could do no better than try to see what lay behind these few hours that were their livelihood. In doing this, the mirrors over which I found myself dangling, revealed themselves in all their depth and profundity, with, as is naturally the case in a looking-glass, the image of the person making the inquiry ready to answer from the bottom of the pool when it is least expected and a still greater depth might be presumed.

What did they do with all the long hours of daylight? The dwindled morning broken into two halves by breakfast, and with its first half never seen by them except at an early start in the provinces, when it climbed like a static blue dome above the open end of the railway platform in those few moments before the train started. All this part of it, as well as all the rest of it, was doomed, condemned already to be wasted. Just now it was sure to be motionless and without any sign of life, but on other mornings it was decked out with a few clouds like sailing-ships, with banks of cloud-like shoals of sand, or it would even assemble these different images into a set of ribs and bones for its own skeleton, which hung still, or drifted very slowly, shaking asunder, over that immense journey.

On such days as this it tries to draw attention to its changes by a rattling upon the window, or stretches down a long hand of light between the clouds, and gives a sudden stab into the room followed by an answering darkness. This mood, with the quick limelight changing into complete and utter black, is one that mates very well with the constitutional sleepiness of a profession that can never get to bed till after midnight, and its alterna-

tions would match the series of little sleeps drifted into
after breakfast had been brought in, and while that
unrelished meal was growing cold.

Luncheon, for this simple reason, was far more like
breakfast, and signalled the real start of the day. They
would go very late to some fashionable restaurant for
this purpose, and now this part of their lives, spent away
from the theatre, becomes just as curious and unreal
in its procedure. For these habits of life are the creation
of the last twenty years, while young men of an exactly
parallel talent and advantage to myself have existed for
some twenty-five centuries, at least. I might equally
well have been writing my poems with a stylus on a wax
tablet while I lay under an olive tree and watched the
nodding asphodels and the goats climbing among the
rocks; have imitated this same mood in the difficult
rhyme and difficult script of an age which had few flowers
beyond the rose, the carnation and the blossoming fruit
tree, and kept these jealously guarded behind a girdle
of walls; or have written odes to the farded cheeks and
swan breasts of that last age of a non-Gothick romanticism when nothing was left unhidden or unexpected
that could by any device of ingenuity grow into a conceit
or simile. But why enlarge upon the rest of the day and
try to draw out its hours into a length that, in any case,
can never compete with the lives of whole numbers of
people as they are seen reduced, but without a sign of
compression, in the few hours at a theatre?

This may be a confession of how little difference there
is between realism and artifice, and of how difficult it
is to choose between them for accuracy; but it is in
this kind of half-light, of neither the one nor the other,
that we must move through these pages occupied with

genuine feelings or pretences of mood, and so no excuse need be offered for any overlapping of the shadows.

When I turned my attention back to it I found the piece was nearly over, and I could guess the unsatisfied mood in which its conclusion would leave me. This hazard reached its fulfilment a few minutes later when all the audience who had been in the theatre were emptied into the starry night. This was lit by an unreal light apart from that given forth by its myriad pin-points, and down the street at the only point where the horizon could be seen, the sky flickered and shook a little at its edges. It might be that strange thing, the Northern Lights, or perhaps it was simply the glare of the town, but whichever it may have been, this phenomenon served to strengthen and intensify the mood of the theatre.

Anything, and every possibility, had crawled up nearer under the loose tent-flaps of the sky, and now lay close at hand waiting for its chance. It was a phase of time that could not last long; and Joaquina and I began walking home.

To-morrow she would be gone, and there would be nothing to do, no one to see, and hardly a person even to think of, as everyone was away, but not for long enough to make their absence a matter for anything deeper than the most passing regret. But the night air turned this little impermanence into something long and lasting. It held ready its romantic paraphernalia of casement and guitar, and even arc-lamp and motor-omnibus could not hide them.

V

CASEMENT AND GUITAR

WE decided to walk a little way. Motor-cars and great crowds of people were pouring in and out of Piccadilly Circus along Shaftesbury Avenue, and there was the same noise and confusion down Regent Street. But the two or three streets between Regent Street and Bond Street were silent and dark enough to be a temptation, and we chose one of them in order to have a moment's lull.

Down towards the end of it an open door poured light on to the street. At the same time, lights were streaming out from a row of three windows at the top of the house, and there were the sounds of voices and music.

We went quickly past, each of us thinking how dull a party in the late summer this must be ; but we were too engrossed in our last few minutes together to pay it any attention, and here was the door of Joaquina's house before we had time to realize that separation was upon us.

As I was coming on my way back again, a heavily-built woman, whom it was difficult to see properly because of the darkness, was airing a couple of dogs, walking them up and down by that open door we had noticed. As she was ahead of me and had arrived nearly in front of the doorway she turned round on her beat, and one of her two dogs took this opportunity to escape from her, trailing its leash along the ground. Instinctively I put my foot down on the end of its lead, stooped to pick it up with my hand, and advanced on the substantial woman to hand her back her dog.

"Oh! Thank you very much. You're a late comer," she said, and I hesitated in some doubt, because I saw that she either expected, or pretended to expect, that I had just arrived at the door and intended to go upstairs.

"I'm sorry. So you aren't a friend of my son's. I thought you must be on your way here."

"Well, I'm pleased to have been able to catch your dog for you. It's lucky that both of them didn't take it into their heads to run away together."

But my joke brought out a vein of pleasant, if vaguely bibulous, humour in her, and I could see immediately that her mistake had been a genuine one.

"Yes, it's lucky. I'm too old now to move about as fast as that. But though you haven't been asked, do please come upstairs. Don't think me rude to press you in this way, but my son and his friends would be delighted, and, anyway, I'm his mother, and will be responsible for you."

"All right. I should like to very much."

And still slightly in spite of myself I went up the steps with her into the house.

There were no coats or hats in the hall, and we began going upstairs at once. The ground floor and the first floor must be offices, I thought to myself. My new friend, from the way in which she was airing her dogs. must live here, and I imagined that she and her son had rooms above some office or business that belonged to them. I had quickly and rightly given up any idea of there being anything at all sinister in her invitation, and

I panted upstairs after her, a little curious about this new world into which I was on the point of breaking.

On the way I noticed the name of a new weekly paper that had just started, in big white letters on the glass panel of a door on the second landing, and my inquisitiveness told me that her son must be the editor of this rather struggling new paper and that I should find they lived on the floor above this.

I was right. When I got to the door on the landing above there was a small visiting card pinned on to the woodwork with " Editor " written in pencil, and a short notice to the effect that this was his private address and that letters or people coming on business must go to the floor below between certain hours.

All this looked safe enough ; and I followed her through a little hall into a square and brightly-lit room.

For all its yellow walls and shadeless lamps, this party had a drab and nasty-smelling air to it which suggested to the mind cups of strong tea left half-drunk in a bedroom into late in the morning. However, the disarray was of a more alcoholic nature than this simile depicts, and a great deal of tousled and arty talk was in progress. I shook hands with my friend's son, a kind-faced, weak young man who was evidently trying to develop his manner out of nervousness into the critical silence and saline wit that he thought an editor should possess. So far he was keeping his comments down in number, and seemed resolved not to give away any information. Why should he talk much when writing was his *métier ?* All the same, his voice could be heard denying that certain well-known names in painting had even sufficient importance to be said to exist. Nor, need it be said, was anyone else present trying to defend them.

I was given little opportunity of talking to him. His mother felt responsible for me, and was also by now keenly interested in finding out who I was. We were able to establish several points of contact in mutual like or dislike of certain painters or critics. In fact, she knew my name, once she had extracted it from me, though there was obviously not much of a label attached to it in her mind and she would have to search about and ask questions of other people before it meant more than its mere sound to her.

There were no painters in the room, but every other profession to do with painting except that of being an artist was represented. Besides the editor-son there were critics, gallery-owners, exhibition-secretaries, and one or two of the young women who do all the work and dawdle through the long hours in a picture gallery at the desk, in front of a heap of catalogues and a marked price list.

Presently when the mother had gone upstairs to bed I moved away from the corner where I had been sitting with her. I went over and sat next to the editor, who was in the centre of a little group. Among the listeners were one of these secretaries, and a most beautiful young girl, who was obviously a friend of hers. She was so silent that it was evident she was the only person besides myself who was in no way connected with pictures or the picture trade. At the same time she was well known to them all, and although she talked so little I was able to see that she was a person of importance to them. I wondered if this was simply because of her good looks; and the more I looked at her the more beautiful she became.

She looked little more than twenty years old, and owing

'to her silence it was next to impossible to make out anything more than that about her, for she had the kind of mask-like face at which it is the most exquisite pleasure merely to look, while the moment speech begins you know that the mask will break and a new expression about which it is useless to conjecture will make its appearance.

To begin with, the whole mouth must alter and keep on changing with its words ; while the immobile lips make up at least a half of that continuity of which we are speaking, and it is no use thinking of a mask without its mouth. It was the whole point of the Venetian domino that the fresh and natural mouth you hoped, or hoped not, to recognize, lay underneath that uniformly pallid shield to the eyes. But in this case the mask had, so to speak, to unmask itself before it was possible to form the slightest opinion about its wearer. This could only be achieved by engaging her in conversation.

I led a desperate hunt through all the possible subjects in my head, and then said—but to the editor and not to her—something about how much more exciting a time of year this was than the conventional May and June of summer, when I felt that such an adventure as had befallen me this evening could never have been possible. This same party, given then, would have been too full to allow room for a single stranger ; or, on the other hand, it would have had to be organized on the most guarded basis and almost in secrecy, so that, then again, I could have had no chance like that of this evening.

Everyone seemed to agree to this.

The elder of the two secretaries thought that by the things I might have missed I meant my introduction to her, and then made a joke out of pretending to believe this. No one saw the underlying truth in what she pretended to pretend. There was no flicker of a smile on any face, not even on that I was trying to approach and get nearer to by means of these feinted conventionalities.

I must try something else.

"Do you suppose I shall ever see any of you again? We should have an engagement to meet once in every five years, like the survivors one reads of in the newspaper, who gather on the steps of St. Paul's and then go off to a melancholy dinner to discuss those of their number who have died since the last occasion. And they know no more about each other than I know of any of you, or than you know of me!"

"And how does it get into the papers?" (This was the editor.) "Aren't they all really just members of the staff?"

"Why not let's test this," I said. "Won't this young lady you have never introduced me to, dine with me to-night, and we will dine together every night through September until we know all about each other, and until our compact always to dine together gets into the papers? But there would be more of a newspaper story in it if we engage never to ask each other's name, and never to meet any of you again until our compact has broken down, so that even your channel of information is cut off from us. What do you say to that?"

"I will dine with you to-morrow, but never again."

But I was too slow to catch any change of expression that I could remember, and so this immediate purpose of my manœuvres was put off till to-morrow.

Then we arranged where to meet, and the party began to break up. I walked home, thankful to get away from that evening of banalities, but a little curious about the next day, with, perhaps, a little more than mere curiosity in my expectation.

This was how the adventure started that I had felt was waiting for me all that evening, and, indeed, ever since the hot and easeless afternoon. Certainly it had not the sort of epical opening to it that I would have chosen, but at any rate this was the beginning ; this was what the starry night had brought me, and this was its casement and guitar. I felt grateful, but with not too much enthusiasm. In fact, it seemed to me, up to that time, as though the starry sky might have done better for me.

VI

LOVE SCENE

WE met next evening according to arrangement.
The new horizon I had arrived at became
quickly crowded with statues. In fact, my
interest in this possible futurity almost prevented my
studying the model of these hieratic suggestions, and I
was so intent on examining them and thinking of their
possibilities that I nearly ignored their original, and was
called back to her time after time by the necessity to
snare her strange silence and copy it on to these masks
that I was making.

All the time there was ordinary conversation, but more
staccato than usual. I was so glad that she was here.
She was so pleased that I had asked her. What would
she, or would she not, eat ? Did she like what she was
eating ? Did she like the restaurant next door ? Had
she been to the play I had bought tickets for ? It was
the same piece I had been to the night before with
Joaquina ; indeed I had come straight away from the
theatre into this adventure in which I was involved. It
gave me a peculiar sense of delight to see the same thing
again and to go over those stages of a longing and a gradual
sinking into danger. It was rehearsing for something
that had already been put into achievement.

But I was living in a life quite outside these little

conventionalities of talk, and I found the small necessary questions somewhere far down in myself and fished them carelessly out of the deep waters of my consciousness, while the whole trajectory of my thoughts was so long coming out of that dark twilight into the purest and most unencumbered possibilities that her answers to my questions hardly left any mark upon me, and sometimes I was afraid of asking the same thing twice over.

She had in her more poignancy and a stronger pull upon the sense of pity than it is possible to imagine. This conscious or unconscious guile was armed with as powerful weapons of conquest. She had greater beauty than need be stipulated for any adventure and, as well, this small bird-like pathos which had so much power in its weakness and which, while I pitied, I longed one day to hurt a little and make suffer. But this was a tired refinement that could only follow on profound experience.

Miriam was her name, for we had quickly broken that part of our covenant; and she was, as I had imagined, just twenty years old—far too old for a horse or deer, but hardly enough for her strange human type, which held in it the warmth, the silence, and the fidelity of these creatures. She had also their speed and their swift change of direction once her calm had altered into mobility. In quick word and quick movement her spiritual as well as her physical tread seemed as light as the deer, who will be at the back of the glade or the far end of the field before it is possible to come near to them.

In the few hours between my first and my second visit to the theatre, I had been thrown under this violent potency and spell, so that I came back to those scenes again quite outside my former self. I had captured and had here sitting by my side just that kind of person who was the point and focus of the play, and who had precisely the type of beauty which, apart from a little dull humour, made up its only *motif*. So I was able to parallel in the possibilities of the next few days just what I would have chosen had I the power to work my own wishes. This was an improvement beyond question upon my situation of the night before and one which I felt that nothing except the mysteries of this time of year could have brought into possibility; but it was made pathetic and robbed of its guilt by that other half of her personality which faced away from these scenes into child-like qualities that I could never have the cruelty to break and which contrasted the false innocence of the prettiness I was watching with their own genuine realization. So I was breathing a double world of artifice and of truth; I was more than ever an actor, and more than ever a part of the audience.

We went home together after the theatre. I suggested going somewhere for supper, but she said her friend was away and that she could give me something to eat in her flat. She lived in two rooms above a greengrocer's shop in a side street not very far from Selfridge's.

It was just a day since we had met by that strange chance of the party. Now the wheel of time had made one more turn, but if it had carried us forward, at any rate we were carried by it in the same direction. If it were possible I was anxious to give it some small irrevocable turn that would make it difficult for Miriam and myself to separate our fates for, at any rate, some little time—perhaps until these days of uneasiness and transition were over. But instead of this, I gave it a violent push that has sent both of us running down the slope ever since. Yet it was not my strength only that achieved this, and to make each clause binding on us both she had to assert her will as well.

But it is little use trying to treat this situation by stages, or to break its phases into words. Instead, it is better to draw its parallel in a set of images which can build themselves up side by side with the truth and keep to the straight lines of its track, avoiding unnecessary corners and stretches of monotony.

In the meantime, if it is possible to lift up this story of the ordinary into anything that is a little better than itself, the stage properties may be transmuted and it is not imperative to insist too much upon the square, bright box in which we talked. We can let alone the wide settee, too near the ground to either sit or lie upon in any comfort; the pictureless walls; the rows of cups hung by their handles from hooks, these being, indeed, the only sign of plenty in the whole flat; we need not listen for the traffic in Oxford Street; we can ignore the glare of lights from the windows opposite; forget the four flights of dark stairs and pay no heed to the tap dripping into the sink behind the door with the insistence of a coldly deliberate clock that hurries on the hours to a faster pace than their true speed. In fact, we can become entire arbiters of speed and may tighten or extend its rate at our will.

This cold statue I began to love had now turned into the most complicated machinery gifted with everything that a carved image lacks, just as though life were grafted on to that incorruptible and changeless death.

I had first of all been hypnotized by trying to think what expression the lines of that mask led into, and I was willing to sacrifice all that its spell meant over me for the uncertainty that lay the other side of its calm.

But a whole universe of the senses was contained between these two static conditions of her mask-like immobility and the smile into which it was eventually broken. I could envy no one a knowledge of all the wisdom in the world or want to borrow for this moment any power over visible or invisible creation while I lay under her potency. Instead, there were more worlds of poetry and wider spheres of music burning into creation and as quickly fading into others in each phase of her than the life of any poet or artist lasts long enough to conquer.

This machine had its thousands of little engines drawing out all my power. She was no longer about to give me anything; she was receptive and was borrowing all my own life, which she magnified a million-fold in order to materialize her ghost into living. She drew out all my vitality, and her machinery of increase had made a spiritual entry into my own self where I could feel it working and preparing the strength without which all her efforts were in vain.

Then, this appearance of her body and limbs being some kind of an engine, this slightly spider-like depredation and danger-stirring vanished completely away from her, and her whole nature now lay before me like a bed of flowers looking up at the sun and wanting rain. They were still, absolutely still, or if they moved it was in a wind that was not of their own volition; it was something from outside arrived to them by force of circumstance, and it was no use their resisting its force.

I seemed to be blown, cloud-like, over to this world of flowers. Night and day, or moon and sun, which made me sleep or wake, plied their strength in a compelling sun and a cool and silver-sounding wind playing out of night, whose joint force brought me nearer to this feat of creation that they had delegated to me.

But I was not ready for it yet, since it is a poor summer that is born into creation with so little trouble, and in place of the rain that these flowers expected, the rolling of drums and the clangour of thunder broke from the cloud. All my forces were imprisoned in me in martial and heroic continence, and she fled out of her flower-heads into a tower that looked brassy and forbidding against my strength.

Her limbs, the instruments of this engine, lay waiting and motionless. They were as still as the mask I had rattled a few hours ago with a chain or two of words, and their whole geometry ran into this expectancy to give it point. They were now the walls of this tower, and they would lie quiet and strong, hiding their own purposeful weakness until attacked, when they were planned at once to crumble and let out the prisoner inside, whose pleasure and very sustenance hung upon their collapse. All the inconceivable irritations out of which the attraction of beauty is made were now put into operation, and every one of them was a little life to be taken and drunk. The whole of them were fused into one possible sacrifice which was stored with every enticement of the senses.

The visual world, all the objects among which I moved, and even the oblique things that spoke to the spirit more than to the eyes, became heightened and transformed. It was an hallucination of the nerves that poets, and only poets, can know; and it was a dance of all the senses before they create something out of nothing and leave this tangible increase behind them when they fall back into the ordinary and the normal. They built themselves up through the clouds and flowers of metaphysics into a series of transcendencies of the actual so perfect in their colouring and proportion that the martial and heroic mood coming up at their back to seize and to create cracked and broke the still and glass-like vision of these pictures and faded through them into a fiery rapture that fast died into pity and weakness.

But, first of all, it was the turn of the actual to become transcendentalized. The room became the platform belonging to this beautiful and intricate machine; it was simply the engine-room that housed and contained its strength, and it was filled for this reason with the strongest radiation of its principle. The most ordinary objects were kept down to their environment, but their volume and pitch of importance became magnified out of all precedent with their past or with what they would relapse into once this enchantment had ceased to work.

Each chair—there were about three or four of them in the room—had no longer the appearance of having been pushed back against the wall, but seemed to be alert and living; not only did it wait to be used, but it stood at so vital an angle with the other chairs that it must share with them some community of heart or nerves. It was no longer just dead wood; if it had dropped its leaves and branches it had adopted this new life instead, becoming, indeed, a kind of minor and dumb hostess, and kept alive by its interest in its owner and her friends, and in the social relations of its sister chairs. It must be treated gently and not banged down or knocked about. Exactly the same condition applied to the tea-cups; not only to those hanging from their handles by the row of hooks, but also to the used ones standing on the table. They had arranged themselves into a vital pattern of angles towards each other, and their respectful silence among themselves was like the wordless attention of the butlers in a rich house. Even the walls of the room were not so much blank walls as discreetly restful screens pushed up by themselves to what they considered to be the most suitable propinquity to the persons in the room.

This heightening of the tempo of everything made the hour and the moment of very little importance, and it was daylight as well as night. The sun came through the windows and began building inside the room. The red bricks of the houses across the street had no longer their usual colour and consistency of mud, but were made of good, red clay, each one of the cubes filling itself out to the utmost limits of fairness, like satisfying chocolate or a full weight of something rich and sweet. A change of this same nature came over the boards of the flooring that now shone and glistened like glass, so that anything standing on them lost its separateness and became, while you looked at it, the centre of the whole room. A pair of red slippers, that should have been isolated and lost except as a hindrance and a thing to trip over, became drenched with personality and regulated the disposition of all the other objects in the room until they fell into proportion with its new assumption of importance.

The four boundaries of the walls had the power to completely alter their own scale, and if they had been a series of screens a few seconds ago, they were now absolutely arbitrary in their arrangement and had allowed the sun to erect a whole series of constructions within their territory, made of his unsubstantial golden timbers, out of light rods of shadow, and from wall spaces of vibrant and clear light. At moments, the whole affair would vanish—this was when a cloud passed over the sun—and all the time the whole thing was slowly sliding along, not fading at all, but moving its apparatus across the blank space between this window and the next, until its beams climbed through the second window and now it built itself again, rod by rod, timber by timber, inside the room.

Miriam's white body was curved and recessed into an architecture to be attacked. In order to achieve this, she was fortified with an easy barrier of nerves, a zone of shyness ; and this had to be advanced through in order to reach to the spirit or soul beyond. This spirit or soul needed wings to lift itself out of the body, and these flights were more frequent than a purely spiritual experiment would require. It was just a wish to shake and flash her wings in that purer and less encumbered air, but in order to reach to it and to attain the speed that was essential to its success, there had always to be some small area of resistance, some little bastion to be broken through. The whole of these fortifications were now defended, and that naked and frail geometry lay still to be a victim.

Then, all those walls and battlements turned over their whole nature and became, instead, a tree bright and heavy with fruit.

These wanted just a small effort to be taken, and they hung where a simple movement could snare them. One of them, and it was impossible to tell which, held the secret and the very matter of the whole tree's life. Her body, the stem from which the branches and the leaves hung, was bigger than my two hands by themselves could hold, and as soon as my arms had also to be used, then her body itself claimed all my attention, and there was none left over to capture the fruit above. If, though, I stretched towards them and did not hold her, it was with the greatest difficulty that they surrendered themselves to me, and by the time they were in my power, she had fled out of where my arms might have been into some deep-hidden fastness of the tree's green heart.

So I pinioned her frightened and yet willing boughs with one hand that swept their different sweetness into obedience and then the heroic continence that I had practised broke from me in iron and violent impetuosity. Hundreds of trumpets sounded in my ears, and I could have put a whole universe to the sword.

All the music and poetry of the world, but in their martial moods, poured themselves into my iron strength to help me, and then, having assumed flesh, ran out from me in every direction to do my bidding. They conquered together; and after that it was an ambrosial feast enduring into what seemed to be the heart of eternity, though, since this cannot be measured, its duration may have been of utter and most lightning-like speed as well as of eternal length. Then a lull like the gentlest and most insidious sleep came over them.

In this sudden quiet, my contentment was spoilt a little by the descent from the cruelty which had been a part of my impetus and one of the weapons of my equipment, and the other side of it as it cooled back into normality made me feel sorry for this soft and gentle thing that I had robbed, though if I asked myself what I had taken from her I found it was something of which I had given her the half while its rest had been her own emanation working upon my beginning. So it seemed to me but a fulfilment of the necessary and the obvious, with no more excuse for sentiment than that of any

R

condition which is about to change into another. The quality in virgin innocence, like that in virgin soil, seemed to me to lie in its angle towards improvement, and the slope is always out of the immature into the perfected.

But now she seemed sorry for what had happened, and could hardly be comforted. It appeared that this one valuable thing in her possession, the intrinsic side, as it were, to her beauty, she had parted with for no return. Her solace lay in the invisible nature of this robbery which nothing save a repetition of the same incident could reveal; and then a kind of balm flowed out of her heart with which to heal this wound, and I knew that I would never be able to leave her, and that I was tied to her for evermore by this pathetic communion. I now found in her what I had never hoped to find before, a real spiritual and emotional appeal to me over and above her loveliness to the eyes.

We were now hopelessly the captives of each other, and were tied to the two chariot-wheels of time, so that we could never escape from each other or from that insidious and quickening descent into the darkness. I was fastened to her in a contemptible way that began to excite my disgust, and I wanted to stir the dust in which I was floundering and to fight and annoy the heavy weight I had to carry. But this mood soon changed into one of a vicious and despairing pleasure in the awkwardness of my burden; and looking down on myself from outside my body I almost relished the slavery to which I was condemned.

So I turned to it and tried to hide myself in that pillar of dust. Its shape and girth were the same as that of the tree-stem I had held before in my arms, and while my arms encompassed it, the dust began to turn

golden, and its particles glistened like strands of hair
or boughs of leaves. Also, it lost its brackish heat, and
had the cool that a shower of rain must have when it
has just left its cloud. I was altogether lost and hidden
in that sudden shade, and all signs of my aggression of
before left me. But, all the time it lasted, I knew the
deception that had been practised upon me and had to
insist with myself upon the truth of this mirage. I
knew that it would surely vanish and that the dust it
turned back into would be black and hopeless with no
trace in it of the things that had cooled and refreshed me.

In a moment, it crumbled and fell, and even the pillar
that had been the centre of this storm, and that had
changed by this miracle into the stem of a lovely tree
and into a silver fountain-foot, springing and leaping
in my arms, now vanished. It was not hidden ; it had
gone away for ever and would never come back.

A terrible sinking horror came over me. There was
some appalling ghost living in that dust and clinging to
me for life. Yet it was more material and less bodily a
phantom than could be imagined ; for there was nothing
of the spirit or soul left in it, and yet it was breathing in
that darkness like a horrible octopus in some dim corner
under the rocks. It drew its vitality, its life-blood, from
me and it would not let me go. All my strength ran
out of me into its stringy veins. Unless I could get away
from it, I would be borne down to be nothing more than
its blood-store, its vat of life.

But then, although its struggles continued, the force
of their terror upon me began to weaken. There was
something pitiful in their frenzy ; and those familiar
lines of architecture, that look of an engine about its
curves and corners, started to come out of the tangled

and convulsed darkness. So this had been the purpose
of that machinery ; and I could not forget, while I
watched it lapse into stillness, the impact that had
thrown it into life and the long and smooth slope down
which it had to travel with gathering speed before it
could begin its flight. Not only had I to impel it out
of its stillness, but I moved along the track with it and
was carried into the air as much by its will as by my force.
The miraculous changes that it had the power to work
were shared with me, and I was the accomplice in all
its transmutations of the mood and spirit. All these
things I owed to it, and in thinking of them I could not
grudge the few moments of slackening speed, and the
coming to earth again of this incredible engine of the
body. It was asleep now, and I was left outside its
influence.

The night was perfectly still and quiet. The lamp-
light never faltered and made not the slightest stir or
noise. It was as dumb and impassive as before, con-
structing nothing and changing nothing. It was an
absolute neuter between the loud day and the feline
night. Its only purpose, this lit and theatrical darkness,
was to hold a lamp to see by, and I much preferred the
black and authentic darkness with no spy upon our
secrets. These lamps were so many dumb servants set
there to report upon what they saw, and I hated their
acquiescence and obedience. But these witnesses were
inevitable, and no bribe could lure them away.

There was a delight to be found in taunting them,
and in enjoying the contrast between their alert uselessness and the utter and profound silence that lay everywhere round them. So late as this, there was no one to
listen to their secrets, and the lights in the room having

been turned out, this poor parody of day came in at the windows, but could get its beams little further than the curtains. And they stood still there. They never moved or tried to build themselves into any convincing shape.

So, not being able to see with any clearness, I lit that twilight and its dark corners with my mind and peopled them with figures.

There being no restrictions, save the limits of my fancy, I was given complete freedom of creation. The room and the square, drab situation in which I found myself, was open to the four winds, and their clean speed purged the air of the dust that had lately clung there. Instead, the hillside shook down its fleeced clouds into a wood of fruit trees. These stood close together, though not near enough to mingle their boughs. This wood, and the meadows below it, were perpetually filled with fresh shapes. The shadowed branches made a theatrical difference for the figures seen below them, and the people who had breathed and been seen for a moment in that unreality lived again here and the vibrant and violent blue sky shone down through the leaves. What was forgotten kept itself in that pleasant darkness ; and the remembered, that needed but a moment's span of life, burned into an incredible realism against that cloudy scenery of the blossom.

There was an idyllic and Sicilian languor in the air. A great snow mountain with dormant fire in its bowels lay so near across a gulf of blue sea that the cannonings of that Gargantuan wind of sulphur and of fire could be plainly heard across the distance sounding the note of danger and menace which must ever be there in contrast to the crystalline clearness and safe happiness of the

scene. A beach of fine sand ran round the circle of the
bay and made a terrace for this naked poetry to parade
its figures, who climbed out of the sea on to golden sea-
soil, or left it for the fields of flowers beyond. Their
limbs, with the blue water left upon them and just taken
up by the sun, shined and flashed like swords, and this
brilliant light of water was a new and positive race of
shadows to which the ordinary dark and empty echoes
were so many ghosts. These lights moved with them,
so that their bodies were the answer to this scintillation.
They ran and walked in a whorl of fire. These were
the heroes of the poet and the models of the sculptor
and painter. The groves of philosophy were some
stunted olive trees near to the asphodels, for it was too
early in the day and in the age to want shade. The
flowers that grew near to the ground were all wild and
were quickly bruised by the feet, though this left little
mark upon their profusion and nothing broke out of
the coloured ground except one or two boulders which
had their answer and parallel in the rocks rising out of
the painted sea.

Both the boulders and the little rocky islands were
platforms on to which any of these figures climbed to
rest, or to be posed in the amber that the air formed round
them. Fierce points of the cactus sprang up in their
violence too near to them, and were the rods and arrows
to these games of war. The rocks in the sea and out of
the flowers were crowded with statues that stood or
lay in all the beauty that the engine of the body can
achieve. Since they narrowed down their maturity to
the early age when it is rare to excel in anything except
in games of speed and in poetry, nothing pleased them
save the stern and heroic flesh which, until it was old

enough to become a warrior and take the lives of others, was their vehicle of pleasure and their whole inspiration.

Almond trees, too low to need a ladder, stood on the hillside like so many clouds. They grew in two kinds —the pink and the white—and the first sort held the sunlight while the second seemed charged with snow. They were so small and powerless as to be easily mastered by the body, and these figures leaned against them and made their rest into a danger for the blossom. The cactus broke up the stony soil and made its points into so many spikes to tear the limbs, for no protection was worn except where one or two of the figures had a helmet on their heads. These were brightly burnished and had a horse's tail trailing down the back on to the shoulders, which formed all their theatrical property and made their trappings of poetry, symbolizing triumph and its tragic consequences.

A little further away, Joaquina, whom I had not thought of for so long, showed in her tidy and gleaming casque of hair among the leaves. I was able now, in this convincing nearness, to see that her eyes, which I had remembered as being blue without close thought, were really of a kind of burnt or tawny yellow, which turned her whole being out of a bleached paleness into a burned and gypsy fairness, and made her appeal to the senses with a much fiercer intoxication. Yet she was cold, cold, bone cold in her husk of golden armour, and I knew that though I might never stop seeing her, I could not reach to her true feeling or find out if she was anything more than an empty shell. Often I thought there was not even a ghost living under that lovely surface. But whenever she was in my mind, even in the radiance of warmth given out by Miriam, who made a kind of daylight of the eyes and senses with the running lines and gentle curves of her whole body, Joaquina's cold and formal architecture moved into an incredible and wonderful life by the same sort of miracle that a beautiful and intelligent animal might become suddenly gifted with speech. In fact, she was nearer to that naked figure that I had seen shaking the almond tree with sunlit and flashing limbs.

Even as I thought this, that shape climbed out of the flat sea and crossed the shore, avoiding the armed cactus points. It came towards one of the almond trees while Joaquina stood by the other, and made a contrast of its warm flesh with her cold and marble restraint. Each time it moved was a sip of honey in the air ; but now the statue at its side came to life and her dark fairness snared all that sweetness from the winds. But there she stayed, taking and asking for everything and giving nothing ; and I turned away from her, knowing this was all her life, into the quick and lively machinery of my third phantom. She blew into reality with a sudden and aching pleasure, while the two forsaken ghosts faded into the dark ends of the room.

VII

EPILOGUE

THIS is as far as I have got with it, and in a short two weeks there is no time to write more than this. These are the present fictions accompanying a created past. We may think of time, for our purposes, as a long measuring line. Every hill or valley can be reduced into some sort of harmony with this set proportion, but this does not prove that these heights and depths have not their own scale of comparisons. Where we actually lift up the measure with our hands, a kind of fictitious posture or emplacement is achieved by which the real relation to what is known and determined, or proved and historical, is most difficult to describe. But my eyes and my hand, as on the first page of this book, are now directly concerned; they are grasping, or even bound by, this line of distance that is now so near and obvious; indeed, the letters flowing out from the point of my pen become the rate of speed and distance that we are travelling. So everything for a few moments is tied down on to these pages, until time springs back or forwards in obedience to my wishes.

This is the best that I have been able to do with two hot and empty weeks, and their tenuous structure has been developed and ornamented into the fullest blossoming that it can stand. The sad ruins we live among I have hung with this trailing mantle of flowers, and the cold stones and sharp edges are somewhat cloaked and softened by this covering. Behind this fortnight, and on the other side of its lived or merely written adventure, I can see a few mornings of September mist. Its last moments move like smoke among the crockets and buttresses, and I remember the promise that my name would be invoked as they sat sketching those cracked moulds and broken metaphors of beauty. But it is not time yet to recall them with their relics, though their true return from that land of cream and cider is due for to-morrow. There are still a few hours before me.

My two friends would seem to have been concerned only with the deadness of that past and not with its life. I accused the present of being as dull because so little effort is made to palliate its uniformity, and now I have taken up the challenge that I threw down. There were the alternative treatments of broad humour, or of a sharp and photographic realism, but in their place I have tried to advance along a series of metaphorical parallels, hovering over and keeping pace with the truth. This has been the only method that gives enough play to the sort of abilities that are mine. Anecdotal and fictional writing should not be expected of a poet; while, at the same time, there are certain heights of emotion, and certain degrees of interpretation where I hold the mastery and am seldom approached. This book has been designed for their display.

There can be few others of my generation who have spent five or six months of every year, as I have done, writing poems all through the day. Indeed, I could write a most novel and revealing book of memories about these periods of my life, for where the lives of painters, of musicians, or of novelists, are on such full record, the mysterious art of poetry, self-taught and almost too subtle in inspiration and in texture for its origins to be understood, has never been chronicled in its strange and tumultuous procedure. But two things about it may be stressed in order to help my present purposes : first, that this incessant practice brings out, as in pianists of first-rate talent, a remarkable level of virtuosity, the benefits of which a poet should be able to convey without much difficulty into his writing of prose ; secondly, that a succession of many weeks spent in this way is equivalent to supporting life on a diet of cream, and of things as strong and yet immaterial as triply-distilled essences. In fact, such a life as this is dangerous for the nerves and for the senses, and the writer has not yet been born who could support it for more than a handful of months on end. He is forced to turn, because of this, into some other direction, if half of his working life is not to be wasted and useless.

But the choice of these new directions is one of immense difficulty. It is no use, with this new and powerful battery of instruments at his command, to start along the sort of path where such strange advantages are of no avail. And having renounced the novel, because there is no room, and because half the possible material is not allowed and would draw down a too deadly persecution on its embodier, we arrive at what is termed " fine writing," only to find that this has been wrecked and twisted aside by the morality, the aestheticism, or the naughtiness,* of last century's apostles. So some new treatment has to be attempted, and, since it is difficult to avoid the achievements of Italy, at any rate her

* Ruskin, Pater, Wilde.

triumphs must be celebrated away from Tuscany or Rome.

I found for myself, as I remarked in a dialogue at an earlier part of this book, a mass of material in Naples and Sicily, and I treated this as a composer would treat a whole universe of folk-songs of which he came suddenly into possession. Their merits were re-set and they were given a symphonic treatment. It was an age of bustling and crowded cities, far removed from the new churches and idyllic meadows of the early Renaissance.

Music had been born and airs were sung at the street corner. A fine and scenic architecture gave play to all the proud and rapid emotions of its patrons; church roofs were recessed and fretted so as to receive the roulades and cadenzas of the choir; monasteries and convents took to themselves majolica cloisters and fine pharmacies to sell their fashionable distillations; the palaces of princes had a pantomime grandeur about their twisted and double staircases and the huge saloons were multiplied into infinity by mirrors. A great school of fresco painters was ready to prolong the realities of wall and ceiling into a false world of perspective; even the foulest slums were never far removed from these evidences of a wealth which the taste and habit of that day always shared to this extent with its poor neighbours; the houses where travellers lodged had their drab doorways brightened by the spangled comedians coming back to their rooms, or going out to the cheerful trestles in the hot square; and there was not a single street down whose vista you could not see the heads and banners of a passing procession.

There is a tropical depth and brilliance of colour about these scenes which lends itself quickly to treatment by these powers and this technique, which one art, that of poetry, has developed, and which, as I have described, must often find themselves out of necessity in unemployment, and so are converted into the instruments of another medium in the intervals between their proper and authentic use. These same qualities, when applied to a strictly contemporary focus, must penetrate deep below the surface into the heart and nerve and mind before their product justifies this effort ; and to satisfy its requirements, either persons of a formidable sensitiveness must be chosen, or else the dark and hidden corners of the spirit have to be investigated and dragged into light. A number of barriers have to be pushed back and built up again on the further side of this possible extension until some new energy makes another recession and these curiosities of the soul can be followed a little nearer to their place of birth. So a complete technical perfection is impossible of achievement, and this is the poet's one superiority over the executive musician whose twelve hours of daily practice may ensure an impeccable finish and a lion-like battery of martial violence, though these mutations of the lion and dove are at the dictation of another and the half-safety felt in this reliance and lack of responsibility cannot atone for some amount of chagrin at being the vehicle and not the real instrument of creation.

But I must not let time stray away from the table where I write. It should cling to the point of my pen and follow it in tacit obedience as a shadow-dancer on a darkened stage whose lighted wand follows and outlines all his hidden movements. It has a span of a day in front of it before those two figures come back, who, since they have been created out of nothing, are no further away than the shadowed corners of the room, are, in fact, here all the time and have never been away at all.

As I think of their curious situation, so remote and yet so immediate, I am reminded of the hotel where I stayed a night this year at Casablanca, a horrible modern town, all suburb and no centre, which has been the gift of Europe to Morocco in exchange for that country's incredible legacy of careless beauty and careless cruelty, now ensured to her, in return for this, some degree of conservation by what would seem to be a set of Museum regulations which make every Moroccan more than ever anxious to save up his pence for a visit to Casablanca, where he thinks all the arts and inventions of the West must flourish.

The porters on the jetty have the look of corsairs, and the hybrid population has produced a horde of monkey-like children who sleep all night under the tin tables of the cafés and who will fight over a thrown penny with dreadful, animal ferocity. There are two or three hotels, at one of which, resonant with its noisy band, I found myself waiting through the night, for sleep was quite impossible. A number of its tunes remained behind long after their bray had died down, and they haunted and preyed upon the mind. Some of them I remembered as once being new and fashionable, and now they had got as far away as this, just as though they had been so many demi-mondaines once known and recognized in happier surroundings and found now in these cheap cafés, because this was a garrison-town and, at any rate, the officers have a regularly paid salary. Others of the tunes had the air of never having been better than this, as if written especially for such emotions against a cheap background. This set me thinking of the newest popular tunes I had heard before leaving London, and I wondered how long they would take in reaching Casablanca. It might be many months, perhaps a couple of years, and I could see myself in two years' time here in these same surroundings and present at the dawning of those once familiar characters; but then it occurred to me that with a wireless installation perhaps this particular tune I was thinking of could now be heard played in London, and in my mind I kept on putting this miracle into practice and turning on this new tune in the intervals and even in the midst of the loud and confident band from below, mingling in this manner the several generations of these cheap-toned and prettily-finished personalities.

This is not for the first time in this book that I have said that two years is the least time it can take to write any considerable work, and I hope that this illustration of the births and deaths, the subtle changes, and all the intermingling curves without which this span of time cannot flow past will stress and emphasize why I have thought it better to contrast the particular past that I had chosen to work and delve in with some scenes taken from the present. My aim is in this way to alternate and enrich the main subject so that there should be as many sculptures on the pedestal built up to carry this fine and antique statue. Its knightly armour towers above these contemporary scenes and does not suffer from what is carved below, where a few incidents, based on the artist's life, signal his own wish to be remembered and show him in the costume of his time surrounded by the symbols of his life and thought. But when it came to choosing these I spurned both the exact camera and the wilful eyes of the naïf, preferring, instead, to be seen where my particular skill has the advantage.

The ruins of our sad times are seen here gilded with
their own setting sun, and some of the emphatic shades
of the dark night that lies ahead are already to be seen
threatening the horizon with the coming changes in all
conceived values ; with money counting for more, and
therefore for less, than it ever did before ; with an
infinite multiplication of both pleasures and pains for
the nerves ; with every art tallied and knocked out by
its mechanical equivalent, beginning, already, with
photograph for picture, and gramophone, or cinema, for
all situations, spoken, played, or sung ; and with poetry
perhaps extinguished altogether since it is the art of the
amateur and a massacre of these drones would seem to
be one of the certainties of the future.

Out of this twilight I have tried to collect some of the
sparks and flashes by which it is lit.   It seems that these
are no more substantial than idle thoughts changing to
the pace of the blind as it taps against the window ; than
gusts of music blown out as the swing-doors open and are
sucked back again by the draught ; than the changes
that a mask-like face can work ; or than another mask,
its opposite in all things but impassivity and troubled
depths of shallowness, that seems in all its marble calm
and the happy colour of its gilded hair and sunburnt
eyes, where everything except these two fires is pale and
cold, to both ask and never answer.   The movements and
reactions of a piece of sensitive metal between these
two magnetic stones gives us the action and all the incident of the piece ; or it is a ship tossed between two
rocky shores ; or the choice, expressed before now in
poetry, between two trees of fruit, hung with different
kinds of apple, plum, or pear, or resolved by the earlier
year into two towers of blossom, as almond, pink or white,

whose lovely differences divide all beauty into two halves, as in the choosing between a milky skin and raven hair or a sunburnt and gypsy fairness, tawny as to its yellow and lion-like eyes.

These are the two alternatives to the soul, and here they are to be seen plumed and metaphored to the best of my ability, for I have no wish to be a Hamlet in modern clothes. Above me, guarding, as it were, the ramparts, but in reality confined to the small space of his pedestal, so that his home is no bigger in area than that of a Stylite, stands this iron and emphatic shade in his knightly armour. His beaked shadow moves with the hours round its pedestal as a menacing hand upon a clock, sometimes dwarfed by his own self so that he cannot reach even to the rim where the tents of time are written and that old wanderer is hidden for a moment among dark walls, and, at other angles of the sun, stretched and swollen to gigantic stature so that he threatens far-off things and holds some dominion over the future, outside and beyond his ruled and dead path.

None of the Caesars is near, for they passed by and were quickly gone out of the North. This, then, is the first statue in these parts, and it is significant that his place is on a tomb, or high on the ridges of some Gothick church, for the Caesars feared their soldiers and were elected by the mob. Their images are found, therefore, either upon some arch of military triumph, as if carried in acclamation on the shoulders of the legionaries, or else in public in the market-place, close to where farmer and peasant bargained and as though appearing to them and soliciting their votes. Nor did the Caesars seek in their appearance to make much difference between themselves and their subjects ; they were typical merchants

s

or typical centurions fattened by a special diet into some slight travesty upon those qualities of ordinary soldier or everyday citizen. If gods, they were gods by election and not by inheritance. So unique, though, was their situation that there was no foreign equivalent to their grandeur and no one of a like rank for the daughter of a Caesar to marry. It was difficult, therefore, for a line of Caesars to be aristocratic except on its paternal side, and at this stage it is not necessary to emphasize the very different ideals and inheritance of the North.

If we try to search out the secret of that dead age we find that dissimilarity, lack of sameness, was the main ingredient of its beauty. No two suits of clothes were alike, for the art of copying was not understood, and in order to balance any design or ornament a natural fertility of invention preferred the making of a fresh equivalent. Now the growth of this sameness and uniformity is our greatest present danger. It has come out of America and is but the latest of the ills, venereal disease may have been the first, which that hostile and alien soil has sent forth from itself, perhaps in revenge, to ruin Europe. I have tried to suggest in an earlier part of this book that the haunting and sinister types to be seen by lamp-light, for they are only travestied by night, in the great German cities may be a definite effort on the part of mankind to counter the levelling effects of shop and factory and to work some hideous variety and ornament on to that uniform surface. Nature, which has the common sense to intervene in the birth-rate after a great war in order to balance the ratio of male and female, has surely the resource to counter even by these extreme means a more lasting and insidious danger to mankind.

Religion is fast going. Priests are seen to have no

more efficacy than witch-doctors. Church services are
no more useful than the hire of wizards to bring down
rain. The very survival of religion is an anomaly, as
though doctors, or lawyers, had formed themselves into
a corporation hedged round by magical rites. Have not
doctors, or lawyers, as much right and reason? Why
should not they, instead of the priests, preside over
marriage, birth, and death?

The hereditary principle is gone. Fathers are told
they have no right to save up riches for their sons. No
architecture is to be seen. Football-grounds and cinemas
give the only opportunity, and this is never offered, for
there is no one to accept it. There is nothing left at
all with clothes. The dress of men has been abandoned
and left unchanged for two generations, while women
are nearly arrived at the same stage. Their cropped hair
may mark the last fashion before a permanent uniform
is evolved. Already actress, prostitute, and fashionable
beauty are impossible to distinguish between.

Murder, and to a now curtailed extent the divorce-
court, have been thrown open to the public as permanent serials run gallantly by the competing newspapers. Practically the only time in which the great
public comes into anything that can be called contact
with the arts is in the dance-hall, or from their own
gramophone. There are some qualities to this kind of
music which no one could deny, though any excellence is
outnumbered by ten times its amount of sentiment and
vulgarity. The hysteria attendant upon daily results
and daily news leaves no time for anything but this.

In order to foster these very results of wage-earning
the United States have introduced prohibition to increase
the efficiency of the worker. It is to be hoped that the

workers of Europe will prefer to keep their efficiency
undeveloped by this means, and that the odious effects
and arid deserts of ugliness which America produces
and stands for will soon produce a definite desire on the
part of European countries to develop their own means of
defence against these invasions of stupidity and barren-
ness. Both Russia and America should be hateful to
our eyes, for they spell death to all our achievement,
past and future. But of these two the most dangerous
is America.

No sooner did the nations of the East come into contact
with Europe than they fell to dust and ashes. Their
art, their power, and all their institutions crumbled and
fell from them. As regards things of the mind or spirit
America has no greater strength against us; they are
stilled and paralysed by our history, held so fast in their
wonder that the act of creation is beyond their strength.

It should be easy to take advantage of this hiatus. But,
unfortunately, the cult of the primitive, silliest of all
artistic affectations, has made the painter lose all his
inherited fluency and caused his position to be invaded
owing to its obvious simplicity by the hordes of amateurs
who since the artists have renounced their skill find
this an easy victory, and, in fact, often make, judged by
this criterion, better painters than do the professionals
themselves. It is essential to regain this lost fluency;
to throw off, for they would drop easily, the parasites
who cling to this dying body; and to connect ourselves
with the chain of tradition that has been wilfully broken
and cast aside. As far as painter, poet, or musician, is
concerned the Church may be mourned as a patron, if
its creed is disbelieved; and, so long as rich men spend
their money in the right way, it matters little if their

wealth had its sources in a Norman charter or a soap-factory.

In order to start this mood of creation again a kind of trance has to be induced. Any artist who has gone through a period of unproductiveness can testify to the truth of this. In such a situation it is no use thinking too much, the results of which are only so many laboured and abortive experiments. Instead, it is essential to let the senses lull themselves into a trance till this gradually works into the intoxication that brings confidence and is the indispensable accompaniment to work. Therefore, in so much as any small individual effort can help to bring about this state, the poet, or the musician, has now an unrivalled opportunity and his career has never been more needed. Unfortunately, it would seem as if the members of these two professions were born in an inverse ratio to the general increase of population, so that, until some radical change takes place, their number, few already, will be diminished. Then, we shall be as extinct and pathetic as the brother and sister whom I have chosen as being typical of a dead and useless attitude towards the past.

There is, though, an equal probability that, with music at any rate, the very opposite of this may be true. Music, compared with poetry, is a newer and immensely reinforced means directed towards the same end. Its deeper intellectual scope and greater excitant properties are too obvious to need emphasis. There can never be another age when poetry is the aim of life and poets are heroes, though there have been many such in the past, in Japan a thousand years ago, in Persia of the fifteenth century, and during the reigns of the Valois kings. But music, and many kinds of sports, will be the recreation of the future, and, indeed, its successes have hardly begun, and it will conquer where poetry has tried and failed, and when the great powers that once lay in a poet's hand have been forgotten and relinquished.

In order to restore things to the normal after the hundred years' smoke of the first industrial age a greater effort must be made to beautify life than has ever been made before; and the naïf and the wilful primitive must be kept out of the way, for their only achievement is to impede and obstruct. The eclectic, also, must disappear, as must those associations of intelligence with tiresome affectations of the voice and manner that are only to be met with in England, and that never appeared, even here, before the time of the Pre-Raphaelites. In fact, these are the legacy of that now despised brotherhood, and persons catching this infection may be said to antedate their intelligence by nearly a century.

Such are these sad ruins. They have no chance of being rebuilt, but it is just possible that fine and new structures may rise up beside them. There are voices speaking under the low arches.

They sound hidden and muted by some cold corner of stone, being no more seen and recognized than are the tramps under a railway-arch on a wet and windy night. Such are the signals for a quiet and hurried passing-by, for it might be dangerous to disturb them as they dry their clothes and warm their hands at the fire; and, in the same way, we must not stay too long beneath the roofless walls.

Just at this present the scene has only its own imminent future and its own immediate past. This confines itself to the actual, or possible, background for its characters. The drawing-master and his sister, being the first artists

I ever met, form its outermost boundaries, for it is no use moving them further away than the limits of our own lives, and I only wish to think of them in situations where the missing of a train or a breakdown of the motor-car could have prevented this fulfilment.

The sounds and tones of but a few days back are still ringing in my ears, and if I held a shell to them the empty volutes would reply to me, not with the punctual and breaking tides, but in the speech of cheap and slangy sentiments, as of that music issuing from the swing-doors I have been constrained to open more than once before.

Unfortunately, there is one concept, one conceived idea, that has attached itself to the two figures seen against that floral scenery, and this has its weaknesses which are difficult to explain. They can only be illustrated in this manner. There can be no one who has not at moments in his life wondered how much to the safe side of the line of sanity he was situated. The symptoms and peculiarities that mark the crossing of that frontier must be gradually approached and imperceptibly crossed, until things which seemed forced and fanciful become natural and unnecessary of explanation to the person concerned. Once this stage has been reached nothing is any longer odd or unconvincing; indeed, life must be more sensible and logical than to the normal senses. In the same way, the stores of simile and metaphor which are thrown open to the poet are never seen by him to be a part of life's principles in urging him towards the objects that his heart or mind admires, but they seem really to emanate from the person or thing itself, and not to have been placed there solely by the eyes that behold them. That is to say, the credit of these discoveries belongs to the writer and not to the person out of whom they seem to emanate.

VIII

LIFE IN THE DEAD STREET

S. S.: Oh! Come in!

C. C.: I'm disturbing you.

S. S.: Good heavens, no! Thank goodness you're back, or I should never have stopped writing. I finished the task you set me two days ago, but have gone on, nevertheless, all yesterday and to-day.

C. C.: Well, stop it, for the moment, and come round and talk to us. Hilda has got our sketches out for you to see, and there's a bottle of Benedictine we've smuggled home from Fécamp. Of course, it's the same as you buy at the "Six Bells," but somehow it tastes different.

S. S.: I've always admired that bit of Shakespeare's England, but d'you know I've only once been in a public-house.

C. C.: When was that?

S. S.: I was taken to the "Blue Posts," behind the Café Royal, to see the fat landlord and his collection of pictures and photographs of fat people. I went with the "Icelander" and with Guevara, you'll know who I mean!

C. C.: I know. He did your sister's portrait in the Tate.

S. S.: Do you like it?

C. C.: It's magnificent colour. You'd guess it was

296

by a Spaniard. It's a good likeness, too, I should say ;
is it like her poems ?

S. S. : Isn't that rather a leading question ?

C. C. : Well, all those bright colours, and that
shimmering, dazzling effect ?

S. S. : I wish you could see her picture by Tchelitchew,
a Russian painter. It's painted entirely in dust and
ashes and is more melancholy, more sunk, so to speak,
into its own personality than any portrait I can
think of. It's just as much like her as Guevara's
picture. In fact, more so. But isn't this your
door ?

C. C. : No, the next. This is it. Here we are.
Hilda !

H. C. : Is it Mr. Sitwell ? So our fortnight's tryst
is kept to the day.

S. S. : And almost to the moment. We suggested
ten o'clock. How faithful we've been !

H. C. : Carl has told you about this Benedictine ?
Some coffee, too ?

S. S. : Thanks. Oh! I like that. Isn't it the chapel
at Amboise where Leonardo is buried ? The chapel of
St. Hubert with gilded antlers on its spire ? And you've
arranged Carl's on the other side of the room, have you ?
When we've finished our Benedictine we'll walk round
and hold a regular exhibition.

C. C. : We've done five or six dozen sketches, each.
May I ask how many pages you've written ?

S. S. : Forty to fifty of the actual story, as arranged
between ourselves, and another twenty, or so, in the
last two days waiting for you to come back. Sixty to
seventy in all. In fact, about a page to each sketch of
yours, but of course you outnumber me, two to one.

H. C.: You'll read it aloud to us, won't you?

S. S.: I'll leave it here for you to read, if I even do that. You're both inside the frame, and I can hardly let you out without spoiling the picture.

H. C.: Will we recognize ourselves?

S. S.: You were in it long before Carl came up and spoke to me in the café at Blois. Then, I was travelling round collecting material. I've got it all now, all I want, and have reached the stage of putting it into its final form. This book has not much more than a hundred pages to run. Three-quarters of it is finished and done with. I hope you'll like the love-scene. It puts some of these novelists in their places.

Your figures have leaned out of it at times, like the things a painter brushes into his fresco to give it realism. The plaster has been simulated into a boulder jutting out, or the corner of a cloud trails down from the ceiling on to the wall and has become concrete and anchored, as it were, into one dimension more than its own strict flatness of coloured plaster. Or, to repeat a simile I was thinking of a few hours ago, your personalities are part of the sculptures I have designed for the pedestal. A few incidents, based on my own life, show me in the costume of my time, surrounded by the symbols of my life and thought. They alternate and enrich my main subject, and are so many decorations below the plinth of the heroic, iron statue I am setting up.

H. C.: You say it is three-quarters finished.

S. S.: Well, for the moment, we're only concerned with the part of it that you and Carl directly suggested to me, aren't we?

C. C.: Exactly, and what have you tried to do in that?

S. S.: I have applied my method to a transcendentalized account of the fortnight since we last met. The
ordinary things of life, if I've been successful, have been
transmuted and lifted out of their focus into some more
permanent level of experience where they are not incongruous with the rest of my matter. This has been a
direct frontal attack, such as no poet has delivered for
some stretch of time. But, if my medium can combine
this wretched present that we live in—when else should
we have liked to live ?—with the riches of its past, in
the tattered old clothes that those ghosts are reduced
to wearing, then my project will have been realized and
my poetics can be excused by their results.

C. C.: In fact, it comes to this. Besides showing
yourself choosing out a subject to write upon from those
that suggested themselves to you, you have given a picture
of yourself in the process of collecting material for your
book ; now, you are dealing with things that actually
happened in your mind or were typical of it while engaged in this process of composition ; lastly, at the end
of the lens, so to speak, the subject itself appears, set up
and fully coloured by your vision and experience. That
is how I understand you. Am I right ?

S. S.: So correct that it sounds suspiciously like my
own voice speaking through your lips. But I'm hoarse ;
give me some lemonade, or a little more of that
Benedictine !

H. C.: In fact, it is a portrait of yourself at work.

S. S.: I've had two things in mind as models. One
of them is the self-portrait of Vermeer in the Czernin
collection in Vienna. But realism has not been my aim,
and where, as in this second picture, part of my subject
has been a study of the light coming through a window

and the blind tapping and beating in the afternoon wind, it has been the effect of these things upon the mind that has interested me, and not the exact patterns thrown by the reflections on to the silk and velvet of my clothes as I sit thinking. That, and the tweed or serge of my suit, have made the difference. But, even in a silk doublet with slit sleeves, I should not have dwelt for long upon that even surface, for having chosen a noisy and pugnacious age to study I need to be set round with trophies of lance and trumpet.

C. C. : That reminds me. I must say, this time, I was very disappointed with the tombs. There's nothing I enjoy drawing so much, but I suppose it's the Revolution, we hardly found a single one worth sketching. Hilda thought the same as me.

S. S. : In fact, you didn't enjoy yourselves as much as on our trip to Naples ?

H. C. : I'm afraid that started us with new notions of the picturesque. I'm a little tired, now, of frosty mornings and green grass afternoons. Carl can't forget that view.

C. C. : You're quite right, Hilda. I've lived in another dimension ever since I saw that incredible perspective. I don't think we shall go again to Normandy. It gives me a pain in my heart. The buildings are sad and aloof, and have the sort of helpless regret that an old ballad or song gives to one.

S. S. : At last you've seen how useless they are! An entirely new standard, a fresh criterion as it were, has got to be set up, somehow. And yet it is no use living in the present without any tradition at all. The past has got to be made use of. But, to begin with, a new set of enemies must be declared. You know what

I'm going to say! The novelist, the business man, the
art-dealer. But I mustn't say any more. After all,
they won't last for ever. What are business-men but
money-beetles, rolling the little balls of mud and manure
that they've collected in front of them! As for the
dealers, let's try to extol every single thing that's no use
to them!

C. C. : I must say, there's not exactly a rush for my
sketches. One summer they let me hang some dozens
of my things in the hotel at Dinan. By the end of the
season only two of them had sold. Nobody under fifty
would look at them. Never mind! How do you like
this one? It's a street of old houses at Valognes in the
Contentin. D'you know the place?

S. S. : Yes, I've been there.

C. C. : I sat the whole morning, sketching. Not a
child came to disturb me, and Hilda will bear me out
that the whole three hours I was drawing not more than
a half-dozen people, old women at that, passed me in the
street.

S. S. : I can well believe it. I know Valognes, and it's
as dead as any town I've ever seen. It's so rare to meet
a human being abroad in the streets that the houses
lose all their scale. After looking at them for any length
of time, as you had to do to draw them, their reality
must seem to leave them.

The top of Carl's sketching board, as he drew at his
easel, was as high as the roof of the next house. So he
must be as tall as that.

The street died away in flat perspective like a theatre
scene built up in stone, and the houses were all of the
early seventeenth century. They were as clean as at

Bruges or Haarlem, and had no more of the Renaissance than satyr's head, or mildly conceived cornucopia, could give them. They had high gables, and the window in each gable was like the front of a cabinet.

It was an autumn day with a great deal of its sunlight still to burn. All the peacefulness of that particular life came back to the dead street. The window-sills were bright with flowers. Smoke climbed straight from the chimney into the bare heaven, and the tiles glistened as though a golden brush had been passed over them. It was a paradise for Carl and Hilda—or had been, till it crumbled and was too dead to hold them.

All the afternoon nothing happened. Flowers breathed into the open doorways, and leaves of shade flickered against the walls. Sometimes a great bee, like a golden ball, knocked upon the window-pane but was beaten back by the glass. Nothing happened, and apparently nothing ever would happen.

The evening had a faded freshness while you breathed it, as though seasoned with quince and clove. Nothing had happened, and morning came again.

It was the time of Henri Quatre, who used to dance under the oak-trees with the pretty peasant girls, and this was the last age that interested my two artists. Its tunes were happy and untroubled. The houses were well-stocked with food, the orchards deep in fruit, and a sunset breeze moved the boughs to the measure of the farandole. The past was sweet and scented.

It broke in a little foam of spires and bells at their feet.

These were all the things they had loved. But the middle-ages, whose very name implies their supposed fixed point in time and the apparent summit of history so wildly ridden by the poets and artists of the Romantic Age, were now drifting, slowly and deliberately, into the distance. They were as dead as a broken machine, the wheels of which you can still turn with your hand but which will never move by its own power again.

These are the authentic sad ruins. And they are turned more melancholy still by any ghosts that try to shelter in them and are left outside the roofless walls. Such were Carl and Hilda.

But the airs that had echoed so lately with the farandole now resounded with an alert and live music that carried nothing except its own direct messages. It had no associations save these, being sprung only from garish scenery and from the cheaper kind of prettiness that looks best against painted roses. This it had done because all the arts had failed, and because there was a hopeless bankruptcy in everything else except this unaffected need to please the eyes with pretty limbs and soft faces.

The winds rolled like drums announcing something special, and Claude and Cordelia walked past. It was their holiday, and they had come to the country.

Seeing the English brother and sister from their hotel, Claude took out a far too golden cigarette-case and began smoking. He looked half matador, half hairdresser, and Cordelia was in her usual long clothes and wide hat. The two brothers and two sisters would meet in an instant. Carl and Hilda had been much puzzled by them. Claude and Cordelia had guessed them at once. But they were beginning to like just what Carl and Hilda had started to despise.

This is the sadness of life, that no knowledge can be inherited, and that everything has to be started from the beginning with each new comer. The dead street with its two façades propped up, and with nothing behind them, was no gayer from these lessons that have to be learnt over again.

Behind them, the street jostled and swayed with a crowd of masks. The satanic Algerian; the small dark woman with her hair brushed straight and a man's collar and tie; her wigged friend, bleached from natural darkness into that Scandinavian pallor as of painted wax; the pair of brothers—or were they sisters?—with their odd smile as of a simple secret, dear to them both and holding their means of livelihood; all these had come here for their holiday, for a trial of bucolics.

They advanced with their characteristic walks, recognizing old tunes and dragging them out of the sunlight, as though pulling fruit from boughs. The horrible, haunted future lay just in front, and soon their shadows would mark it. The kings of old tragedy lay in the dust they kicked.

This was the flood of ghosts I let loose to people the waste spaces and fill the emptiness of those two sketchbooks. They came to complete these pages of an interlude between two serious acts, allowing time for my more heavy machinery to be moved. Yet their obvious importance to the whole scheme excuses this interference.

They typify some kind of life against so many dead admirations. They could have no better scene, and this street of old houses can never have held a more spirited foil, for it brought out every quality that had lain dead there.

We may imagine both scene and characters as enjoying themselves to the same high degree; and, watching them, I had no time to think of my own degrees of sadness, and of the figures I should have liked to bring on to complete, or contradict, this faded town and the sketch-books that tried to chronicle its dead merit.

NOTES

1. I am bound to admit that this denial of mine was reversed and put to nought the first time I set foot in another continent but Europe. So far my experience has been limited to Morocco ; but, even in this small scope, there is enough to disprove my contention. This is not Asia, but North Africa, never famous for the arts, and lying on the uttermost limits of the Moslem world. The grand mosque of Tlemcen with its openwork cupola, its mihrab, and its court paved with slabs of onyx ; the smaller mosque of Sidi el Haloui ; the ruined minaret of Mansoura ; the mosque of Sidi Bou Medine, lying like a little Umbrian village upon the hills above Tlemcen, with its bronze doors and the gilded honeycomb of the porch above it ; the Kairouiine mosque at Fez, and the Medersa Attarine ; the Kasba at Rabat, the broken minaret of Hassan, the ruins of Chella ; the Koutoubia tower and the tombs of the Saadian Sultans at Marrakech ; these were the revelations of an unknown land, nearly omitted from every history of the arts, and only treated as the poor refuge of the Andalucian Moors. Of all the buildings named, those at Rabat and at Mansoura, and the Koutoubia tower, are twelfth-century work belonging to the age of the Gothick cathedrals, while the rest are affairs of the fourteenth century, forming a parallel to the lighter, filigree Gothick of that date. After these, what can be the buildings of Koniah and of Brusa, of Persia and of India ? But I still hold to the truth of my footnote on page 16.

2. A few details may be of interest as to the castles of Syria and the Holy Land. The Castle of Belfort, called Kal'atesh-Shakîf by the Arabs, lies about 2,500 feet above the sea and commands the pass from Sidon to Damascus. It is first

mentioned in 1179, but had surrendered to Saladin by 1196. In 1240 the castle, together with the town of Sidon, was bought by the Templars, but it was taken from them in 1280, and has been deserted ever since. It is protected by a moat hewn in the rock to a depth of from fifty to one hundred and twenty feet. On the south side, only, it is connected with a narrow mountain-ridge. The walls slope outward to a distance of twenty to thirty feet.

Blanchgarde, or Specula Alba, named from its conspicuous white chalk rocks, and called by the Arabs Tell es-Sâfiyeh, was made into a castle by King Fulke of Anjou in 1138. In 1190 the castle was taken and destroyed by Saladin. It lies between Gaza and Jerusalem in a great river valley filled with mimosa bushes.

The fortress of Toron, between Safed and Tyre, was built in 1107 by Hugh de St. Omer, Lord of Tiberias, for the purpose of making forays into his country of Tyre. The Saracens captured it, and it was besieged without success by the Christians in 1197-1198. Scandalion, or Iskandarûneh, was fortified by Baldwin I, in 1116, to help him in his attack upon Tyre. In spite of its name the site has nothing to do with Alexander the Great, but was so called from being situated on a Roman road built during the reign of Alexander Severus.

The last, and greatest of these fortresses, Kerak, lies on the far side of the Dead Sea, upon the road to Petra. It commanded the caravan-route from Egypt and Arabia to Syria. The castle was held by Rainald de Châtillon against Saladin from 1183 to 1188, but was at last captured by him, together with the castle of Shôbek, or Mons Regalis, built by Baldwin I. Kerak is one of the finest mediaeval castles in existence, with huge bastions, great galleries, corridors and water-cisterns. The military architecture of the Middle Ages is nowhere seen to better advantage than here, in a waste land removed thousands of miles from Coucy, Pierrefonds, or the Welsh castles of Edward I. It is at the moment undergoing expert restoration.

3. The pair of pictures referred to are by Fedele Fischetti, and were painted in 1808, the year of Joachim Murat's expedition

to Capri. The first of them shows the force embarking at the Punto della Campanella under the supervision of King Gioacchino. His flag is flying above the Royal villa, and among the officers of his staff is Colletta, the famous historian of Naples. The second picture shows the actual taking of Capri. Sir Hudson Lowe, the future gaoler of Napoleon at St. Helena, was the English Commandant of the Island. The youth in a high shako and salmon-pink trousers is Achille Murat; but on grounds of accuracy it is better to admit that his alternative appearance, in no clothes at all, takes place on a painted ceiling at Caserta, where he rides with his father in a chariot after the classical fashion. While dealing with this subject and however far removed it may seem from my *fons et origo*, William the Conqueror, I cannot resist drawing the attention of travellers to the quarter-length portrait of Murat in cocked hat and dark blue coat, also at Caserta. This is the pirate of children's stories personified, and is probably an excellent likeness of the Gascon adventurer.

Achille Murat, the subject of so belated an anachronism, calls for a few more details. Napoleon Achille Murat, whose mother was Caroline, sister to Napoleon, was born in 1801. After the fall of the Empire he emigrated to America, and was postmaster for many years at Tallaharsee in Florida. He married a greatniece of Washington. His brother, Napoleon Lucien Charles, only two years younger than Achille, was recognized by Napoleon III as of imperial blood, had his debts of two million francs paid, and was granted a generous allowance from the civil list. He was the progenitor of the present Murat family. At one time Napoleon III schemed to restore his father's throne to him on the expulsion of the Neapolitan Bourbons. He died as recently as 1878, while his daughter, the Duchesse de Mouchy, a person of Proustian importance, survived till two years ago.

4. " It was at Naples only that I expected to have my ears gratified with every musical luxury and refinement that Italy could afford. My visits to other places were in the way of business, for the performance of a task I had assigned myself; but I came hither animated with the hope of pleasure. And what

lover of music could be in the place which had produced the two
Scarlattis, Vinci, Leo, Pergolese, Porpora, Farinelli, Jomelli,
Piccini, Traetta, Sacchini, and innumerable others of the first
eminence among composers and performers, both vocal and in-
strumental, without the most sanguine expectations? . . .
In their manner of executing music there is, at Naples, an energy
and fire not to be met with elsewhere, perhaps, in the whole
universe : it is so ardent as to border upon fury, and from this
impetuosity of genius, it is common for Neapolitan composers,
in a movement which begins in a mild and sober manner to set
the orchestra in a blaze before it is finished. Like high-bred
horses, they are impatient of the rein, and eagerly accelerate their
motion to the utmost of their speed ; as Dr. Johnson says—
that Shakespeare, in tragedy, is always struggling for an occasion
to be comic." (Cf. Dr. Burney's "Musical Tour in France and
Italy," London, 1773.)

Of all these composers, the only music that is known, now,
is a capriccio, or a pastorale, by the younger Scarlatti. Dr.
Burney was right about Haydn, the Bach family, Mozart, Gluck.
Is it reasonable to suppose that he was wrong about these others ?
Are they not undeservedly forgotten ?

5.   It will not be very long before this kind of scenery is extinct
altogether, and it will be a sad day when that happens. The
peculiar excellence of the Harkers consists in their rendering of
river, or sea-scape, and in their gardens bedded out with flowers.
Their technical cleverness and optimism are prodigious. I was
privileged, once, to see the rose-covered studio of this delightful
and deleterious* pair of painters from a boat. It is in the
neighbourhood of Bosham, in whose church a daughter of King
Canute is buried ; and a few moments later we stranded on a
shoal and were nearly drowned. My companion in this adventure
was the author of " The Waste Land."

---

* This epithet was applied, in my hearing, by the late Sir Edmund Gosse in
1921, to a pair of brothers whom I will no further specify than this.

BOOK III
THE FAIR-HAIRED VICTORY

I

MONASTERIES

TWO things that happened long ago much impressed me and directed my thoughts. When I was a child, I saw a hermit in the streets and churches of Genoa. He had come down from the mountains for the Easter services in the town. His long raven-black hair nearly hid his face, though it was possible to see two flashing and fanatical black eyes through that strange kind of mask. He was a young man; I wondered if he ever saw or heard from his relatives, and if he ever read a newspaper; sometimes, now, I wonder whether he was conscripted in the war.

My other inspiration was a mendicant friar, dwarfish, red-bearded, and hunchbacked, whom I saw creeping in and out of the lava-built slums of Catania. I expect he was selling amulets. He was the most primitive human " throwback " that I have yet come across, while I must admit that his presence in Sicily was not to be wondered at, for this island, of all Western European lands, possesses the most tattered and aboriginal of monks.

Some day I shall write a history and a handbook to beggars. These lines of this present book may be said to act, in part, as a spiritual introduction to that future work, for there is no doubt that, the lunatic asylum always excepted, we can study early man to better

309

advantage among beggars and monks than anywhere else.
The most powerful actors I have ever seen play all day
for a few coppers in the slums of Naples, and their art
is nearly approached in such unlikely settings as Rouen
or Nancy. But before I desert my twin-theme for the
remainder, at any rate, of this present book, I will draw
a little sketch that can hang safely beside the two monkish
incidents just noted.

In the spring of three years ago I was on the road
between Leon and Oviedo in the north of Spain. These
two towns are separated by a jagged and appalling range
of hills in which there are many coal-mines. The colliery
villages put to shame even the most disgraceful of those
to be seen in Scotland, while there is not a football-match
or a picture-house within miles. Upon this icy road,
for at the summit there was a good deal of snow upon
the ground, I passed three beggars. They were fit
companions to the hermit and the Capuchin I have
described. I stopped the night at Oviedo, and on my
way back to Leon the following day came across them
again, only about four or five miles further advanced
upon their road. They were two old men and an old
woman. At this second view of them the woman
and one of the men were a mile behind the other man.
Was he the vanguard of this extraordinary march ? Why
had his two companions fallen behind ?

Their appearance was beyond description. I can
only quote from a note-book some sentences which will
give an idea of their effect upon the memory. " A
terrible ape-like hair grows upon their lopped and twisted
limbs ; they seem like an attempt at a vegetable man
which has been manufactured and cast aside as soon as
finished ; their piece-made limbs have been assembled

and strung together with a mechanical heartlessness of
invention ; their limbs are covered with coarse, spiky
points like those the clown exposes when he pulls up his
trouser and shows the calf of the leg sprouting with a
thick noisy hair in one of the frightful demoniacal jokes
of the circus ; their boots, below that horror, are splayed
out at their ends to show the gnarled toes that writhe
convulsively, in socks that show each toe separate as
would a glove ! All three of them are heavily wadded
in successive layers of rags, their pace is slower than that
of an ox, and they lurch along under their bundles,
staff in hand, with heads dropping on to their chests.
On neither occasion that we saw them were they speaking. Are they two brothers and a sister ? Two husbands with the same wife ? Three Platonic friends ?
A whole history of extraordinary conjecture builds itself
round them."

I wondered what language the woman spoke through
those wooden and red ventriloquist cheeks ; was it a
few words—they surely could not have many in their
language—of some incomprehensible Spanish patois ;
was it Basque, or Gallego, or Maragato, for this latter
rare race of men, of unknown history and origin, lives
not far away in the mountains near Astorga ? I wondered what the name of the woman could be ! She
can never have been baptized, having been born probably
in some ditch or beneath a stone wall's hard shade,
but the two tramps must have some name to call her
by, and my fancy suggested Dolores, Anita, Carmen,
an echo of Andalusia into the high, cold land in which
they moved. Had they any friends left, any companions
who had huddled round the same embers and whom
they met, now and again, upon the moors, or by a

village of caves ? Or were they simply a tribe to themselves like some of the Indians in the Mexican states
who are reduced to no more than a single family ? And
then I imagined a meeting with them in the night,
having lost the way, and what an unearthly experience
it would be to have to trust to them for a scrap of supper
and for their advice upon how best to avoid the wind
when lying down to sleep in their company. This was
less than a year ago, and I suppose those three extraordinary beings are still wandering to and fro, having
by now, it is likely enough, got deep into Galicia, the
wildest and most inhospitable of lands.

It seems to me that this double encounter upon a
Spanish road is in the same class of experience as the two
incidents I described a little way back. There always
have been, and there always will be, ascetics and beggars,
and in their extremes of achievement these two strange
careers come nearer to each other than might be imagined.
Alas, that I must now desert the latter for the former !
But I can soften the separation by proceeding, as
tramp or monk might do, down a road of common
experience.

Everyone who has been in Europe knows a little hill
up which there climbs a slow and steady staircase. At
the top there is a great pile of buildings, and to the world
of typewriter and gramophone in which we move such
terraces as these are as strange as Maya temples in the
jungles of Guatemala ; they are anomalous and incredible and have this advantage over any of such
serpent-haunted ruins that they are often still inhabited
and put to their original purposes.

A projecting porch is built forward to the edge of the
hill and comes out over the steps. Through this it is

our duty to gain entry, for we have come to study and examine the honeycomb that such busy workers have built and stored for themselves. When the bell has gone back into silence a tortoise-like step comes down the long corridor and the door is unbolted and unbarred. The church lies across the flag-stones of a great court, and beyond this are the cloisters and the cells. A number of monks are crossing a corner of this courtyard into the refectory, for it is the hour and the day, coming but once in a week, upon which they eat together and are allowed to talk. We will enter and watch them.

It is a high vaulted hall, narrow and long, with great openings on either side into other refectories, as though this was nave and those were aisles. The pilasters between these arches are niched with statues of huge saints, and between their intervals there are other tables far away into the distance, while this chief hall is lined with tables that are crowded with monks. These are the oldest of them; they sit with their backs against tall wooden settees and age comes to its climax with the Prior at his high table looking down the hall. In front of him down the centre of the room is a narrow plank table at which the novices are sitting on benches without backs to them.

Several of the serving-brothers are going from table to table in pairs, carrying between them a trestle of bread; others, singly, are on their way with smoking dishes of meat, or with a water-jar in either hand. The food has not altogether gone the rounds yet; a novice is feeding a dog with a crust while he waits for his soup to arrive, another is teasing a cat with the ends of his rope waist-belt. Thus have they been painted by

Alessandro Magnasco, the delineator of monastic life, and there is another picture by him of the common room, or calefactorium, with a great open fire where the monks can be seen warming their feet and hands at the flames. It is a pity there is no picture of the frater, or dormitory, in which they slept, for we should then possess a complete epitome of their lives out of church. The painter of these two canvases added a new subject to the somewhat threadbare conventions of his age, and his pictures of monks, taken in this case from the thriving convents of the plain of Lombardy, are true even of a place so remote from his age by distance and by time as Fountains Abbey. These, then, are two general illustrations to my theme, for they give us the strange being we have come here to study in surroundings the most typical of the ordinary divergence of his life from that of soldier, sailor, shopkeeper, or peasant.

The effect of seeing so many tonsures together is, to be frank, rather repugnant—like an outbreak of ring-worm in a boys' school. There are so many freakish and ugly faces, and those that are cast in a better mould seem condemned to their environment and inspire pity. Yet for many hundreds of years there was little hope for mankind outside such walls as these, and life in their shelter was the only refuge for those who were not prepared for blows with any chance person they met. The sight of this meal, taken as a whole, was not unlike that which might be witnessed during a workhouse dinner. Not much better food, still cheaper and plainer clothes, the architecture of the hall being the only main difference. So here, at any rate, the monks have still preserved their original vow of poverty, though it amounted to hardship in fine surroundings; and they

THE REFECTORY

From the painting by Alessandro Magnasco in the Civic Museum, Bassano

have still another freedom, that of speech. They are all busily talking to each other, which would not be true of all refectories ; indeed this small licence may be said to give the clue to their identity, and we must follow it into recognition. In fact we have arrived at our list of dramatis personæ.

They would seem at first to be a drab kind of actor, very different from the spangled knights of the drama ; yet, for those diamonded untruths, they may be more humble in their sackcloth, but they play in a permanent stone scene of hall and corridor, to mention but the barest of their palace cells. It has been an endless repertory for two thousand years of ritual. Their power over the audience lies in the contrasts of great riches with bare halls, wooden pillows and crusty bread with coffered ceilings and gilded walls. These terraces, leading, so they hoped, into eternal life, had, as even they would admit, various degrees, various heights and depths, and such differences we must now enumerate.

The Holy Men of Egypt were the beginning. After so many thousands of years of urban life with, at the end, the Greek and then the Roman crowd-life super-imposed upon their own, it is not difficult to understand how silence and discomfort had an attraction for the serious-minded. The discontented began to rally behind certain confirmed grumblers in the desert, and with so deep a zest did they enter into this new diversion for frayed nerves that their celebrations amounted to perpetual Olympic games of privation and self-imposed torture. Over a couple of centuries the ascetics reached to superb and at the same time nauseating heights of sacrifice, and the Thebaid was big enough to raise an army. This was from an artist's point of view the most pure and least alloyed period, and its values demand a volume to themselves.*

Asia Minor, the oldest land of luxury after Egypt, was the next to catch this infection, and the anchorites recruited from Ionia and Antioch suffered a spiritual reinforcement out of Persia and the lands beyond Tigris and Euphrates. In fact they took on many of the attributes of the Indian fakir. St. Simeon the Stylite may be remarked as a ringleader, and it is a thousand pities that I cannot describe and perhaps illustrate the masterpiece of architecture that was built round his life-long column.(1) That chapter could well continue into Byzantine history, so Oriental were those lives and that art. It might flow on, were I able to read Russian, until the death of Rasputin, but I should restrain it, save for Mount Athos, at the fall of Constantinople to the Crusaders. The Jewish and the Armenian, the Arab and the Persian, entered, as I have just hinted, into that art, and indeed it is the first phase in which we find anything to do with art associated with the ascetics, who, till then, had been content with hut or cave.

There was, and there still is, but one order of monk in the Eastern church, so that there was none of the competition and the divergence of style to be found in Western Europe, where the different orders competed with each other in their monasteries.† But from this

---

* In the fourth century the Thebaid and the district of Nitria swarmed with hermits and anchorites. One of the most famous monasteries was that founded by Pachomius and 1,400 monks on the island of Tabenna, near Denderah, where Rufinus afterwards found 3,000 monks. The city of Oxyrhinchus, according to the same authority, had 10,000 monks and 20,000 nuns. In Nitria there were said to be 5,000 hermits and 50 monasteries.

† For example, the churches of S. M. Novella and Santa Croce in Florence; SS. Giovanni é Paolo and the Frati in Venice; S. Domenico and S. Chiara in Naples. In each of these cases the first church named is Dominican, and the second, Franciscan.

point we must leave the eastern world on one side,
while in the Roman church the rôles become infinitely
multiplied. Since then, but little has been added and
of what there was some little yet remains. Those ward-
robes, once so full, can still dress even the stage-crowd
without whose aid we could not bring on our big scenes.
Benedictine, Franciscan, Dominican, Capuchin, are to
be seen in number to this day ; while the Cistercian, now
turned Trappist, the Olivetan, the Camaldolian, and
the Carthusian, are still to be met with in certain
appointed places.

But their virtue has left them. Now, monks are
objects of pity, condemned to an uncomfortable imprisonment among the ruins of their broken illusions.
The works of their hands, that side of them which
interests us, we must remember to be the mere product
of their hours off duty. The most of their time was
prayers and penitence.

Their tortured senses, deprived of everything else,
imagined the utmost luxuries of light, shuttering and
dyeing it through painted histories. The more austere
orders were denied even this, and their only satisfaction
came from the chalk-white cliffs at the feet of which
they knelt in prayer. Each wall of their churches is a
steep precipice, and the eyes recognize such far-apart
places as Alcobaça and Fountains, Tintern and Santas
Creus, as individual attempts towards this same effect.

We can distinguish several types of ascetic. The idiot
type, lolling in slothful inactivity and credited with holy
inspiration from his mysterious, haunted movements ;
the hard, unpleasant grumbler gloating over the inevitable pains to which his prayers condemn all enemies ;
the easy, punctual lover of a quiet life ; the creeping,

curatical conspirator; the benevolent French missionary; the athlete in austerities, trying one after another for all the prizes in suffering; these are some of the actors of the cloister.

They formed, as I have suggested before, another sex over and above the accustomed, procreative pair. We must expect their lives, then, to attain to the normal through other directions; though this normality would naturally exceed the average as much as their privations put them below it.

We may imagine their pioneers as inquiring anxiously for the whereabout of the most uninhabited corners of the land. They wished to found new monasteries for their order, and this ambition could only be satisfied by finding an improbable locality for building. It must be far away, hidden in dense forest where they could clear the ground, or in a marsh where they could drain a little island for its foundations. It was the contrast that pleased their starved senses; the contradiction of a great monastery being built in a wilderness, and then the inner and perpetual difference between their hard lives and the stone bastions and lattices of this winter and summer prison, this palace where they toiled in sackcloth through the heat, and shivered barefoot in the cold.

We enjoy in a few seconds several centuries of their work, but are appalled and stifled if we think of their hours of prayer. Each monk will have spent a quarter of a century, if he lived to any age, upon this problematical insurance. Another third of their lives was sleep, and there remained this other part, made manifest in these works of stone.

Each of the great monasteries was a miniature republic,

supplying all its own needs and with no necessity for its inmates ever again to come into contact with the world of towns, once they had taken refuge in its walls. There was enough energy to drive out sadness, and we need not waste our pity on them. The drably uniform clothes, the regular routine of life, the strictly sufficient diet, left little of the individual. Each monk walked past his burial-place hundreds of times in a year, he was taught to look forward to death, and in the days of that real faith something approaching the corporate life of the insects must have been attained. Ants, and other communistic tribes of insect, have no fear of death. Science cannot explain this, but may it not be that they, too, think they will be born again ?

If we consider the monasteries to be the greatest manifestation of mediaeval energy, we must grant them space and time in their lives for an unparalleled finish to any task they set themselves. Given unlimited wealth ; a store, an accumulation as it were, of time to spend ; generations of skilled and anxious labour ; all the peace they had, and the inspiration their faith gave them, we should expect to find certain instances where they reached to a supreme expression of themselves in architecture. This hazard is justified in its examples, but the inquiry should begin on a humble scale by an examination of how much any one person could accomplish, whose whole life was passed in such surroundings of safety and tranquillity.

All the action is in a little room. A door leads from it into another cell where a bed, a table, and a chair, are the only incidents. The door into this second cell he never opens, save on his way to and fro from chapel, where our own conscience forbids us to follow him.

There is a view, and a little garden hanging below the window reached by some steps through a wicket in the passage. For a flagged corridor runs the length of the two rooms and joins this prison on to the outside world. Here is the third door that he passes on his way to prayer, and food is given to him through a doored trap, at shoulder-level in the wall.

But the inmost room with the garden below it is the focus of his whole life. It has the high desk and the railed chair of the scribe. Quill-pens, fine brushes of hair, precious colours in cockle-shells, agate burnishers, leaves of vellum, give point and animation to the incessant cold air. For it is seldom, or never, warm, and the hand is always chilled upon the vellum, slowed down and steadied, as it were, by this breath out of vault and tomb.

Good handwriting was expected of the author, or poet, in the same way that a composer of music is credited, till he always contradicts it, with a gift for the piano. Failure in this respect will always throw doubt upon his other talent ; and where so few people could write at all the mediaeval author who was not something of a calligrapher had his career seriously affected by this shortcoming.

The professional scribe, then, filled the rôle of virtuoso, and his task was an interpretation of someone else's themes. His ornaments and flourishes were inspired out of the subject and were held to enhance the beauty of the original as so many cadenzas and scale passages enliven the bare tune in the piano arrangement of a song, or in a fantasia upon an opera.

This art of illumination had two golden ages. The first was in Ireland, and it produced intricate mazes of basket-work, hidden in and peeped out of by toothed dragons and by all the sea-mythology of the North. The saints are shown red-haired and blue-eyed, in trousers and coats of what can only be identified as tweed of the Hebrides, dyed with sea-lichens and smelling of the peat-fire. The masterpiece of this school is the Book of Kells, now in Dublin. The second great period was in Carolingian Germany, where uncial letters, of purple and gold, ornament the most elaborately conceived architectural fantasies. But neither of these schools give us any indication of the details of life. The buildings in which we are interested had not yet begun, and it is necessary to leave these two formalisms some centuries behind.

Nor can we find satisfaction in the ivy-leaf borders of the French school, and in the tessellated, damasked, and diapered backgrounds to the figures, which thus imprison them and allow no effects of realism to be achieved. The Horae of John, Duke of Bedford, one of the treasures of the British Museum, marks the culmination of this attempt. Its burnished gold, as loud as a brass band, but applied sparingly, as though the strains came from far away, is the beauty of this particular manuscript; but it is difficult to think of the hand, or hands, that worked upon it as having belonged to an artist, for this is merely ornament and nothing else. Its effect is extremely monotonous, and a mere half-dozen pages, out of the hundreds that the book contains, are sufficient to satisfy curiosity and to stimulate a wish to move on a step further among the manuscripts.

But with careful search we can place exactly the things we have come to look for on the crowded desk in the chilly cell of the illuminator. For, at last, the most

U

delicate and gifted artists gave up their lives to the task, and there is no nearer approach than this to the truth of appearances and of the imagination in that day. It is probable that several of these trophies may be the work of lay artists, but their handiwork was the complete and final development out of the cloister, and so we can attach this last generation to the many centuries that went before it and think of this art's culmination as an intrinsic part of its whole history.

We shall be able to find certain paintings in manuscripts that have all the personality and characteristics of the individual. They will be the work of forgotten artists whose whole output is put away in some few books. Where one of these volumes is in a public library, it may be exhibited in a glass case with just one open page showing, and all the rest of it shut away and only accessible to the patient student. Having examined some few of these hidden things, there will be a chance of comparing them with the only other rivals to them in perfection, and in this same quality of being kept away and invisible. Even so, only the available examples out of the vast material that exists can be discussed here; and then it will be time to move off towards those places where the monks attained to the utmost freedom of expression in their architecture.

One of the most beautiful of these manuscripts is illustrated thrice over in this book. It is part of the Huth Library bequeathed to the British Museum, a tiny Book of Hours not much longer than the fingers.(2)

The volume opens with several pages of prayers written out in a microscopic hand of incredible delicacy and clearness. After this, comes the Calendar of the months illuminated with little roundels, no larger than

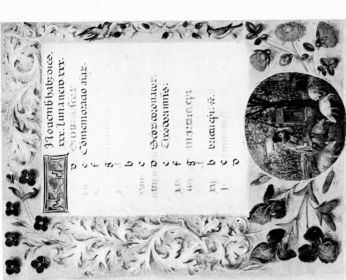

TWO PAGES OF AN ILLUMINATED BOOK OF HOURS

From the original in the British Museum

a half-crown in size but forming a series of compositions complete in themselves. Two of this set of pictures are here reproduced. The real text of the Book of Hours follows after the calendar, and here are several full-page paintings, one of which forms the frontispiece to this book.

Through every page there are flower-paintings of exquisite fineness and poetry. Sometimes these are arranged upon variously treated golden backgrounds, and occasionally against a simulated silk, or brocade. Some decoration of this sort occurs on every page. In all, there are twenty-four full-page paintings and thrice that number of smaller miniatures, and it is no exaggeration to compute that a decade of years must have gone by before this Book of Hours was finished.

There are several remarkable points of interest attached to it. In the first place, in spite of the late date of this manuscript, its period must be about 1480 to 1490, no clearer instance can be found of the impression made, as it were upon the very landscape, by the armoured knight living in his castle on the horizon. Twice, already, in this book, have I stressed the manner in which a castle, or castles, are put by the artist into every single scene, holding the background by force and brandishing a drawn sword out of the air. This was the temporal, as the Church was the spiritual, subjection of the peasantry. The ruling race lived in these forts, and great bastions and capped towers were never far distant.

The second feature of this Book of Hours, once that triumphant feudality has been recognized, is the presence in it of several miniatures that make a really memorable contribution to the store of pictures that an intelligent eye can carry in the mind. These can be summoned up in all their beauty to join with the fine Flemish primitives; while the usual book-ornaments, however intricately designed and minutely executed, fade away entirely and are forgotten.

The coloured frontispiece at the beginning of this book is taken from the most successful of these full-page paintings. This hermit, praying in the green wood beside his lath and timber retreat, is an interpretation of the subject that takes its place beside the St. Jerome of Antonello da Messina, and the St. Jerome, or St. Anthony, of Dürer. These three world-famous eremites, one of them hunched on a hillock in front of Nuremberg, and the other two in their elaborately comfortable libraries, are now joined by a fourth and forgotten companion.

This very young, spring wood that is the scene of his prayers is typical of Northern France in its fresh, almost shrill colour. There is a wonderful spontaneity about the picture; its Northern, and most un-Italian, qualities are expressed in a rapid smallness of touch that it is difficult to match in the works of any other painter. In many of Dürer's water-colours the same lath and plaster houses are to be seen, but they have become essentially German, and have the curious rat-infested look that goes with those piebald villages. The green lakes and jagged fir-trees of his water-colours are the accompaniment to the houses; but Dürer snaps and pounces upon his sketches and then finishes them to the bitter end in a very different spirit to the calm, tranquil mood of this miniature. It is coloured with the very green of the leaves.

The third, and perhaps most lasting, impression left by this Book of Hours is the extraordinary talent dis-

played in the flower-paintings. More especially where
the calendar is concerned they follow the seasons in a
regular order. The occupation chosen as being typical
of each month is accompanied by a display of the flowers
to be seen in the same span of time, and where this is
within the bounds of fact insects and butterflies are
shown hovering, or as though standing, on the worked
gold of the background. In this latter respect, in the
mingling of flowers with insects and butterflies, the only
artist to compare with this unknown and anonymous
talent is the famous Maria Sibylla Merian.(3)

This lady, who came of a family of flower-painters,
was the only good Dutch artist who had the curiosity
to convey her talent into any of the new countries
colonized by her countrymen. She set forth with her
daughter for Surinam, in South America, in 1698, and
stayed there two years drawing the plants and insects
of the country, returning thence to Amsterdam, where
she and her daughter passed the remainder of their lives
colouring the engravings that she caused to be made
from her drawings, and selling them in bound volumes.
She was the first person to study the chrysalis and to
draw its different stages of development, and for this
and other similar discoveries she has a scientific repute
only second to her skill and renown as an artist. But
her talent is in no way more remarkable than that of the
unknown person who drew the flower-borders in this
small Book of Hours.

It is a study, complete in itself, of all the flowers and
insects of the land. Many preliminary drawings must
have been made for each flower-border, and we may feel
certain that in some instances the project will have been
set aside till the following year, when the particular flower

wanted was eagerly waited for and at last the day came to search field or wood once more.

There is here all the enthusiasm for flowers of the Flemings and the Dutch, and it is easy to understand, after seeing the patient excitement expressed in these miniatures, how it came to pass that rare bulbs became the objects of maniacal gambling and speculation, so that whole families were ruined over them, only some century and a half after this manuscript was finished.(4) Then, the importation of flowers from newly discovered continents had begun, but, by the end of the fifteenth century, this had hardly started and only the indigenous plants grew in field and garden. Even so, there must have been great rarities, rich prizes for the enthusiast, and we may think of the artist offering a small reward for the bringing to him of an unusual flower or insect. Without this incentive his choice could not have ranged over such wide varieties. Indeed, it is possible that close examination of the book by an expert botanist might discover some flowers now lost and extinct.

Especially successful is his portrayal of some of the earliest spring flowers, coming, in fact, so near to winter that the hardiness of anything so delicate and fragile is difficult to credit. The snowdrops are treated several times over, having each time a page all to themselves in their whiteness. The more simple kinds of blue flowers, periwinkles for instance, are also rendered with an amazing fidelity and in a freshness of blue colour that must have been obtained after endless search. The powdering of the butterflies' wings comes out in all its flaunting and extravagant texture ; and with their gilded and painted sails these insects hover above the flowers, or are at rest upon a band of gold which is rayed and striped as though with the sun's beams.

This book is an epitome of all the strength which that age did not waste in war. Peaceful and pretty cleanliness, as of a béguinage, speaks of a low horizon and a landscape continually washed with floods. Where everything was so near and so comfortable, the strange and the romantic dwelt only in marshlands, where the far-off mewing of the seabirds gave a mystery to the tepid shallows ; and, to some slighter extent, in the little woods of the land, when the first flowers climbed out of the thinning snow and it seemed as if no feet had trod here since the last bonfire smoke in a blue autumnal afternoon.

Apart from this, nature was tame and lay in easy reach of the hand. None of its terrors came to disturb the harmony of life, which could go on, day after day, year after year, to exactly the same pattern, thus allowing, and, indeed, insisting upon, the same traits being reproduced in the works of men's hands. Nowhere else could this particular masterpiece of patience have lived into its own completion. But this was the land of tapestries, where those wonders of the North were woven, and they share the same qualities of steady breath and slow endurance.

As for the cell of this illuminator, we can think of its windows as within sight of the swans on the canal. Trees, men, and houses were timed, like so many hour-glasses, to bring about their punctual and anticipated effects. The trees rattled their bronze leaves, and then dropped them to be swept into mounds where they lay like so many thousands of pairs of brown boots, tremendously shrunken and crinkled in proportion ;* later on, the bare

* I am indebted for this image to my sister.

branches moved in little tongues of fire and green leaves began ; or the fruit trees heaped themselves with snows of blossom.

This was the time when so many flowers were brought into his cell that work fell some days behind ; and they stood waiting in vases, or lay neatly dried ready to be drawn into a final version after their colour had been studied from life. But he came up inevitably to the surface of his work again by incessant application, never allowing himself to be turned away from the object he had in mind. No sentiment, no feeling of nostalgia, ever disturbed this Flemish calm. In all other places, life, inevitably as dull as this when it was peaceful, brimmed over with dangers.

The next manuscript from which a miniature is reproduced has been chosen as representing an entirely different world from that of the bourgeois tranquillity of the Book of Hours. Its interest is of a directly different nature. It moves among the creatures of fashion, mirroring their vagaries whenever opportunity allows.

This manuscript contains the poems of Christine de Pisan.(5) It has, like the other, a miniature on nearly every page. The frontispiece to the book shows the authoress reading her poems to Queen Isabeau of Bavaria. The Queen is sitting in a high, narrow room with her ladies round her. There is hardly another miniature of the time as valuable as this for its treatment of dress and its view of an inhabited room, giving the exact appearance of a scene of everyday life among the capricious elongations of their buildings, and with dresses, furniture, and every object in use, conforming to those strange and improbable principles.

Our eyes are too familiarized to appreciate it in all its strangeness. But there has never been such a transformed reality. Everything true and obvious is hidden, or worked round to some other purpose. Wherever possible, the lines of the human body are concealed, and if this cannot be done, the truth is exaggerated out of all conformity to fact. A fanatical affectation against the ordinary and the expected was the reason for this, and this, in its turn, came from the tired monotony of aristocratic life, where the established nobles had held undisputed dominion and been in possession of all the wealth for many hundreds of years, for a longer space of time, in fact, than has elapsed between the death of the Gothick Age and our own century.

War and rebellion were the only dangers, but, even then, treaties were honourably kept. Wives and daughters had never to fear for their own safety, the huge edifice of chivalry protected them. They were beginning to be tired.

As against the new and growing burgher merchant class, whose civilization is typified by the Book of Hours just discussed, even if this particular manuscript may have been ordered by an aristocratic book-collector, we have here, in these miniatures to the poems of Christine de Pisan, a specimen of the delights of the dying feudal age, and a record of the form they took. Their diversity and extravagance show how old and recondite they had become.

The age was isolated from all contact with any other culture. Until the revived learning came upon them, driven into the West by the Turks, there was nothing to break this spell, and changes of fashion were confined to variations upon somewhat limited themes, so that imagination worked wildly in its search for something new. But a young and vigorous stock was exploiting these faded principles. They were beginning to tire of their confinement into such limited directions, and this sense stemmed up the energy which flowed into the Renaissance as soon as it had the opportunity. But in the miniature we reproduce there is no foreshadowing of that new adventure.

You would imagine, to look at it, that art could take no other form than this and that it was anchored, for ever, in this dimension. This has happened in other cases, more particularly in Mohammedan countries, where there may have been three or four revivals of art, at intervals of two or three centuries, and in each case exactly the same principles have been resuscitated into life, and at the end of it hardly any new discoveries remain to be added to the total of the race's achievement. So might it have been in Northern Europe had classical literature perished during the centuries of barbarism, and this might easily have been so; in fact, its contradiction of truth is one of the miraculous events in human history. Had none of the poetry or philosophy of the old world survived, its remains in sculpture and architecture would have deserved little notice and could never have received adequately documented study. Then, the alert vigour of the Northern races would have had to perfect new developments out of their own racial beginnings, and the pointed arch might have remained for ever as the symbol of European man.

It was only the feudal age, only the possessors of that hereditary power, who were beginning to show fatigue. Under them, the masses were starting their serious multiplication into the unwieldy and unled hordes of this present. Kings were consolidating their positions at the expense of the nobles on every hand. A paralysis was setting in, and the castle-dwellers were growing into an anomaly, into an unnecessary precaution, into the holders of privileges that could no longer be upheld.

The third manuscript to be discussed here is the Prayer Book of Charles the Bold of Burgundy, now in the Imperial Library at Vienna. We give an illustration of one of the miniatures in this wonderful volume. It shows Maximilian and Maria of Burgundy kneeling at prayer in a great cathedral. The view into this is through a casement, with its mullions flung open and lying back against the walls of the room. The whole exterior scene is framed in this way. At the side of the window, a lady in the high steeple hat and flowing wimple of the time sits reading her missal, which lies, with her beads and a pair of carnations, upon the window-sill. The missal has its wrappings still round it, so that it is like a parcel packed in cloth, instead of paper, and just arrived. On the opposite side the thrown-back mullion, with a hint of reflections, never quite made manifest, in its cobbles, has a glass vase of tall irises set against it, and this is made the occasion for a miraculous piece of painting. The great nave of the church lies in front of all this, with the sun's spot-lights darting through the painted windows. Maximilian and his wife are kneeling before the Virgin, who is enthroned, much larger than life, upon the altar-steps. A carpet is spread in front of her, and on the corners of this there are four angels, prostrated by the side of four great brazen candelabra. Maria of Burgundy wears the exaggerated steeple hat, that would be expected of her, and her three ladies behind her have headgear only diminished by the necessary conventions of rank and distance. Of this beautiful miniature all that can be said is that it is one of the supreme achievements of Flemish art. Indeed, it is as beautiful as the triptych of the Seven Sacraments at Antwerp, which is the masterpiece, rather similar in subject, of Roger van der Weyden.

Such are the comments of these three manuscripts upon the life to which they were witness. Even so, they are nearly unknown examples, chosen rapidly from the nearest available sources. This was the North, in its own indigenous appearance. It was centuries old and had reached to an alert, busy state that was only contradicted by the tired, dulled nobles. The art of the miniaturist, taken, now, out of the hands of the monk whose monopoly it had been, was at its culmination. Printing was already invented, and soon this particular kind of trouble would no longer be taken.

Meanwhile, as though to afford a parallel by which to judge it, this same art was flourishing to an equal, or greater extent, far away, in another part of the world. It was in the service of another aristocracy, yet more idyllic from the opportunities its wealth afforded it. This was in Persia.

The Persians, who were not of Semitic origin, had not the same hatred as the Jew and the Arab for a graven or painted image. Painting, therefore, was occasionally practised among them, but was confined almost entirely to miniature-painting. Apart from this one direction, the artists had to find other outlets for their activity. In the cases of Sultan Muhammad and Mirak, two of the greatest among them, the first was a bookbinder, a clockmaker, a designer of carpets, and a painter upon porcelain; while the second was an ivory-carver and an expert

MAXIMILIAN AND MARIA OF BURGUNDY AT PRAYER
BEFORE THE VIRGIN
From a miniature in the Prayer Book of Charles the Bold

calligrapher, for it is said that all the old buildings in Herat are decorated with inscriptions from his hand.

It is these two artists who painted most of the miniatures in the poems of Nizami, the finest Persian manuscript of the sixteenth century, which has just been made available to the public for the first time by its recent publication.* Until now, only students have had access to its beauties, for the Persian manuscripts are hidden away from the world to an even greater extent than are those of European origin. Their miniatures illustrate a literature which is invariably badly translated, if even this amount of attention is paid to it. But the best artists of one of the most ancient of civilizations put their finest work into these small limits and painters of the quality of Carpaccio, or Cima da Conegliano, are in this way withheld and kept out of experience.

The greatest of them is Bihzad. He was born about 1450, and passed his life between Herat and Tabriz, but chiefly in the latter city. Strictly speaking, then, Bihzad was Afghan in nationality. Mr. F. R. Martin knows of ten books, containing some ninety miniatures by his hand. Two of these are in the British Museum. They, also, are the poems of Nizami, and they contain, between them, thirty-seven miniatures by Bihzad, so that it is possible to see in London more than one third of this great artist's still existent works. The larger of the two manuscripts (Or. 6810) is dated 1494 and contains seventeen works by Bihzad and five by his pupil Mirak; the second manuscript (Add. 25900) is of minute size and is dated 1442. It has twenty paintings by Bihzad, but these have been inserted at a later date,

---

* "The Poems of Nizami," with an introduction by Laurence Binyon, *The Studio*, London, 1928.

probably about sixty years after it was written, when Bihzad was, himself, an old man.   They were painted into this older manuscript to the order of Shah Ismail, the founder of the Safavid dynasty of Persian Kings.

It is not necessary, therefore, to go further than these two manuscripts to get an idea of Bihzad's powers, but his talents and execution are reinforced by two other things.   In the first place it is difficult to conceive of the care exercised by the Persians in their choice of paper.   Various sorts were manufactured by different, devious processes, and, once this was done, the surface was incessantly polished for weeks together with an egg-shaped crystal.   Leaves of good paper were valuable and commanded high prices.   Secondly, the style of the calligraphy was as important as the beauty of the paintings.   It was the subject of much technical discussion and criticism.   The pull and balance of each curve was taken into account and all sorts of details were considered important which even trained eyes can hardly appreciate. Some of the finest gold writing was done with the nail point of the index finger, and a virtuoso of this sort must have taken as much care of his one finger as a Paderewski ever did of his two hands.   These minutiæ of technique are refinements and delicacies of which no European has ever been capable in the arts.   It is not only patience which is lacking, but it may be thought with reason that these artists who never touched alcohol or tobacco must have possessed a steadier eye and hand than has been granted to any European, even in the virtuous vacuum of the cloister.

These two manuscripts, whatever their present sale-room value may be, were esteemed at a much higher price by the Moghul Emperors.   There were never more

than a handful of good Persian artists, and the Moghul
Emperors, who were arduous collectors, paid sums
equivalent to a hundred thousand pounds for fine manuscripts illuminated by any of the three painters named.
Of these Bihzad had the greatest reputation, and his works
were nearly unprocurable, even to the massed wealth of
India. Persian was the court language, the great poets
had been Persian, and these written and painted masterpieces were the greatest works of the world in which
they lived. There was nothing better for the dilettante
to buy.

Let us try to imagine this world so strange to our
experience! Tabriz, which is to us a name fringed with
daggers, was in Bihzad's day a city of poets and scholars.
It is covered in snow for four months of the year, but
after that the spring comes and the whole town breaks
into blossom. In climate and in general character,
Tabriz is said to much resemble Brusa. If we want to
think, then, of the things which lay in front of Bihzad's
eyes, we need go no further than Brusa. This is a Persian
town built nearly into Europe. Its mosques and
medersas have none of the honeycombs and stalactites of
the Moors, but are mosaiced with tiles. The floral designs
on a green, or blue, ground are as though flowers had
been dropped on the grass, or were held in the sky. All
round, the cypress, the flowering peach-tree, the flowering rose-bush, give the motives that Bihzad loved to
paint. For, in his miniatures, sprays of blossom hold
themselves in blinding detail against the sky, and have to
cross the green bars of the cypresses in order to do this.
As for the sky, it is either as blue as lapis, or is literally
burnished with sun.

If it is the country, and not a garden, the glare of the

desert is wonderfully imaged in gold, but he always seems
to choose that fortnight in the year when the desert
breaks into flower and the sand is sown with blossom.
A plane-tree will be growing among the rocks, for Bihzad
had a particular talent for rendering this tree with its
smooth bark and tinted leaves. A little water-spring
may be flowing away in silver, which the age of the
manuscript has oxidized and turned black.

Where buildings are concerned, Bihzad facsimiles all
the tile-work in a minute fashion which Van der Heyden
could never attain to ; in the smaller of these two manuscripts (Add. MS. 25900) there are occasions where
literally some thousands of tiles have been separately
painted in the space of a few inches. And, apart from
this gleaming detail, hundreds of the most intricate
tile-patterns are shown. Where he signed his name,
Bihzad's signature is so small that it has escaped the eyes
for hundreds of years and is only now become visible
again with the help of a strong microscope.

Only mosques were built with an idea of permanence,
and the tiled pavilions typical of these miniatures were
quickly put up, and as quickly abandoned. They occur
in Bihzad's pictures wherever there is an excuse for portraying the interior of a palace, or whenever a prince
grants an audience. They had little more importance
in the owner's eyes than a favourite tent, and, as in a
tent, he was here surrounded by the same easily portable
properties, rugs, trays, porcelain cups and beakers.

Sometimes his pictures actually deal with tent-life.
The encampments are made from gorgeous rugs. At
the back stand the black, goatskin tents of the nomads ;
they are lighting their fires, the goats feed in the crevices
of the rocks, and the shepherds in their striped clothes

play their pipes, or lean on their crooks looking down at the royal encampment. Such scenes, by a device which Bihzad invented and his followers specialized into a habit, are divided and emphasized by the tent-cords. These blue and white, twined ropes are tied to pegs at various strategical points in the picture and give perspective to the composition. Figures are seen in front of, or behind their lines, and are in this way secured and proved in the positions their feet give them in the landscape.

But Bihzad had a sense of realism that none of his followers inherited from him. There are two instances of this in the manuscript we are discussing; a mosque is being built and the blue-robed workmen are shown busily at work on the scaffolding; and, in the second picture, the interior of a bath-house is shown, the figures of the bathers are seen, and their blue, or black robes are hung up and used to the best advantage in the picture. These two miniatures are without parallel in the stiff and formal art of Persia.

After looking, even for some few days, at the beauties of these Persian manuscripts, their conventions become necessary and unavoidable in the mind, and it is difficult to believe in the existence of another art of the same kind devoted to a different climate, an alternative race of men, an alien religion. The turbans; the serious beards; young men and women conforming to the same standards of beauty, being, thus, most difficult to distinguish between; the minaret and the muezzin clinging to the parapet for utmost shrillness to his voice; the patterned and crenellated town-walls; the delicate gazelle-like horses; the spread, or pitched rugs for floor, or tent; the flowering trees; the cypress; the red-legged

v

partridge; the stork on its nest; the adder in the hollow of the stones; all these are points which add up into the total, detailed presentment of this one kind of life. How should it be possible that in another part of the world these same things, based only on their own essential differences, should reach to the same finality, as if to cancel out any parallel excellence?

But in these few score miniatures out of a handful of manuscripts we find a great artist imprisoned who was allowed no other outlet, and given no opportunity bigger than this for his talents. He is a Carpaccio, a Benozzo Gozzoli, confined within these tiny limits, but moving in a world which we find more interesting because of its strangeness to our eyes. Nothing like this ever came out of the North, and the patient, cold fancies of the frost lose their poetry beside the possibilities of this Persian art.

When it had become freed from its own primitive chains, perhaps the greatest beauties possible to a Gothick, a transitional epoch might have been attained. But no Moslem culture has ever got further than this stage, and none has ever outlived the lives of two generations. Nothing came of it, and the last good painters of the school were men who had been alive in Bihzad's lifetime.

In Western Europe men of less talent than this were numbered in their hundreds, and were allowed all the tranquillity that their sex ensured to them—for so we may term it where a monk is concerned. This was, in itself, another advantage over the Moslems, who have no clergy and no monasteries, if we except a few societies of dervishes who are occupied only in hysterical pandemonium. Their artists were individual persons and not members of a corporation, let off military service, guaranteed food and lodging, and given a presumption of eternal life if only they would behave in the present. Monasteries had privileged immunity in time of war, and, indeed, the only enemy they had to fear was accidental fire. But for this, nothing ever came to disturb their centuries of slow growth.

The more poetical and less assured alternative to this lived by no continued breath, but flickered now and again into life. It was transplanted out of Persia into India, but stayed there no longer than its customary two generations. Since then, it has never lifted its head, and vitality would seem to have left it for ever. The Moghul palaces were the scenes of its last signs of life. The jewelled inlay, the pierced lattices, the marble swimming-baths, the arches, fretted like shells and of lucent, pearl-like marble, these were the items of its most emasculate stage, and, since then, there has been nothing. These limits of the Aryan world have given no more to the senses, and the mosques and palaces of Delhi and Agra are the last contribution of this other mediaeval tradition. But the dangerous perfections of this Moghul work range themselves with the filigree courts of the Alhambra as something too finished to afford any further inspiration to the artist. They are no use to him, and he prefers something that his imagination can complete.

As for the strict and authentic Gothick of the West, building activity was on such a prodigal scale of magnificence that very few projects ever reached to oriental finish and perfection. The nervous suppleness of the Gothick mind caused constant changes of plan, and it is not rational to expect the sort of homogeneity over a long stretch of years that is to be found in some buildings of the Baroque period, or in Southern India.

There, Fergusson cites some twenty cities, each one of them representing as much architectural and sculptural energy as is contained in a cathedral in France or Spain, but all of them absolutely formal and continuous in method. Thousands of hands worked upon them over a long period of years, but ideals never altered from age to age. Such temples have a servile patience that makes their detail painful to the eyes. They are the unpleasant memorial of a population whom an era of peace caused to swarm like insects. They lived like flies and died like flies ; and their fussy, teeming works remain behind them, as useless as the galleries of an old ant-hill.

Nevertheless, it was a true cathedral-age that produced them. It was the fashion at a certain stage in man's development, like the megalithic age that produced Karnak and Stonehenge, rude echoes, perhaps, of the rumours of Egypt. The Hindu temples are the works of a second cathedral-age standing parallel to the stone doxologies of Northern and Western Europe.

Specimens of this are the Dravidian temples of Trivalur and Vijayanagar, and the Chalukyan temples of Hallabid and Somnathpur. At its most Northern extent are the Black Pagoda of Kanarak, the temple at Bhuvaneshwar, and the famous Juggernaut temple at Puri. All of these, being English property, are un-advertised and comparatively little known, but they form a most interesting parallel to the similar activities of Christianity. Their date is mainly the thirteenth century, but some of them are much later than this; indeed, the temples of Ramesvaram and Madura are of the seventeenth century, being certainly the most curious products of the age of Charles I and Louis XIII.

At the very furthest extent of this movement are the

temples of Borolbudor in Java, and the Khmer buildings in Cambodia, of which Angkor-Vat and Angkor-Thom are the most famous examples. These, again, have strict affinity to what Celt and Teuton were doing ; and it is necessary to think of this when the works of Cistercian monks are being extolled as the unique glory of our twelfth and thirteenth centuries. There were other enthusiasms just as vehemently elaborate in the forms they took.

With regard to these Javanese temples, their origin was Buddhist and not Hindu. Their great epoch of construction was in the ninth century, so that they form the latest Buddhist buildings of any considerable scale ; but the inspiration behind them was undoubtedly influenced by the Hindu and Brahman constructions. They must represent a sort of Counter-Reformation in Buddhist architecture, and are the last vigorous contradiction to the new order that was coming in before the Buddhist religion had to forsake India altogether. Its centres remained in Ceylon, in Burma, in Japan, and in China, and so the Javanese temples we may consider as an effort to stem the new religion and preserve the old by adaptation of the principles that were attractive or impressive in this danger to their own tenets. But, less than two centuries after this, not the Hindus but the Moslems, a most distant and improbable foe, conquered Java and the temples of Borolbodur were deserted. The jungle took possession of them, and they are not heard of again till Sir Stamford Raffles, a temporary English Governor of Java during the Napoleonic Wars, discovered them and cleared the ruins in 1814.

A Chinese traveller, Tcheou Ta Kouan, who visited Angkor in 1296, gives a few details that are just sufficient

to rescue it from the degree of historical deadness of
Borolbodur, or of the Maya temples in Guatemala.
He describes the five gates of the town, and the bridges
across the moats.   Guarding these bridges, at both ends,
were one hundred and eight stone statues of genii, like
stone generals, gigantic and terrible.   The parapets of
the bridges were cut in the form of serpents, each cobra
having nine heads.

The King wore wreaths of jasmine, or a golden crown
in his hair, walked barefoot, and had the soles of his feet
and the palms of his hands dyed red.   He slept in his
palace on the summit of a golden tower.   When he
came out from his palace, three to five hundred of the
girls of the palace preceded him, with flowers in their
hair and carrying lighted torches in their hands, even if
it was daytime.   Then followed more girls carrying his
royal insignia, and his vessels of gold and silver, and finally
a troop of Amazons armed with lance and shield, who
were his bodyguard.   After them came golden chariots
drawn by horses, and by deer.   The King rode an
elephant.   He carried the sacred sword in his hand, and
was sheltered from the sun by umbrellas.   Many more
elephants surrounded him on all sides.

The King was a God, the spiritual, as well as the
physical, dweller in the palace.   The troupe of dancing
girls were servants, or priestesses, to his sanctity, and they
filled a hieratic rôle in the constitution, as it were, of
the Khmer Kingdom.   The whole happiness of the
people depended on his communion with his sacred
ancestors, and this was only made possible through his
contentment on earth.   He lived in a sacred maze, or
bee-hive.   It was a monastery, but with a difference.

In fact, the theatre, which imagination always projects

as a possible, or preferred alternative to the church, had here been definitely installed as a religion in itself. Dancing-girls, who were practised gymnasts and posturists of the most alluring grace and symmetry, established the Khmer temples as the scene of the ultimate point ever reached by the erotic senses in their search for beauty. The echoes of this are to be seen in the bas-reliefs with which the temples are decorated, and some poor shadow of it lingers in the royal dancing-troupes of the King of Annam, and of the Sultans of the native states in Java.(6)

The spirit of this monastic civilization, for it was essentially a cult set up by, and continued by, monks, is the very antithesis to the ideals, for instance, of the Cistercians; they are such wide-apart interpretations of what was really the same epoch that they have come back near to each other. They are so little removed that the slightest extension of the principles of either of them would lead into a fusion of their processes.

The battalions of monks, or nuns, with their privations and hardships; their repudiation of the flesh; the solitary confinement for life that they loved to inflict upon themselves; their scourgings and penitence; their midnight masses, so contrived that more than a couple of hours' consecutive sleep was impossible, and so that the snow in the court should have to be crossed before the freezing floor of the church was reached; all these self-tortures are but a little way removed from the sacred licence and debauchery of the pagodas. Certainly these two principles, the complete negation and contradiction of each other, held exactly the same force of stimulus to the artisan of these two cathedral-ages.

The Hindu temples are the most picturesque and

unlikely works ever created by men's hands, and it is no use adopting a too impatient attitude towards them if we want to confess an admiration, at the same time, for abbeys and cathedrals in our own midst.   They are built to a far more severe plan than might be suspected, being definitely in some cases works directed by one particular architect, as, for example, at Somnathpur, where the temple was made to the design of Jakanacharya, the sculptor and architect of the Ballala Kings.

If we cannot afford time, or patience, to think of them, we need only consider the situation of an intelligent Hindu traveller in Europe, who, while admiring the usefulness of our inventions and the pictures by great masters in our galleries, might find it difficult to devote his attention to cathedrals in England, France, or Spain, which he would at once attribute to the same rather mythical, pagan dullness from which he was trying to escape on his travels.

But it is no use denying them their environment. They are as well adapted to this as are the works of Gothick builders to the rain and mist they had to consider.   The mystery and horror of the temple-precincts, many of them, even now, never yet trodden by the white man's foot ;   the placid lakes and their lilied banks ;   stone corridors, like those at Ramesvaram, over four thousand feet in length, and sculptured through all this extent to the height of thirty feet ;   all these have a merely statistical value, with which, apart from questions of beauty, none of the achievements of Christianity can compete.   And the temple of Madura, even in a photograph, is the mysterious and unfathomable relic of something which the eyes find it most difficult to put into reality.   For the Hindu culture is the one, out of all historical periods, which it is hardest to clothe and colour in the mind.

The men of turbans were Moslem, nor must we expect here the beards and fierce moustaches of the Moslem warriors. Neither did their women walk veiled. These are true idolaters, bowing down to wood and stone. Their temples are the triumphal cars of the god, petrified and brought to a standstill. The sculptures writhe and twist their bodies, standing, row above row, upon eaves that carry no roof and only lead into a smaller, diminished row above them. Their contortions are helped by more than the usual allowance of legs and arms, certainly the most primitive method of attributing superior powers to a deity. But these carved pagodas are the only parallel that history can establish to the sculptured fronts and sides of cathedrals, such as Chartres, or Wells.

As for the lives led in these tumultuous shadows, denial of the flesh was certainly only one part out of the immense repertory of holy action, and its exact opposite as a celebration of gratitude for the gift of life was just as reputable a rôle to play. These were the same colleges of nuns as in the Christian world, but with a different end, that of sacred prostitution, for which purpose the nuns were trained from the earliest age. The groves of Ashtaroth stood open in the enervating heat, and the sacred orgy sounded its horns and half-heard voices.

The arts of life were not understood and have never been developed by the Hindus ; their immense pantheon and its complex translation into stone imagery, is the only energy they have contributed to the history of human progress. The life of religious contemplation, as practised by them, was in the nature of an idiot-trance, suggesting the bowed head and fixed stare of the imbecile child.

But the mere complication, the dreary weight of the mythology they had invented, trapped the mind in its mazes.   Life was an elaborate game in which the moves were so many advantages, or losses, incurred from using or avoiding the different, established symbols that were strewn thickly through the ordinary events of life, and had an immediate, an electrical, contact with their corresponding values in the celestial plane.

In fact, this was a strictly urban culture with the slums never far away.   Plague and famine were always present to the mind, and, indeed, an outbreak of plague was the inevitable aftermath of any important religious festival.   All the effects of their architecture were calculated for a noisy, proletarian audience who used to brawl and kill each other in their excitement.   At the same time, these feelings, which were the stimulus they got from worship, had to be encouraged, and, therefore, the excitant, the lascivious, and the triumphant, were the moods that their art set forth and that they wished to be echoed in their crowds of devotees.   This was easy enough in a mob of such dimensions, for the swarming plains of India had a population with which no contemporary European country could compare.

It is the rainy season.   Every human being has a cold. Rain falls in a roaring cataract, drumming and jangling upon leaf and stone.   The proud Indies bow down and are bound with waters.   The rain is as thick as jungle. Its knots and cables trail down from the trees and are impenetrable.   To walk through them is to be hit by a chain of hammers, and to be thrown clear of them soaked and beaten by their force.

The doors of the temples are guarded by rods of rain, which the sudden winds blow forth in a gust as though

the roofs were spitting them out. This is a hammering
on a different note, sucked back again by the eaves and
then thrown out once more in direct personal attack.
The inky sky lies just overhead. It is a bed of sponges
violently discharging their water, as if wanting to
hide, when dry. Lightning cracks its whips ; perpetual
thunder sounds ; the terrible typhoon has come.

It blows in from the sea. The order of the universe
has been changed and the sky has assumed all the waters
of the sea. If you try to walk in it, the storm pounces
upon your clothes as upon so many rags of sail. A
rattling, as of ropes against their masts, goes with this and
a great splitting of wood as the branches are wrenched
from their sockets, to fall, like the refuse of the tides,
on the wind's edges, where they roll along their spoils
before them.

If it clears, thick steam rises and all objects drip with
perspiration. The earth is being sipped up into the
sky and the waters are only taken up to be thrown down
once more. This happens like a timed clock to an appointed hour of the unseen sun. The air is full of fever.
One raindrop booms like a bell under sea, giving warning
of what is to come. For the waters hiss out of the sky
again, having scarcely time, indeed, to sieve their weight
into drops ; they fall in headlong collapse, tumbled out of
the clouds that burst their weight like sacks too full of
grain.

This happens, day after day, night after night, and
sometimes darkness is the more light of the two. Then,
at last, the loud noises are no more than echoes. It is
their reflection and not themselves ; they are growing
old and their forces shake and are uncertain.

The spent typhoon knocks, now, like a ghost in the

wainscoting. The old tyrant is dying and can nearly be mocked. Its far-off thunders, and its little voice of wind can summon no more rain. It makes a last brave show of lightnings to prove it is not failing but has only moved far off, and then the flowers and leaves begin to rise up like springs.

A myriad blossoms, so rayed and petalled that they might drop like insects off the branches, hang down their baits and ask the hand to shake them, which is their child-begetting. Or they twine like parasites into the trees, strangling the living scaffold that they climb, and light their stars high up in alien leaves, dwelling between earth and sky.

The temples are strung with flowers, the sacred cows wear garlands between their horns, and the holy pleasure-gardens are thrown open to the public. Even the tanks bear lilies out of their mud, and blossoms are in the air, on the ground, and in the water. Scents breathe, as compact as clouds, at every step, so small and solid that a way has to be forced through them, and they add a sated weariness to the fatigues of walking. There is such a glare of light that every fixed object moves if you look at it, and more than two things standing together are impossible for the eyes to number. Nor can they remember any details that lie before them, and the multiple carvings on the temples have been arranged by a prodigal hand so as to dazzle the retina, and beat down the eyes before such proof by number. Nowhere is there any peace, or a corner not made loud with gesticulation.

Galloping horses, reared up suddenly at a word of command, are carved in stone at the entrance, and their bridles are held by dwarves, who are men of ordinary human stature. The Gopurams, or gate-towers, stand out in the swooning heat and seem to be rolling away like stone chariots; while the statues, as did the sailors on an old man-of-war, man the yards and cling to any foothold they can find.

The most intense fire of fanaticism burns on every face. The attendants on the god may number as many as six thousand male adults, all living like monks in the temple enclosure, and divided into thirty-six orders and ninety-seven classes. There are distinct sets of servants to put the god to bed, to dress and bathe him, and a great band of Nautch-girls to dance and sing before him. The Rajah is hereditary sweeper of the temple. When the god issues forth in procession from the temple, his chariot, which is forty-five feet high and is supported on sixteen wheels, is drawn by four thousand two hundred professional haulers, who have been worked up into the highest frenzy of fanaticism. It is like a procession in Messina, or Seville, except that all this army of attendants live their lives free, and are supported on the temple revenues, derived from offerings and endowments.*

But these parallels to our abbeys and cathedrals differ from us in this very disparity of numbers. The Gothick places of worship were always built many times too big for their audience, however swollen by a pilgrimage, or some saint's celebration. It was their policy to impress by size, and where a Hindu temple is crowded with sculpture and swarms with its fanatical worshippers, a

* These figures refer to the temple of the Juggernaut at Puri. They may be compared with the temple of Ta Prohm at Angkor, which, at the end of the twelfth century, had 18 major and 2,740 ordinary officials, 2,232 assistants and 615 dancing girls. In its enclosure 12,640 persons had their lodging and accommodation. It may be added that the whole city of Angkor is estimated at this date to have contained nearly two millions of inhabitants.

cathedral must be always cold and empty. The scale that they chose as their instrument over the audience was height, more than length. There must be a hundred, even two hundred, feet of air above each head, a freedom in dimension which would be impossible if, for instance, every person in an audience of ten thousand people had to stand a hundred or two hundred feet away from his neighbour.

The same problem presents itself in the modern city of New York. A skyscraper, seven hundred feet high, but built on a base of only two hundred feet each way, will accommodate on its different floors what is equivalent to a town of ten thousand workers. If this were spread out over the ground, an area of many thousand acres, really equal in size to a town of offices for ten thousand people to work in, would have to be built. Or we may think of it in this way : that the whole diurnal population of the true City of London might work in fifteen to twenty of these towers, built along both sides of a street which would not need to be more than a quarter of a mile long. The skyscrapers are true examples of the Gothick spirit ; their effect is simply that of a cathedral, secularized, with floors put into it.

The men of the Gothick age wanted room to breathe in and room to move in. It was the spirit of freedom and the sense of cleanliness beginning to work. In fact, the further away they could get from each other, the more they were pleased, and the more ideal conditions became for communion with the god they worshipped. Even the small lands they lived in had remote corners where solitude could be achieved.

In the case of our own country it is only necessary to think of the four most beautiful relics of their energy.

The first was in the vale of York, still lying desolate and uncultivated after the ravages of William the Conqueror; the second was in a remote peninsula reached across wild, rugged hills and jutting out into the Irish Sea; the third drew its wealth from the pasture-lands of Somerset; and the fourth was in the loveliest valley in England, remotely peaceful and just safe from the Welsh tribes.* These are four cardinal situations than which better could not be found, each of them in a centre of bucolics, surrounded by farms, woods and pastures, and each of them typifying quite different beauties and profits of nature.

From their humble beginnings these monasteries soon began to acquire great properties. Fountains, for example, had one single estate of sixty thousand acres in Craven, walled round with a ring-fence. But the English monasteries never swarmed with monks, as did many convents in southern parts of Europe, and their wealth was devoted to the elaboration of the buildings and to the comfort of few more than the original foundation of monks. The accounts of the commissioners for the Dissolution are always a surprise upon this point, and the great size of the churches and their riches in plate, jewels, and vestments, are in strict contrast with the few monks appointed to live by them. Their office was more like that of the Fellows in an Oxford or Cambridge college.

Unfortunately, life in such places was broken into and dispersed far too long ago for it to be possible to gather its threads into any convincing colours. Not only are the buildings in ruins, but their destruction came when only one half of their normal history had been accomplished. Where would be the monasteries in Spain, in

---

* Fountains, Furness, Glastonbury, Tintern.

Italy, or in Germany, without their evidence of all the changes in taste between the year 1500 and the middle of the eighteenth century ? Yet this is the situation in England. The epoch of great constructions, which lasted everywhere else for five centuries, has, in our case, been curtailed to half that period of time.

Even so, there was opportunity to work away from the original Gallic beginnings into the one original invention of mediaeval English architecture. This was the fan-vaulting, first practised in the great monasteries of the West country. It was first used, between 1351 and 1377, in the cloister at Gloucester, and since this is one of the monastery churches kept on as a cathedral, it can still be seen, uninjured save by the ravages of time. Indeed, in its way, it is the most beautiful thing to be seen in the whole kingdom.

Its later uses in the small chapels of the Perpendicular age are not so happy, but in this cloister at Gloucester, its delicacy and gracefulness bear comparison with the finest Moorish work in Fez or Granada. No better setting could be devised by the imagination for the ultra-refinements of contemporary dress. Sleeves cut like the edge of a leaf, or a fish's fin, shoes tied to the knee-cap by a gilt chain, the folded turbans that men wore, and the aeroplane or butterfly hats of the women—these were extensions of the ordinary, as forced as periwig or hooped skirt, that demanded something as suited to them as the volutes and rilled curves of that later age.

The love of conceits, the passion for the transcendental, had known these earlier days of licence. It was a fanci-fulness of distinctly worldly type that gave birth to the stone stalactite, and to the pillar branched into a palm. They were the product of a mind working along social lines, no longer terrified of the god it worshipped, but resolved to turn its safety and leisure into comfort and ornament. To reach to this state, there had been an obvious prelude of some generations, falling away from the dogmatic and the categorical into the discovery that this kind of life was a pension, and that it allowed many mitigations in its original harshness and crudity. Unfortunately, poverty ensuing after senseless wars waged to no purpose over the lives of three generations, followed almost immediately by the bullying of Henry VIII, and its culmination of torture, expropriation, and execution, ruined all these possibilities and made their promise null and void.

But now the horizon must be lifted. All over the white man's world these hives of energy were at work. The wealth of a town was reckoned as much by the monasteries and convents in it as by the riches of its merchants, or dues taken at the harbour side. They taught the rich, nursed the sick, fed the poor, and offered an easy and complete insurance system as to prospects in the next world. Results, equally happy for all, were achieved by this, for payments proportionate to the suppliant's income.

These are metropolitan examples, with their steep roofs built thinner still from nearness to the houses of the merchants. For true freedom in their expression it is necessary to go much further away than this, into regions where the monastery was the only power in the country and its walls were the capital of a little kingdom. Kings and princes might elect to be buried there, and their ancestors may have founded it, but now it has grown beyond their authority and is a little state in itself.

w

It is a sacred maze, or beehive, with an abbot in its midst. He is one of themselves, elected out of their number by what would seem to an observer from high above to be as mysterious a choice as that by which, on the death of a queen bee, another ordinary bee out of the community is chosen to be her successor. All the routine of daily life is regulated according to the same unheard and invisible ordination. The lives of the monks are as busily divided; there is the same community of interest; as in a good theatrical company, no " starring " is allowed; everyone has his duties to perform, and he receives no particular praise for doing them. There must be the same mysterious incentive to this incessant labour, for we will count prayer as a part of it, as that which binds the bees to an oath of business and allows them no respite in their lives. They do not procreate, but their number is continually increased. There is an athletic keenness in their search after personal discomfort, but this is contradicted by one end of their labour, which consists in the magnificence of the vessel they have built for their prayers. Here the invisible god dwells in their midst, and is invoked by a formula.

If we want to see one of these communities in its original state, almost, we might say, still at work and with its machinery functioning, we must go to the Spanish Peninsula. Both in Spain and in Portugal the day of ruin only came in the 'thirties of the last century, not quite a hundred years ago. Till then, they had remained untouched, except by the marauding French troops who stole the fine pictures and the gold and silver vessels; but the treasuries are always the least interesting part of the whole, and the architecture has remained nearly intact. In Portugal the monasteries were dissolved in 1833, and in Spain they were destroyed by a popular rising two years later. The Spanish Liberals suspected the monks of being strong Carlist partisans; and, as well as this, the old rumours of dungeons, bones and prisoners—white-haired and maniac—chained in their cells, had given birth to a curiosity which was too strong to be resisted. Since that day they have remained untouched, and just as Ottobeuren, or Melk, must be visited in order to realize what things this same system could accomplish less than two centuries ago in Bavaria and Austria, so must the monasteries of Spain and Portugal be seen for an idea of the Gothick principle working in ideal conditions and miraculously preserved, or frozen, for our inspection.

The subject can be restricted into two groups. There are the Catalonian monasteries, and the great monasteries in Portugal. The first group is in the neighbourhood of Tarragona. It consists of the abbeys of Santas Creus and Poblet. The second group includes Alcobaça, Batalha and Thomar, perhaps also Belem.

The interest in the contrast between these two groups is this. The first two of them developed along perfectly normal lines, making a blend between their original Northern origin and the vigorous Spanish environment in which this foreign seed had been planted. The monasteries in the second group, on the other hand, progressed at a furious speed into the middle of the sixteenth century, as though nothing was happening elsewhere. Both groups can be legitimately included in my subject, for they both of them represent the very antithesis of what was coming out of Italy. The first pair of them are the extreme conservatism of the age, developed, as it were, in full rhyme and metre from the start, while the Portuguese examples are bold innovations, fearless experiments towards new ends. Apart from the Northern, or Burgundian, origin of many of the Portuguese nobles and the Portuguese kings, their isolation on the far Western seaboard of Europe, and their traditional friendship with England, has given to their nation a separate history, unlike that of any other Southern nation, and a character, half Northern and half Moorish, with an absence of any intermediate stages between these two extremes. Prince Henry the Navigator, who was the founder of Portuguese wealth and dominion, was a son of the marriage of John I with Philippa, the daughter of John of Gaunt. The dynasty, then, was half-English and in perpetual communication with England. An access of Northern energy made this small country into a world-power, into the richest kingdom of its day. The Italians were so distant as to have been hardly heard of, and the Portuguese culture pursued its own violent course without any Latin interference.

But, in order to get this contrast, we must begin with Poblet, in Catalonia. It is the largest and most complete specimen in existence of the monasteries of the Cistercian order, now that Cîteaux and Clairvaux are in utter ruin. First of all, some facts about it must be given in order to prove its intrinsic importance. Like all the Cistercian monasteries, one of the main considerations in founding it had been to reclaim new lands for agriculture. All round it there lay different farms, granges and plantations, each one under the direction of a lay-brother, who was at the head of a small community of farm hands, keepers, and other lay-brothers. Among these were La Pena, lying in the middle of lush water-meadows, and Castell-follit, a delicately beautiful name in itself. A splendid forest was under the charge of the dwellers in this romantic grange. The plain at the extremity of the abbey-lands contained the farms of Milmanda, Mediana, and Riudabella, among vineyards, pastures, and tilled fields.

Poblet had rights and privileges in every important city in Catalonia. It possessed shares in the salt-works of Cardona and in the fisheries of Ampurias, and the rights of pasturage on all Crown lands. Among its manors were the castles and towns of Verdú and Menargues, where previously such families of semi-regal importance as the houses of Urgel and Cervara had held sway. Its daughter-houses were El Tallat, Nazaret in Barcelona, the priory of San Vicente in Valencia, La Real in Majorca, Benifassa, at the joining of the three states of Aragon, Valencia and Catalonia, and the monastery of Piedra in Aragon.

The abbots of Poblet, besides their jurisdiction over their daughter-houses, were Generals of the Cistercian order in Aragon and Navarre, had precedence in the Catalonian Parliament, frequently held the post of Deputy-General of the Kingdom, and were given by Pedro IV the office of Royal Almoner. In this capacity they accompanied the King on his wars, going, for instance, to Italy with Alfonso V when he conquered Naples. The keeper of the monastery archives was notary-royal, the abbot and his monks were dispensed from giving their oaths in the law courts, and their simple word had to be accepted. All castles, towns, and villages belonging to the monastery had the right to fly the royal ensign as a symbol of the king's special protection.

Within the enclosure of its walls, Poblet had every kind of workshop and office, so that having once been accepted as an inmate there was never again any necessity

to come forth from its shadow into the outside world.
It is the sacred maze, or sacred beehive, in its most
perfected expression.

The founder of Poblet was Ramon Berenguer IV,
Count of Barcelona and Provence and Prince of Aragon,
and his original gift of land to the community was in
the year 1149.   D. Ramon Berenguer had taken Lerida,
married Doña Petronella, the heiress of Aragon, and gone
to Provence to settle an outbreak of rebellion.   There
he made a donation of Poblet to the Abbot of Fontfroide,
a Cistercian house near Narbonne, in return for which
certain monks from Fontfroide, chosen personally by St.
Bernard, went to found a monastery at Poblet.   The
conventual buildings and the church were planned under
this prince and under Alfonso II.   Abbot Vidal of Fontfroide paid repeated visits to Poblet between 1166 and
1177, so it is evident that Poblet was built under close
French supervision.   Later on, Pedro IV made the
monastery into a pantheon for the kings of the House of
Aragon, and the whole importance of the abbey derives
from its connection with the kings of Aragon.   When
this family became merged into kingship over the whole
of Spain, and the capital of the country was Madrid, the
supremacy of this ancient abbey soon faded.   It was no
longer the burial-place of kings, and their tombs were
uncared for by their more powerful descendants.   Even
the nobles of Aragon moved away to the court.

Before this, their bones had been buried here beside
those of their kings.   The houses of Urgel, Cabrera,
Moncada, Cervera, Anglesola, Pons de Ribelles, Jorba y
Alcarraz, Boixadors, Granyena, Puigvert, Montpaho,
Timor, Guimera, Jorba, Rocafort, Alanya, Copons, and
Vall-llebrera, all these bearers of Catalan names had their

tombs in the church at Poblet. Indeed, there is no place like it for the study of early heraldry.

Besides the ruined church and its multitude of desecrated tombs, the great beauties of Poblet are the chapterhouse and the royal palace of Martin V (1395-1410). The chapter-house is floored with great carved slabs, the tombs of the perpetual abbots. It stands on the east side of the great cloister, and opens by three windows into another cloister with an effect which is a real piece of architectural genius. Apart from this, it conforms to the usual features and has the nine bays and the two double-windows with a door between, which are to be seen in every chapter-house of the Cistercian order.

The royal palace is an affair of the utmost delicacy and precision. Its windows are of a type that is only to be seen elsewhere in Sicily—in Syracuse, that is to say, and in the Gothick palaces of Taormina. Some of them are capped with exquisite sculptures of angels, round-faced and with long golden locks, floating in their shifts, back to back, lute or violin in hand. The two vaulted dormitories of the novices and of the elder monks are in the most marked contrast to this. They are more haunted than any building the eyes have ever seen.

The great arches of their roofs, each one of them making the silhouette of a helmet, sound a scale of ghostly echoes to the footstep. To the novices this must have been their prison, with no hope of release. Long draughts, or sloped ladders of the light, come in at the windows, and often a bird or a bat, whose stupidity in not escaping when all the airs were open to it, was a sarcasm sent to torture them.

But the dormitory of the elder monks was alive with

their own ghostly emanations. It was no company from the world outside, but their own shapes, the peculiar results of the hard, cold life they led, and the strange habits of mind and body that this isolation from everything except their own fellows had brought to them. The vaulted roof must have rung with stertorous breathing, with ceaseless snores, with prayers and secrets mingled together in sleep and betrayed by the lips, with asthma, like a ghostly bellows, plied without ceasing. Sometimes a wind rose up, and it rubbed as though it were a dog against door and window. Or rain fell like a thousand fountains.

The other most utter ruin is the kitchens. The imagination refuses to believe that these were used so little as a hundred years ago. They are on the monolithic scale of a Stonehenge, but burnt offerings of flesh were never seen there, and fruit and vegetables, bread, or a little fish, were the only food from those stone altars, from the hooded fires, and the basins for great cauldrons. These kitchens can hardly have been altered since the earliest years of the monastery; and its decline never changed their size or shape.

Ruin began to come upon the monks, as I have said, when the kingdom increased out of Aragon and the capital of the whole country was Madrid. It was deserted by the kings, but came under the less important protection of the dukes of Segorbe. No more princes were allowed to be buried in the royal sarcophagi, and the coffins of the kings were covered on feast days with scarlet cloths bearing the emblems of the house of Segorbe. This family was of royal decent, and one of them, Pedro Antonio de Aragon, Viceroy of Naples, took the ashes of his ancestor, Alfonso V, from Naples to

Poblet in 1670 and built a tomb for them. This prince was a famous bibliophile and left his library to the monastery. The books from it are all bound in red, with his name and arms in gold upon them. They were scattered far and wide at the destruction of the monastery a hundred years ago, and the discovery of one of them is now a prize in book-collecting. This was the last benefaction that the monastery received, and it decayed slowly for a hundred and fifty years after this, until it was broken into by the mob and was brought by their violence into the state in which it still remains.

The second abbey, that of Santas Creus, is in the same district, not more than thirty miles across the mountains from Poblet. This also was the foundation of D. Ramon Berenguer IV, in the year 1157, but its prosperity was more directly due to the endowment and support of the Moncada family. Building was continued over nearly two centuries, ending, in 1341, with the consecration of the cloister, which had been paid for in large part by Jaime II and Blanche of Anjou. Their arms, the French lilies and the Catalan bars, appear on the Royal Gate at the end of the south walk. The tall church is dark and empty now, but it is of the usual Cistercian type, being, indeed, in all probability, the work of the same French architect from Fontfroide who built Poblet. Its chief interest is the series of tombs that it contains. Chief among them are those of Pedro III and Jaime II. The carved shrine of Don Pedro is carried on a huge porphyry bath, brought from Sicily by his admiral, Roger de Lauria, who defeated the French fleet of Charles of Anjou at Naples. It has much resemblance to the tomb of Frederic II and Constance of Aragon in Palermo Cathedral.

In the cloister there are many more tombs, rich in mediaeval heraldry. They are built into pointed niches that carry the arms of the family of Montelin, stand between twisted pillars bearing the counters of the Moncadas, have the eagles in quatrefoils of the de Selvas, or, above saints in cusped arcades, the stags of the armed knight, D. Ramon de Alemany de Cervello. The customary chapter-house leads out from the cloister; there are the usual hexagonal fountain-house with hexagonal basin, lesser cloisters, and dormitories.

The royal palace of Pedro III and Jaime II is the culmination of the beautiful things in this abbey. In the first court, a stairway, carried on a single pillar of porphyry, leads up to a gallery of pointed arches on slender pillars. These have delicate Catalan capitals, and above there is a painted timber roof. The next court has a third storey, a low loggia of stucco reliefs; in another place a loggia of fine brickwork arches hangs over the wall. The ceilings are timbered, coffered, of artesonado work, or have fine plaster reliefs worked upon them. A whole series of these little rooms leads out of one another, and the monastic atmosphere is altogether broken and dispersed by their secular loveliness.

This is but a threadbare account of these two wonderful Catalan buildings. Their major interest, as I have said, is that they are, in spite of their ruin, the best preserved of all the great series of Cistercian monasteries that flourished once in nearly every corner of Europe. Royal patronage was withdrawn from them in time to leave their original mediaeval form but little touched by later architectural developments. Thus, from a purist's point of view, they are less spoilt than most places of the kind.

At the same time, even in their own day, they were among the most important houses of the order. For Fr. Manrique, the Cistercian historian of his own order, speaks of Poblet as Populetum . . . *toto orbe Christiano nulli secundum.*

Both Poblet and Santas Creus are in a part of Spain which is not much visited, though its situation so near to Barcelona could never be called remote. It is a tract of country which has a remarkable character of its own. Nowhere in the world is fruit-blossom so beautiful as in the orchards of this tract of coast between Tarragona and Valencia. A separate language to that spoken in other parts of Spain is still in use, and everything—people, landscape, and buildings—are neither French, Spanish, nor yet Italian.

A distinct style of mediaeval architecture, quite unlike the Gothick of any other region, was practised here. It is the only indigenous Spanish school, for, apart from this, French or German architects were universally employed. No trace of this particular Catalan school is visible in either Poblet or Santas Creus, but the presence of this talent in their midst goes a great way to explain the interest shown by rich nobles of the time in these two royal foundations. The architect who started the Catalan school was Jayme Fabre, a native of Mallorca, and he built the cathedrals at Palma in Mallorca, and at Barcelona. The immense width of the nave was the peculiarity of his manner, until finally the aisles disappeared altogether and were shown merely by a series of separate chapels. This is the case in the fine Catalan churches of Gerona, Manresa, and Lerida.

The successors of D. Ramon Berenguer were ambitious princes who by the middle of the fifteenth century had possessed themselves of Naples and Sicily. But their condition of civilization was beyond any doubt in advance of that of these two kingdoms they took over. The Italian culture was in Milan, in Venice, and in Florence, and the Catalans in their own country went ahead along their own lines, not bothering overmuch about what they had seen in Italy. Thus, while Poblet and Santas Creus show little influence of the local Catalan architecture, they are still less perturbed by any rumours from Italy.

It is now necessary to cross over to the other side of the peninsula in order to examine the second group of monasteries. With the exception of Belem, which is in a suburb of Lisbon, all these are near each other in the centre of the country. Batalha and Alcobaça are only a dozen miles apart, while Thomar is not more than thirty miles from either of them.

These convents, regarded often as the bastards of their race, are really among the most imaginative feats of the whole Middle Ages. They are products of an alert, vigorous intelligence resolved to explore the secrets of architecture at a time when this same ideal of adventure had changed a small kingdom into the richest country of its time. The Portuguese, born soldiers and sailors, with good architects and exquisite poets of their own race, were in no need of Italian inspiration, and had set their backs resolutely against the Spaniards. Their own energy carried them forward, till its very excess in proportion to the smallness of the population, with Brazil and Africa and the Indies as the perquisites of a few thousand white men, caused the nervous collapse of the whole race. This ruin was completed by the foolish escapade in Morocco when their King and all their best men perished, unnecessarily, in this poorest of all the lands they could have chosen for a crusade.*

Till then, the profits of these adventures had been enormous. There was money to spend, and each time it came back in the ships there were new tales told of the lands from which these riches came. It is only natural that out of these three main directions mentioned it should be India that was most interesting to them. Africa was the land of black men; while America (for Mexico and Peru, two ends in themselves, had not, then, been heard of) they thought of only as an approach to India which might take less time to accomplish than the weary journey round the Cape of Good Hope. India was the country of great kings and fine buildings, and it was only out of India that there was any civilization to match their own progress. The Empire of the Moghuls was scarcely established, and it is therefore from the Hindu Kingdom of Southern India that the Portuguese were influenced.†

They had one architectural genius, whose work, until it is seen and the eyes can recognize it, would seem to be a myth. The same suspicious secrecy surrounds their one primitive painter, Nuno Gonçalves, till his two great triptychs in the Museum at Lisbon make him an authentic, powerful person. But Nuno Gonçalves was the true painter of his period, working only in one laborious convention, and reaching in this to the stature, perhaps, of Conrad Witz, or Matthias Grünewald; whereas this architect,

* King Sebastian, and the flower of Portugal, were killed on the battlefield of Arzila in 1578. This was the very scene of his ancestors' triumph, vide Vol. i., p. 130. The mystery of Sebastian's death gave rise to many pretenders, while this battle brought about the ruin of Portugal, which was absorbed by Philip II of Spain, a couple of years later.

† The Emperor Babar, first of the Great Moghuls, began to reign in 1494.

João de Castilho, has certainly three styles, or manners. There is the flamboyant Gothick of the great doorway at Belem; the Plateresque Renaissance of the cloisters at Belem ; and his third, or most personal, stage is shown in the unfinished chapels at Batalha and in the church at Thomar.

His doorway to the church at Belem is in the full Gothick of Rouen. Indeed the sculptures with which it is ornamented were the work of a Frenchman, Maître Nicholas, who is said to have come from Rouen. It is only in the interior of the church that the Portuguese character of the building becomes evident. The great Vasco da Gama had spent the night here, before he started on his voyage of discovery, and it was at Belem that Emmanuel I received him on his return. The King had promised to build a great convent on this spot if the expedition succeeded in its object of reaching India, and he fulfilled his intention by laying the foundation-stone of the future monastery only a few weeks after the explorer's return. This was in 1499, and the convent was begun to the design of an architect Boutaca, but João de Castilho took control in 1517 and worked on it for the next thirty years.

The interior of the church is supported upon two piers and six ornate octagonal pillars, elaborately groined. The peculiar Portuguese character of this Gothick work is very impressive to anyone who has never seen it before. This church seems to contain the material of a whole new school of ideas not yet put into practice, and the sight of the great cloister confirms this impression, while it carries these latent possibilities further than an ordinary imagination could conceive. For the first few moments the horror of ringworm, projected on an unheard-of scale

ADORATION OF SAINT VINCENT
Central part of a triptych by Nuno Gonçalves

over the heads of some hundreds of Portuguese orphans, makes any close examination of this amazing affair too painful to be considered. But enthusiasm removes all scruples ; and this is the most wonderful conception of a cloister that has ever been realized.

It is a square with blunted corners, and the arcading is double-storied. The Plateresque ornament has a curious quality, for this is Renaissance detail seized upon greedily by a mind which wanted to take over all poetical material that was of any use to him. At the same time, no principles of classical construction have been thought of, and João de Castilho just assumed this new mythology for its fresh stock of ornament. The lovely groining of the stone roof of the lower arcades, the round-headed windows with their carved columns, and the traceries latticing the intervals between these, help the essential square design of the cloister into the form of a well where the sunlight is sifted and made gentle by such an argument of shadows. Its effect must be more beautiful still by moonlight. Altogether it is the most individual architectural caprice that has ever been translated out of the imagination into actuality. Cloisters are the unique glory of Portuguese building, but there is nothing else as beautiful as this, and it is no use trying to describe it in terms of technical practice, for it defies this kind of analysis and is, perhaps, more the possession of the poet or the musician than that of the architect, who will ask too many questions and try to dissipate this incomparable mystery.

After Belem, the wonders of the three great abbeys in the centre of Portugal can be anticipated, but Alcobaça, which Beckford praises so highly, is the only one of them that falls short of expectation. It is impressive from its.

size and from the white bareness of the Cistercian church ;
but its great ornament is the pair of doorways by João de
Castilho that lead across the corridor between one of the
chapels of the ambulatory and the sacristy, which was
restored to his designs. These doorways are of great
height and are white in colour against the steep whiteness
of the corridor-walls. They are the first indication of
his Indian, or marine, style. Their pillars are in the
form of sea-palms rising out of a rock where their roots
mingle with the coral-stems and can hardly be told apart
from them. Then the branches from the two pillars
curve towards each other and meet, with a little clash of
fronds, above the door. It is a conception of the purest
originality.

Apart from this pair of doorways, it is not possible to
agree with Beckford's opinion of Alcobaça. The extravagance of Batalha and Thomar frightened his own small
creative talent. He felt safe with the stream from the
river Alcoa that flowed through the kitchen, and with
the shifts of nine hundred monks who chanted mass day
and night without ceasing.* These were easy, epical
effects that matched with the Cistercian simplicity of
the church. So, out of Alcobaça, this ordinary average
of a monastery, with any quality that it has coming
merely from a magnification of its parts, we need only
concern ourselves with the two marine doorways by
João de Castilho.

The genius of this architect is shown in its origins at
the Dominican convent of Batalha. It was always a

---

* This estimate of Beckford is proved still further by his eulogy of Mafra,
the palace-barrack-monastery of the Portuguese Kings, which is again undis-
tinguished except for its size, while the Royal Quinta de Queluz de Baixo, one
of the greatest marvels of the Rococo age, Beckford will not trouble to describe,
though much of the action of his scenes takes place in it.

much smaller affair than Alcobaça, never having more than sixty monks attached to it. The church is of authentic Gothick, with an exterior crocketed and floriated in the richest manner conceivable. The interior has excellent flowing design, with not as much detail as the elaborate sides and façade of the church would seem to imply. The Founder's chapel opens out of the south aisle. This is a high, stone chamber with an octagon roof borne by eight pillars; the arches, the window-tracery, and the bosses to the vaulting of the octagon all having the same kind of minutely beautiful carved detail that is to be found in the chapter-house at Southwell Minster. In fact, this church is built largely upon English models, and the masons and the building-plan were obtained from England through the wife of the founder, Philippa of Lancaster, daughter of John of Gaunt. The name of a master-builder, Houguet, probably an Irishman, Hacket(?), has been preserved as that of the designer of the church. The bodies of Philippa of Lancaster (d. 1416) and of her husband, John I (d. 1434) lie beneath this octagon in a sarcophagus borne upon eight lions. The tombs of four of their children are in niches in the walls.

But the Portuguese character has shown itself in everything that is not part of the actual church. Most particularly is this so in the Claustro Real and in the Capellas Imperfeitas, while it is here that the beginnings out of which João de Castilho built his originality can be seen at work. This cloister can only be compared with that of Belem. Its character is nearly indescribable. The tracery of the arches is based upon two patterns that recur alternately. One of them is an elaborate network of briar-branches, enclosing the armillary spheres

x

that formed the devise of King Emmanuel; the other is a combination of the double-cross of the Order of Christ with the stem and blossoms of the lotus. These designs are symbolical of the Portuguese attempts upon the Indies. The well-house, at one corner of the cloister, is the most beautiful pavilion imaginable, entered through two very rich archways with the lotus pattern repeated again in front of the eyes in the tracery of the two high windows that look out on to the cloister-garden. Opposite to this pavilion there is a chapter-house of great, if more usual, beauty.

But, strangest of all are the Capellas Imperfeitas. The entrance to them is awkward, as they are not organically connected with the church, but the narrow passage that leads to them ends in a huge archway fifty feet high and twenty-five feet wide. This is elaborately ornamented throughout its surface. It is the most wonderful entrance ever devised by a mediaeval mind, of a general character which is strongly Oriental, but with which no work of Moor, or Persian, can compare.

The chapel is a great octagon without a roof, and its space is surrounded by seven large chapels with six smaller pentagonal chapels in the intervals between them. The great central space was intended by Emmanuel for the body of King Duarte, the son of Philippa of Lancaster, named after the English King, Edward III. The three large chapels facing this magnificent entrance he meant for himself, and for the bodies of Alfonso V and John II.

These chapels only rise to about half their intended height, for when Emmanuel died, in 1521, work upon them was stopped. He had taken it up again at the point where it had been left by King Duarte, some sixty years before. It may be concluded that João de Castilho

ONE OF THE UNFINISHED CHAPELS, BATALHA

was in charge of the renewed attempt to complete this peculiar and ambitious design, but Emmanuel soon lost interest in it and put all his energy into the church at Belem, that he now chose to be his mausoleum. The work at Batalha never progressed very far. The clustered columns of pillars start up again higher, in form like a bundle of reeds, and with an altogether Indian intention. But they never reached even as far as where their capitals should be. The whole scheme remained roofless and unfinished.

In this sporadic building the Manoelino style is seen in two attempts towards its own perfected form, and João de Castilho's isolation as a genius in architectural design is somewhat contradicted by this germination of his ideas. They were latent in the Portuguese mind, and only required development in the hands of someone strong enough to put their theory into execution. This second chance, coming some sixty years after the first suggestion, is an extravagant fulfilment such as is seldom made possible by circumstance. But, in its final state, the Manoelino style must be seen at Thomar.

The Convent of the Order of Christ is on a little hill above the town of Thomar. The order had been founded by King Diniz in 1314 as a military order to fight the Moors, but its days of prosperity came in the next century with the Grand Mastership (1418-1460) of Prince Henry the Navigator. He made use of its revenues to equip vessels for the discovery and conquest of the West Coast of Africa. By the time King Emmanuel had succeeded to the Grand Mastership, in 1480, the possessions of the Order in India and in Africa had made it the wealthiest fraternity in the whole of the Christian world. Soon after his death, and probably because the

Order had become too powerful, its Grand Mastership was merged in the Crown, and the Order was turned from one of chivalry into one of ordinary monkhood. It then rapidly declined in power, lost its possessions, was looted by Junot's troops, was dissolved in 1834, and its ruins only saved from utter destruction by the Count of Thomar who bought it, and whose descendants still use one end of it as their residence, certainly the most deserted and picturesque of all country-houses.

These few details of its history are necessary in order to explain how this remote town, far away on the Western fringes of Europe, can have a building of this extraordinary nature, in a style completely original and outside experience, and on a scale so immense that it contains no fewer than sixteen cloisters.*

The interest of Thomar from our point of view consists in the New Chapter-house, and in the church of the Order of Christ. Both of these were built to the designs of João de Castilho. The church has an ornate doorway, not unlike that of Belem, and the arcading is patterned, as before, with the armillary sphere and with the cross of the Order.

As if to typify the sea-ambition of Prince Henry the Navigator, great stone cables like a ship's ropes are carved on the outside of the church. The doorway is enclosed in an arch, of which the under-curve has an elaborate pendant ornament. Over the door, and within its recess, figures in niches stand under canopies, and upon pillars, in which these and many other devices have been employed. Coiled cables, bossed spirals, floreated pin-

---

* Among these is the Claustro de Dom João III, a two-storied cloister finished in 1562. It is a magnificent Palladian building, with a fountain in the middle, and is the only fine thing of the strict, full Renaissance in the whole of Portugal.

nacles, armillary spheres, and crosses, stand out in high
relief. The lower window, which lights the interior
of the choir, is a tangle of outstanding ropes, each point
being crowned by the cross and the armillary sphere.
Around one of the corner-towers, a great chain, each
link carved entire in stone is braced, and around the other
an equally tremendous buckled belt, representing the
Order of the Garter, which the Prince, who was half-
Plantagenet, had been given. The upper window, that
lights the chapter-house, presents the extreme of the
Manoelino manner. It is a window of great depth
worked into the surface of the wall, and represents upon
the sloping inner face of the circle a series of bulging
staysails, each of them held down by a rope.

Behind this church, and over the rest of the surface
of the hill, stretch the endless corridors of the convent
with the cells of the monks. At one point, three of these
passages meet together in a high domed hall, and six
rows of doors can be seen diminishing into the distance.
At the end of one of these corridors, in the cloister dos
Corvos, live the Conde de Thomar and his family. The
flowers and fruit-trees of their garden lie below the
barred window, fountains still play there, and voices are
heard through the boughs. But, on this side of the
window, the ruin is a labyrinth of stairs and vaults. The
Abbot's House, the Noviciate, the Refectory, the kitchens,
the store-rooms, all of these are empty and deserted.
It is an affair of hours to wander through them. The
only building to equal it in desolated splendour is the
convent of Santa Chiara at Naples, but this is not the
place to speak of its majolica cloister trellised with vines,
of its refectory painted with perspectives, of its tumbled
kitchens, or of any of the other things visible for the first

time only some three years ago, when this immense building, as fine and large as Thomar, but in the midst of the Neapolitan slums, was at last made open to the eyes.* The Convent of the Order of Christ, like the Convent of Santa Chiara, must be seen in order to be believed.

The Manoelino architecture at Thomar is an enlargement in any artist's experience. So are the three other great relics of this style, the cloisters at Belem, and Batalha, and the Capellas Imperfeitas at the latter place. Of all these, the cloister at Batalha is the only one in which João de Castilho was not directly concerned, while at Belem and Thomar the work is entirely his.

There are many more Manoelino buildings in Portugal, but these are the chief. Others may be found at Evora in the Algarve, a little known town which should have much fine architecture, and at Coimbra. This university town is like a mixture of Toledo and Salamanca ; it is among the most interesting towns in Europe and has, besides its buildings in this " national " style of Gothick, including more particularly the Claustro do Silencio in the Mosteiro de Santa Cruz, the magnificent Romanesque Sé Velha, or old cathedral, and the University Library, which has a lacquered interior of red, green, and gold, and is beyond any doubt the most beautiful thing of its date, better even than the library of the Hofburg in Vienna, or the libraries of the Baroque monasteries on the Danube.

* There will be another surprise of the same nature if ever the convent of San Gregorio Armeno at Naples is allowed to be seen. Only the church is visible ; gardens, cloister, refectory, and chapter-house are in the strictest clausura, but this convent, still preserved in its pristine brilliance, and hidden away in the foulest slums of the town, is one of the greatest works of the late seventeenth century.

CHAPTER-HOUSE WINDOW AT THOMAR, PORTUGAL

The impression left by these Manoelino buildings is this. The earlier Gothick of France or England, when the great cathedral-age was over and the Hundred Years War had diminished the energies of both countries, died away and gave place to a small intricacy, a lace-like diapering, without the strength to invent anything but new ornament. The exception to this is the English fan-vaulting. Apart from this, the kind of Gothick that flourished in the district round Rouen added but little to the structural repertory of buildings. Nor is it possible to consider the work of Claus Sluter at Dijon, or the Nuremberg school of Peter Vischer, Adam Krafft, Tilman Riemenschneider, and Veit Stoss, as of more than a very minor importance in the history of art. More particularly in the case of the Nuremberg school, their Gothick is of that obvious, easy sort converted so quickly half a century ago into town-hall or railway station. The continuations of Gothick, where money was at its disposal and the prosperity of new discoveries had fired men's ambition and given them the genius of exploration, was in Spain and Portugal.

But, in Spain, the international character of the monarchy and its contacts with Flanders and with Italy curbed the natural developments of Gothick and invented the Plateresque, a sort of medium between the two, in which the Gothick craftsman could continue to make use of his talent for ornament, increase it by this fresh stock of ideas, and yet not have to learn the new structural system of the revived classics. This sufficed them for their generation.

In Portugal this did not happen, and anyone wishing to see what directions there were still left in which a vigorous mind could advance without going to Rome for his instruction must see these three or four monuments to Portugal's lost greatness, and should pay particular attention to the works of João de Castilho. In them, the untrammelled Gothick of a race which had still much to say in that medium has reached to its final expression. As well as this, these four monasteries mark the culmination of one whole aspect of the cenobitic life. If we are only concerned with monks to the extent to which they influenced the arts, it must be admitted that in these four instances they had devised a setting for themselves of unparalleled splendour, and as strange in its form as it was fine and finished in detail. One apex of their achievement was reached in Portugal, and if we think of the monastic life all over the world, and not only among the Christian races, most certainly these monasteries take their place beside the monasteries of Mount Athos; the Russian convents of the Troitsa, the New Jerusalem, and the Lavra of Kiev; the Hindu and Brahman temples; the Tibetan lamaseries; the Buddhist temples of Kyoto and Koya-San; the Certosa of Pavia; the monasteries of Bavaria and the Danube. This neutral life led in our midst has produced in Portugal some of the most astounding of its works.

At the other side of the peninsula, Poblet and Santas Creus represent the more ordinary effects, found even in France and in England before wilful destruction overtook them. Alcobaça and Batalha, Belem and Thomar, are very different from this, for their strong and vigorous Gothick was alive some century and a half after its quasi-death everywhere else.

The best contrast to these two groups of monasteries is the town of Burgos. The late Gothick work in this place represents the last expiring efforts of the mediaeval

craftsmen. Two fathers and two sons are responsible
for most of it—Hans and Simon of Cologne, and Gil and
Diego de Siloe. It was Hans of Cologne who built the
Cimborio and the perforated tower-caps of the cathedral ;
while his son, Simon, built the chapel of the Constable
of Castile in the cathedral, and designed the Cartuja
de Miraflores outside the town. Of the other father and
son, Gil de Siloe made the tombs of Juan II and Isabella
of Portugal, and the gilded retablo of the high altar in
the Cartuja de Miraflores, while his son Diego built the
Escalera Dorada of the cathedral.

A few words must be said about these works. The
perforated effects devised by Hans of Cologne give an
appearance to the outside of the cathedral as if it were
the work of someone who had made a study of the fox-
glove, the Canterbury bell, and all the other flowers of
the Northern woods. As for the chapel of the Constable
and the chapel of the Cartuja designed by his son,
Simon, they represent the climax of heraldic, aristocratic
art. In the roof of the former place the groinings form
at their intersection a large star of eight points, and the
cells between the ribs of this star are pierced with the
most elaborate pounces and floriations. The crowned
eagles and the pillars of Spain are supported by " wild-
men," the mediaeval satyr, and by figures dressed like the
Knave of Hearts off a playing-card. Two other instances
of this manner, found elsewhere, the church of San Juan
de los Reyes at Toledo and King's College chapel at
Cambridge, fall away from any comparison with the
buildings at Burgos because of their senseless iteration
where the mere manual skill of this decadence has
repeatedly copied its own effects and shows none of the
fertile invention of Burgos.

The sixteen-sided tomb by Gil de Siloe in the Cartuja is an accepted miracle which no one can dare to doubt. It is the most beautiful of all Gothick tombs. Its plan is a square with another laid diagonally upon it. At the four chief angles are seated figures of the four Evangelists, and round the sides are kings and saints, virtues, nude figures, and wonderful foliage. Above, lie the king and queen; he holds a sceptre, and she is holding an open book. Gil de Siloe also made the monument of their son D. Alfonso which stands against the side-wall. There is a great shield held by angels, with men in armour at either side. D. Alfonso kneels at a prie-dieu under a fringe of leaves, below a sculpture of St. George and the Dragon.

The retablo behind these tombs, made by Gil de Siloe in the short space of three years, is the richest work of applied Gothick in existence. Alfonso and Isabella appear once more kneeling at stools with their coats-of-arms above them. An innumerable crowd of figures compose the design and culminate in a great circle made of clustered angels, in the centre of which is a great crucifix underneath a figure of the Pelican vulning her breast.*

The son of this great artist, Diego de Siloe, before he had entirely accepted the classical manner and had left Burgos for Granada and Malaga to undertake the new Christian works built there after the expulsion of the Moorish Caliphs, put up, in 1519, the Escalera Dorada, a great double flight of fifty-nine steps, leading down to the north transept from the Puerta de la Coroneria on

---

* The small Gothick church of San Nicolás, just above the cathedral, contains another retablo, by Francisco de Colonia this time, nearly as splendid as that of the Cartuja.

the hillside above. This is a magnificent example of
the Plateresque, with its worked and gilded railings and
with the balustrades jutting out, as they reach the pavement, into two stone griffins. It is just at the transition
between the two ages and bears predominant signs of the
new civilization come in from Italy. It has just emerged
from the Gothick, but left it in these other splendid
works that have been described, in an elaborate fringed,
or German, leafiness of thought, transplanted into the
soil of Spain and forming a last flowering of those old
principles into action. Unlike the Portuguese buildings,
the last stage of an alert and busy decadence had been
reached; no more elaboration of effect, on only these
lines, was possible, and after this climax fatigue and deadness would have ensued had not these new items come
into the stock of the craftsman and the ornamenter.

Gil de Siloe is by far the most interesting of this
quartet of architects and sculptors who endowed the
town of Burgos with their handiwork. The Cartuja,
because of the tombs and the retablo made by him, is a
supreme instance of the licensed, academic Gothick in its
last phase of existence when intricacy of handling only
suited it for the enrichment of small areas. The aristocratic, ascetic nature of the Carthusian monks took a
particular delight in this contrast to their bare cells and
this reminder of the luxuries they had known and relinquished. Indeed, the Cartuja is but the first of a whole
series of buildings embodying these same principles but
carried out more often in the baroque, which was quicker,
if no less expensive, in reaching its effects. Chief among
these are their monasteries at Jerez de la Frontera, at
Granada, at Pavia, at Pisa, at Padula in the Basilicata,
and on the hill of San Martino above Naples, at all of

which places their wealth contrived some most surprising and original inventions.

Here, in the Cartuja de Miraflores, these white-robed monks, who bear an exact resemblance because of the date of their style of dress with the Moors of Atlas, say their prayers in front of this vertiginous retablo, which is so crowded with little figures thrusting themselves into the first plane of vision and with their less important and less richly-garbed fellows standing in rows behind them, that we are audience at the last scene of some great theatrical ballet. A perpetual grand finale has been achieved, and, as in the masques of two hundred years ago, many, or most, of the figures are in the air on wires.

The mandorla of clustered angels, who surround and support the crucifix under the figure of the Pelican vulning her breast, is the climax of this emotional affair. Its effect can be described in no terms but those of music, and I can think of no musician but Tchaikowsky who could parallel the hysterical cyclones and their alternation of brittle calm, as of patterns of the frost, or leaves shown in water. This is the characteristic of his orchestration, where, if the brass is not playing in four-part harmony, the woodwind and the strings echo themselves in a series of reflections of their action. Such is his procedure in his best moments, in the " Casse-Noisette," or in the scherzi of his symphonies, and there is nothing except these to compare with the infinitely laboured, yet delicate and direct, emotionalism of this great retablo. It is one of the most personal moments in the whole of Gothick history, and in this small chapel of the Cartuja we find ourselves in front of one of the most singular and gifted men of his race. Its delicacy, and the more deep than broad loudness of its climax, are considered for a small audience who had to pass their whole lives in front of it. The mob-public of a cathedral had to be planned for in a quite different direction, but this monastery was a place where the same few people came day after day and many times in each day. It must be something they would not tire of, with an emotional force to sustain the spirit, and a minuteness of detail that always left some corner unexplored and lying fresh to be examined. Or the whole structure hung there before short-sighted eyes as a mist that allowed no one to know its secrets who would not draw near to it.

Burgos, and the works of art that it contains, are within the experience of nearly every traveller, whereas these two groups of monasteries that I have described are nearly unknown. But, together with Burgos, they represent the Gothick art of the monks in three definite stages of their end. With Poblet and Santas Creus it is the art of the great convents in a countryside that belonged to them; in fact, they were little walled states containing everything necessary to their support. With the Cartuja de Miraflores, it is a rich monastery, but of small size, with a church no bigger than a little chapel, lying outside a town where the greatest sculptural and architectural activity was in progress.(7) With the group of Portuguese monasteries the situation is different, and there is an opportunity of following the Gothick into regions where it need never have died, having unlimited wealth and a vitality not contradicted by any cross-current of ideas.

In all three places the monks have arrived at the most intense ornamentation of their principles, and, as I have stressed before, it is this side of monastic life and not its prayers or hardships that we want to investigate. These few short hours of their existence, compared with all the

hours of prayer, of sleep, and the time they passed locked
in their cells, made them into the greatest patrons, and
practitioners, of the arts. Had there been nothing but
monks, and had the human race been preserved by a
parthenogenesis of the spirit, bearing men and women
into the world again after they had been taken away
from it for five centuries, we should still have a most
imposing record to chronicle. Indeed, the aim of this
chapter is as though this were so.

Unfortunately the later labours of the Carthusians
lie outside the scope of this enterprise, so that our investigation must stop at the Cartuja de Miraflores. Nor may
we follow the Gothick any further in its Spanish developments ; into the strange heraldic rhapsodies, for example,
of a town like Valladolid. This has two churches, San
Pablo and the Colegio de San Gregorio, which are
literally festooned with coats-of-arms, held by angels,
by knights, or by " wild men " ; the former of these has
a genealogical tree over the doorway and a pair of cloisters
of an almost Manoeline strangeness ; while a third church,
La Magdalena, has a façade consisting simply of one
gigantic heraldic achievement. We must keep away,
too, from Salamanca, from the façades of the Catedral
Nueva and the University with their incomparable
richness of the time of Ferdinand and Isabella, and from
the Casa de las Conchas, another instance verging on the
Manoeline. Last, and saddest of all, our monastic
burden bars us from the palace of the Infantados at
Guadalajara, the work of the Flemish brothers Enrique
and Juan Guas who built the church of San Juan de los
Reyes at Toledo. The courtyard of this palace, and the
ceilings in some two or three rooms, more especially the
Sala de los Linajes, or genealogies, with its carved and

gilded cornice, its statued ancestors looking down from balconies like the Gothick boxes of a theatre, and the Moorish and stalactitic splendour of its ceiling, are things, hardly known, but of a beauty that drives away any of the more familiar achievements of the fifteenth century elsewhere in Europe.

We must put away all these inspirations and think only of the communistic tribes of monks at work in all the fair valleys that their thwarted comfort chose for them. Their pace was so slow that nothing ever seemed to happen, and any change that came was so long delayed that once it had arrived it was not much noticed. Their centuries last us a minute.

Now, their dull, pained lives seem to us to have been peaceful and almost idyllic from the realization, one after another and in their due rotation, of every scheme that their imagination suggested to them. Time and money they spent freely, having unlimited store of each of these necessities. By no other means but this could such effects have been achieved, and in this present age, more than in any other, is the need for these things becoming obvious and even pressing. No other method can secure such results, and yet the rebirth of these instincts is impossible and can never come about, so that civilization is now for ever doomed to the individual effort—almost, even, to the amateur, since there is hardly an artist in the last sixty years who has been able to earn his living. Under the monastic system anyone who did not like fighting, and had no desire, on the other hand, to be a merchant, found himself safely provided for ; and it is exactly this class of person who is likely to supply the arts for his country. A naïf simpleton like Fra Angelico could have existed in no other condition than this.

The first sculptors, the first painters, and the first scholars, had their unprofitable labours guaranteed to them. But, also, men of inferior talent found no encouragement, and if there were a hundred monks to any one of them whose endowment was worth while, at any rate there were not ten thousand bad painters to a single mediocrity. It is the greatest thing to be said in favour of the monastic system that, if they encouraged true talent, nothing at all was done to help the idle dabbler.

Nothing could be more false than to imagine that the cloistered life was lacking in what can only be termed " motif " and that there was no inspiration except a bunch of flowers, or a chance lizard seen on the summer wall. Far from this being so, there can be no doubt that everything gained from the dramatic force that was given to it by constant repetition at stated periods not coming too near together. Even a footfall in the passage had a symbolical power as overwhelming, if less dangerous, as the tread that the prisoner waits for, expecting his death to come with it.

Then it passed by and was gone ; and it can never have been anything else but the regulation shoes of the monk, either the humble sandal, or that heavier version of the dancing-shoe that they wore, black in colour like that happier omen, and with the white sock of the comedian showing under the equivocal skirt.

But this was all. At other times footsteps made their regular round carrying food. They came to each cell in turn, going back again after every fall of the lattice, so that there were a known number of journeys to be made before and after your cell was reached. Perhaps these latter variations were felt more than counted, for

the little routine pleasures of the rule made it a delight
to finish everything in the exact quantities in which it
was brought, as though this very act was part of the
dramatic action. This was one degree of duty, and by
now those footfalls were silenced and there was an
appointed time during which nothing was to happen.
But the very silence was moving in an ordered direction
towards the next ordained event, and the heat or cold,
the rain or snow, of these intervals had been regulated
by the same code of laws, allowing only for a wider pattern
for the theme to move in, so that a hazard seemed
to attach itself to these really fixed changes of the
elements.

Nor were the communal, apart from the solitary,
phases of this existence less emphatic in their appeal to
the senses. Often there was silence in the refectory
while some holy work was read aloud from a pulpit high
in the wall. Or it was a feast-day of the church and the
gift of tongues had descended upon the diners. Then,
it was as though these men, whose lives were separated
from each other only by a few inches of wall, met here
at certain days in the calendar having passed the intermediate time in a round of furious travelling. Nothing,
save such mutations of the mind and soul, could account
for their gabbling hurry of talk.

The forced marches in the cloister were another most
curious spectacle from the different degrees of acting
and behaviour possible under the strict uniformity of
the monk's cowl. Some struggled round, beaten down
by their load of conscience, others walked in strings of
four or five, or in familiar pairs, busily talking. There
were some who came into this light of day, into this
publicity with their fellows, as though reluctant to leave

Y

the darkness of their locked cells, with puzzled step and
eyes yet blinking with the light; while many others
lived only for this seldom recurring day and were disappointed with it when it came from too great an
anticipation of its liberties.

Scenes just as strange and forced as these were acting
in every corner of each huge barracks of the self-willed
eunuchs. They may be imagined, too, working in the
fields or vines, driving a cart and horse, or, oddest of all,
rowing a boat of provisions with a long oar from a high
rowlock, as may be seen to this day on the way to the
convent of S. Francesco all' Deserto across the lagoons
of Venice.

Within the enclosure of the walls we may think of
them coming out of the cellar-mouth from a parliament
of great barrels, or sitting to wait for their turn in the
barber's shop. Here they came, in some places, twice a
week to be shaved and to have their tonsures attended
to; while, in the strictness of the Cistercian rule it was
the custom to be bled profusely at certain intervals in
order to lower resistance and meet temptation with too
little strength to follow its cajoleries.

In the chapter-house the general of the order, or a
visiting abbot, would be received, and the impersonal
affairs of the community were discussed and decided
upon. From here the edicts of each fast were promul-
gated, and offenders had their confessions examined and
were told their punishment. This took the form of a
yet more stringent privation, so that the most devout of
the monks, and those who never committed any offence,
were in the process of perpetually punishing themselves
for things they had not done.

The usual conspiracies among themselves which always

break out when people are thrown together were not so
true of fact as in any other kind of community of human
beings; for, though the monks passed a greater portion
of their lives together in a propinquity as close as that
of camp, or prison, they were barred from nearly all
contact with their fellows; and even in the less strict
orders, where refectory and dormitory put life into
terms of common or mutual experience, they were their
own jailers in their own self-appointed prison and could
be depended upon to enforce the most drastic interpretation of the code. Thus, the most direct approaches in
dramatic action were lacking in their lives, since the
passions had no play, and we must take away intrigue
and subterfuge and put in its place the shallow, quickly
noted peculiarities that habit induces when every happening of life has become settled into a rhythm which
nothing breaks or disturbs. Then, idiosyncrasy rises out
of the dullness to relieve its monotony, though it must
seem to the individual inventor of each trick merely to
be a system of doing things quicker and easier, a saving
of trouble and a short road to what is necessary and
expected.

This rich theme, and all its workings and changes, comes
out of that drab, or black, start; with, at its farthest
possibilities of expression, the plain white of that aristocratic variety, or the magpie division of the Dominicans,
conceived by the Spanish saint to indicate the pied, or
mongrel, humility of his followers. But they are the
only alternative to the glittering, spangled chivalry of
the age; their history was safer and more continuous,
and their achievement in its vastness cannot be compared with the castles of the knights, and with the
tapestry, or poetry, made to please them.

The great and apparent permanence of the cenobites suffered but few darts of sentiment to shake in its sides. All its incident was too carefully planned to shut out this possibility. Regret was not allowed to be a part of penitence. At the same time, no power could keep away every feeling of this kind, and, in itself, the soft dove-throat of the sky was enough to cause a trembling of the senses.

The fruit-trees made the only clouds there were, and these were shaken continually by a sigh of wind, or by a bird leaving one of these islands for another. Then, and because of this gentle playing of the air on those coloured coasts, everything except their message became worthless and hollow. The horrible yawning prison loomed behind, with a doubtful heaven at the end of it, and, if there, only to be enjoyed by a continuation of the same rigid rules into immortality, surrounded by the wan, graceless athletes and militants who made life ugly in the convent. This spell of a few days would be gone in a moment, and the only way to enjoy its beauties was to keep absolutely still as though listening to every sound. This is how creation begins in the poet's mind, when things, seen only with the eyes or touched with the fingers, become changed into voices which speak their words into the brain. The gradual darkening of each day, delayed a moment longer every time, let all the ghosts escape from their cob-webbed corners, and from their green cabinets in the woods, that now built themselves again, leaf by leaf, branch by branch, towards the summer.

During its burning days and torrid nights only the cool snow or rain could be thought of, but when the light began to shorten once more, the same longings but with a different form to their expression will have loaded, since they could never be realized, the mind of any monk who was not as stony-hearted as his prison.

The morning came in mist. It hung like smoke in the high branches of the trees, and had come down lower at every alley through the woods. It started from the ground at a step, and felt dank and acrid in the lungs. Soon the sun began to draw it up through the branches and none of it was left, except in a corner under high rocks, or where any long view through the trees left some traces of mist along the avenue.

Far away, down the distance, came the winding of a horn.

There was nothing else, no figures could be seen, but it sounded once more, and so far away that its direction was difficult to tell. Immediately, the different world that was the alternative to this built itself before the eyes, but now it was too late. The distance, up to where the hunting-horn was blown, seemed immeasurable, and by the time it was reached there would be no trace left of it. They would be at the far edge of the wood on their way to some castle where they could not be followed.

And so this autumn day when the hunting-horn was heard made the last sadness before the bitter winter, when it was too cold to have any regrets, or to think of anything but an alleviation of its pains. Meanwhile, the knights and ladies were hunting every day, and to anyone not a prisoner at a definite spot, the horns and the horses' hoofs could be heard wherever their fancy took them.

II

THE FAIR-HAIRED VICTORY

NEW palaces in peacock marble rise on every hand
and the chequered pavement has been sprayed
with water and freshly strewn with flowers.
A fringed canopy, or tented passage, leads across it and
the empty background seems to wait for figures. It is
not easy to people this childlike paradise except with the
children who would delight in it, but the builders cannot
keep away for long from its conscious pride of newness,
the church bells ring, and a gentle amorous fanfare
announces the shadows thrown by the early morning.

They walk, two by two, in meadowed dresses, with
fair hair falling to their shoulders, or built into the
towers and sails of fashion. There are no drums and
trumpets to marshal them. The happy adolescence of
their stride moves in time to the sweeping of harp-
strings, and to chords touched again and echoing. Harps,
and the plucked strings of this music, suggest sails ruffling
in the wind, the smooth neck and blown mane of the
horse in his speed, with the clean sands that would be
true of both images. Here, the morning air is just as
fresh as this, the marbles shine and sparkle as though
spray from the sea had reached to them, while the blue
waters of the sky show not a sail upon their emptiness.

It is the world of the cassone panels, and the painters

of these marriage-chests imagined many another scene
where the fair hair of the North lit the fields, shone like
gold out of the green woods of spring, or burnished the
hill-crest when a full moon climbed half into the sky
and such beauties as a preened cypress standing sentinel,
or an antlered stag breaking that round mask with its
points, could be seen in this magic half-world between
two days.

Sometimes the dead legends of the past were revived
for once more, and their actors were painted with the
gay colours of the North. Andromeda is bound against
the rocks, and the painter has answered both riddles of
the Gothick age, for her knight is shown in his full
panoply of armour, such as a stranger who only saw him
in his ordinary clothes would require of him in order to
satisfy the rumours of iron men riding out of the mists,
while Andromeda is painted naked, as if washing to shore
in a shell of pearl, and this answers the mystery of what
things were hidden beneath the folds and pleats of the
ladies' gowns.

Or, again, it is some other episode with only two
actors to its story. A daisied field is the scene for this,
and all the action is at one end of it, where a little brook
sings in the sunlight. The arms of Daphne, held up
as she runs, are already turning into branches. Her
fingers have lost their tapering ends and have assumed,
in terror, the sprouting leaves of the spring wood that
she hoped to reach for cover. She does not want to
vanish out of sight, but only to be something that can
be touched by him and not given any injury. She must
be one among a myriad trees, and must cling to just that
chance of being passed by him ; or he may even pause
by her green sleeves and the gold tresses of her highest

leaves, while he listens for a footfall and hears nothing but the sighing boughs, and whispered words whose meaning he cannot catch.

But she is too late in her metamorphosis. Her pursuer is leaping over the brook, with his hair blowing into a red mane behind him, and he will reach to her side when she has lost her human shape. For him, also, it is too late, and her last change is in his arms; her dying breath cools him while the gold locks of her hair turn into screws and twists of yellow wood like the shavings upon the floor of a carpenter's shop. She is sadly imprisoned in this ghostly shape, but can never escape from it again, and is immortalized in a condition just that distance away from death that he would have reached to her in life if she had fallen in the meadow and lain fainting in his arms. So she misses his hot breath, and the pulsing of his heart that she would have heard, and he has lost the rescuing of her shape from the tree into which she was turning, and the recovery of her eyes, her hair, and her hands.

Sometimes it is a battle of the Centaurs. This is among green hills and serious woods. The cornfield is a solid honeycomb, with paths cut waist-high through its richness, and this was too beautiful a thing for the painter to allow his harvest to be trampled, and so its summer peacefulness is left untroubled by the fighting. The death of any one of the warriors would be just as sad, yet many of them are stricken and lie dying. They have no armour, save a shield, and their fair heads and naked legs are as they would be in schools among the myrtle-groves, in contests of poetizing, when making love in the soft shadows, or in any contingency except this, of death. It does not matter. Here they are fixed in an immortality that is incorruptible and that does not allow them to grow old, or even suffer the harvest to be cut.

Another time, it is the legend of Perimedes the blacksmith. His forge is like a fiery cave where the flames sing madrigals in place of the dripping melodies of the damp, so it is a more cheerful place than ever a cavern can be with its stalactites that toll their age away in steady tears. The Centaurs thump in here as loud as a troop of horse, and their voices, as they speak to Perimedes, come from high up, from a taller stature than that of any man. Their faces are lit by the flames of the forge and Perimedes lets his irons go cool and shares his dinner with them.

In other panels they are to be seen coming away from their discourse with the blacksmith and standing at the cave-mouth, nosing the wind, and listening for the sounds it brings from the valley beneath. All their history, and every known fact about them, are made use of.

The Centaur that Pliny saw, embalmed in honey and brought from Egypt, lies like a curious statue in a mass of amber. Its hair and beard are golden, clearly seen through the opaque liquid that preserves them. So the Centaurs are given the fair hair of the North and made as ruddy as the pupils whom they teach. These youths, fresh from the glades of philosophy, are shown the use of the bow, some of the arts of war, and are, perhaps, counselled in the heavier and more galloping metres of poetry by the learning of the Centaurs. But also the Centaurs are shown in their troubles with Hercules.

When Hippodamia married Pirithous, his neighbours, the Centaurs, having drunk too much wine at the marriage-feast, offered violence to the women who were there. This irritated Hercules, Theseus and the rest of the Lapithae, who rescued their women, defeated the Centaurs, and forced them to retire into Arcadia. This was only half of it.

Their insolence was punished a second time by Hercules, who went into Arcadia to hunt the boar of Erymanthus. Here the Centaur Pholus gave him wine to drink, which was the property of the rest of the Centaurs, but had only been allowed to them on condition of their treating Hercules with it whenever he passed through their territory. They resented the liberty that Hercules took with their wine and attacked him with uncommon fury. The hero defended himself, and his adversaries fled for safety to the Centaur Chiron. Chiron had been the preceptor of Hercules, and they hoped that he would desist in his presence. But Hercules, though awed at the sight of Chiron, did not desist, and in the midst of the engagement, wounded his preceptor in the knee, who, in his excessive pain, immediately changed his immortality for death. The death of Chiron irritated Hercules and made him still angrier, and all the Centaurs present were extirpated by his hand. Indeed, but few escaped this common destruction.

All through these scenes Hercules is a fair-bearded giant, a prophecy, in fact, of the Farnese Hercules, who was to be found half a century later in the dust of Caracalla's Thermae. The Centaurs are the same, and are thus portrayed through all their histories, starting at their very origin, which is given, and painted, variously, as the fruit of Ixion's adventure with a cloud in the shape of fair-haired Juno, or more simply, as the procreation of the Centaurs themselves (thus their continuance and not their birth is explained) with the mares of Magnesia.

However this may be, both Hercules and the Centaurs are credited with the fair hair that is my theme, and which we may attribute, in the case of the Centaurs, either to the encounter with a sunlit cloud, its snow being metamorphosed into breasts and limbs belonging to that morning forehead, or to the glistening coats of the mares that had been rubbed, so it seemed, with gold dust.

So universal and uncontradicted is this truth, that it is difficult to find a single figure out of a cassone panel given the dark colouring of the Italians. The ubiquitous gold has triumphed everywhere, in contemporary scenes, and in legends, secular or religious. Nowhere, in this poetry of the house and street, is there one exception to this canon of beauty, and such typical and multitudinous evidence must be accepted in its assertion of what was admired.

Often a tournament has been chosen for subject, and the pages who hold their master's equipment, and who, alone, are not in full panoply of helmet and visor, show the same long heads of yellow curls that are credited to the heroes of Greek legends, to angels fluttered out of the sky, and to youths and maidens walking against the fruit-like domes and lily towers of the town. For this is essentially, at its present stage, the art of Florence and of her subject cities, so that the clean angles of her new buildings and the freshly realized beauties of her hills are never far out of mind, and come into any legend, or any reality, that is pictured.

New bricks and new woodwork with the grain still showing, are two of the most typical things in the spick-and-span, naïf art of Fra Angelico; and most certainly it would be impossible to question this painter's preference for the fair-haired Northern races. So now that smaller world of the cassone panels has been left behind for the great and serious art, of which it was the outcome, and, making a beginning with the mere mention by name of this pious and tranquil genius, we find his ideals of physical beauty in association, always, with an earth that was being reshaped and rebuilt. The Gothick branched into strange leaves and flowers from his hand ; palm-trees and wild-flowers that never grew in the North, and that can only have existed in Kingdoms washing in seas of poetry, in Cyprus or the Counties of Little Asia, grow in his pictures by the side of buildings that have already a hybrid, suspect foreshadowing of change about them. In his figures, not even the beginnings of maturity are in sight, and he paints them as children and not even adolescents, so that none of the curves and bends of beauty are noted and they have only an appealing pathos, without any of the dangerous irritation and enticement that a little flight of time will put into their limbs and faces.

Such changes are already arrived in the figures painted by his pupil, Benozzo Gozzoli, and they are helped still further by his exquisite inventions of trees and hills. The cypress and the pine-tree in a hundred forms break the airs. The flame, or plume-like, male, and the ragged women that make the sexes of the cypress, stand in their groups by pine-trees shaped like a cloud above a crater and as flat and steady as the column of a stylite. Nard and cassia travel down the gales, or must lie, so still are most of the days, in little places where they can always be breathed, so that this certainty might be marked for fair weather on a map. White oxen, yoked together in their pairs, by love as well as duty, tread slowly down the hillside looking before them with lustrous, calm eyes and scenting in their nostrils, if not those spices of the grove, at any rate the warm smell from the bean-fields. Or perhaps it is autumn, when the candle of day has dwindled down to lessened hours and the vines are hung with grapes.

In the distant green valley lie a dozen towns, unless they stand on hills that are bent round into a crown above the horizon. The procession riding through the fresco is a journey of some hours away from any town, and they pick their way carefully through the rocks giving every opportunity for the noting of their richly elaborate dresses. Many of the riders, even, can be recognized, and so their dark hair and burnt features are truthfully given, but whenever children are painted by him, or he is given any latitude for his fancy with angels, heavenly lute-players, young pages, or the blonde daughters of the tyrant, they are painted with the fair hair that was by now the tradition of every beautiful legend.

This is the character of his frescoes in the Riccardi palace, in that wonderful dust-obliterated series at Pisa, and in the box-like compartments into which he poured his poetry at the church of San Gimignano. His art may be also seen at the Umbrian town of Montefalco, which I have never visited, and in an illuminated Livy of the Riccardiana Library at Florence. This must be of extraordinary and rare beauty, and in its probability of trees and flowers should be compared with the minia-ture-paintings by the Persian artist, Bihzad, that were mentioned in an earlier chapter of this book.

The loosening of those classical prose columns of Livy, formed by neat habit like the folds induced by continual wear in a familiar toga, into the wooded hills and terraced vales of Benozzo must be among the strangest transitions of art. The legionaries, turned by the antiquity of their deaths into as many pale statues, lose their stone, forbidding calm and take on the adolescent graces of this idyllic spring. They are made of the earliest and natural poetry of the Mediterranean, but have been painted with the colours of the North. They are few in number, compared with the armies of Roman fact, and their battles are in woods where there are never more warriors than the trees they fight among. This is at a hazard, for I have not seen the manuscript, but imagination pitches their pavilions for me, and all the panoply of serious war, that was associated inevitably in the minds of that time with memories and reports of Crusading armies, shapes itself into Gothick armour. The cedar branches stir with trumpets, rabbits run for their tunnels, and the cloudless day lies more still than ever ; but it is only the silence in which poetry is born, and it is this, and not these tragic truths, that interested the painter. To him, Livy was no historian, and we can part from this invisible book with the assurance that he made those dead pages into a flowering paradise where everyone was young.

By now, the supremacy of this physical type in the imagination is firmly established, and, indeed, its opposite of the normal Italian darkness is usually made use of whenever the forces of evil are portrayed, or this world of idylls has room for a villain to spoil its peace and endanger its safety. Then, the fullest contrast is in this casting of the rôles, and the Gothick type coming out of the uncertain mists of the past is called upon to play the most important part in myths that held a very present and contemporary truth to their beholders.

The most beautiful form that it was possible for the mind of the painter to imagine, or for his hand to make

alive, comes to shore from the summer sea. Her bark is
a cockle-shell that rides upon the waves so that their
lapping in the fluted rills of the shell can be seen. There
is a strange wind in the picture, not strong enough to
cool the day, which does not need it in any case, so mild
is the hour, and this is made visible by the inevitable
manner in which every wave brings the shell nearer to
the coast of sand, and by the disposition of the flowers,
dropped out of the air, and all blowing with one accord
in her direction and toward the shore. She is naked,
and her fair hair, braided into a long tress, climbs over
her shoulder, falls between her breasts and reaches with
its golden strands into her fingers. This was the beauty
of the antique world risen out of the sea and come to
earth once more. It was a symbol that such things had
lived before and that they could be born again.

Not far inland there is an orange-wood, and among its
trees the young men and girls are celebrating the sacred
rites deduced from this arrival upon their shore. The
spring gale, a little brusque and inconsiderate in its
strength, is personified and blows down with distended
lips upon the scene. There is not one Venus, but
several, and three of them, the fair graces, dance hand in
hand through the trees. Another maiden, with her lover
running after her, shakes the fruit and scatters the
blossom no less violently than that figure of the wind.
But more than this must not be said of the picture;
the persons playing in the legend are all characters from
the greatest age of the Mediterranean man, and my
theme must not break down, out of its intention just to
stress upon the inevitable fairness of the types chosen
by the painter, into a long thesis upon that Florentine
world.

It will only be necessary to mention one more picture by this unrivalled genius, and this, being a Christian and not a pagan subject, will prove that the same physical principles were true of both sides of his talent. This picture has a most extraordinary quality of surface approaching the finest lacquer in richness. The interest of it lies in the young girls who simulate angels and hold up, or pull apart, the curtains at the back of the picture. It must be admitted at once that their faces are the most beautiful ever immortalized in this manner, and that they represent what is surely the highest point ever reached in the physical development of the white races, just as certainly as they were chosen from the loveliest children of the greatest age of European art. The form and colouring of this Gothick type has now altered out of its straight strictness, and its pale, or too roughly red, hue of skin, into all the benefits that a genial sun and the blessings of poetry and the arts can give it. From this summit of every beauty of the mind and body nothing but a decadence could follow, and we cannot expect to find the chronicle of such perfections belonging to any other race, or time. It was attained but once, lasting, apparently, only for the childhood of a generation. Already, the hintings of a dangerous heterosexual future are evident, particularly in the young armoured saint in the foreground of the picture, for it is difficult to tell whether he is a boy or girl, and, indeed, his appearance is most easily explained as a boy pretending to be a girl dressed as a boy. His armour shows with intense realism out of the impasto of the picture, and difficult adventures of the spirit lie ahead.

The same traits and the same leanings of nature are to be found in the stern, dry art of Signorelli. He has left only one secular picture, the Pan and Apollo, now in the gallery at Berlin. The goat-god, crowned with the crescent moon above his shaggy hair, sits on a rock with his pipes held ready to play. A naked woman, playing a long shepherd's reed that stretches nearly to the ground, stands beside him, and the naked figure of Apollo is between them with his white back and pale limbs making a contrast with the darker body of Pan. It is a very early morning, lit by both sun and moon, and so new and old in this joining of those two forces of light that this ghostly mythology has an almost probable reality. This is one of the most beautiful paintings ever conceived by mortal mind and of a poetical force and originality that surpasses the powers of description. The painter has wisely chosen, not a wood but a lonely valley full of rocks for his scene; the sort of deserted solitude that only a shepherd could ever know.

There are many naked figures in the background, standing or sitting in positions that the nearness of a river deep enough for bathing in would suggest. They tie, or untie, their sandals, stay still for the air to dry their bodies, or are tired and stretch their limbs, but sleep lies not behind them but ahead of them, for the dawn is their day and the steeper hours hide them and keep them invisible. The heads of fair hair that have been traced all through this history are equally true of this picture, but they are associated with a darker, burnt colour of the limbs. Indeed, in their physical type these figures bear the suggestion that they were taken from the companies of Landsknecht that wandered and fought over Italy in the time of Signorelli. Their fair hair is bleached, as only hair of Teutonic, or Nordic, paleness will bleach, in the strong rays of the Italian sun, and their bodies are

z

blackened in the same unaccustomed manner, as of foreign bathers on an Italian strand. The same thing is true of the naked bodies of the youths that were his excuse and motive for painting the Madonna in the Uffizzi.

Even in his frescoes from the life of St. Benedict, in the cloister of the monastery of San Oliveto Maggiore, the young knights in armour are not of the expected type. It might be imagined that they would approximate to the ordinary Umbrian personality, to the pert, bustling pages in piebald hose, with yellow hair falling to their shoulders and a feather in their caps, as painted by Fiorenzo di Lorenzo in his set of eight panels at Perugia from the life of San Bernardino of Siena. Instead of this, they are of the same marked Teutonic type. They were the only thing that interested Signorelli in these frescoes, for his groups of white Olivetan monks lack any dramatic force and were difficult protagonists on whom to build up an imposing and severe drama. For this reason, only some two or three out of the ten frescoes painted by Signorelli can be said to really show his powers to their full advantage.

The uniforms of his warriors are almost exactly of the date and style of those still worn by the different city-wards of Siena at the celebration of the Palio, but their heads and features are of distinctly Nordic type, fiercely shaved, and alertly loud in bearing. Of the two finest frescoes in this magnificent series, one shows St. Benedict discovering the trick played upon him by Totila, King of the Goths, who, in order to test the saint's wisdom dressed up his shield-bearer, Riggo, in his royal armour and insignia and sent him at the head of a great retinue to visit St. Benedict. The saint at once saw through this trick and ordered him to drop his disguise, a feat of

perception that struck Riggo and his companions with
terror and astonishment. The Gothick warriors are
pinked out in the piebald finery of the time and are huge
giants, taller than any Italian, with long fair hair falling
in masses upon their shoulders. This is sufficiently
indicated by the eloquent phrasing of a book written by
a modern monk of Monte Oliveto, who says of them,
" *masse di biondi capelli sfuggendo da piccoli berretti
cadono sulle loro spalle.*"

The other fresco shows the saint receiving Totila in
audience and prophesying to him that he would enter
Rome, reign as King for nine years, and then die. The
composition is almost identical with that of the preceding
fresco, but the King has been given a more numerous
following and their disposition has been worked out by
the painter with a more convincing phantasy. Two
warriors on horseback are most wonderfully rendered,
and their mail is painted a cold, watery blue, such as this
present age, to whom armour is extinct, have never had
brought before their eyes. The foot-soldiers are no less
gorgeous in their accoutrement, and their Northern hue
and long fair hair are more easily emphasized. The hose
they wear is of white, blue, and red, worn in its alternation on each leg so that the tongues, or flames, of red that
flicker at ankle and knee into the white ground of the
stocking are answered with their equivalent blue at the
knee and ankle of the other leg. Their arms, chests, and
backs are plated, and they wear long swords at their
waists, while the blue steel of their halberds shines
against the rocks above them. For the strangeness of the
landscape round the monastery has inspired the painter
and given him the background for this magpie, piebald
finery.

Monte Oliveto Maggiore is built of bricks made from the red clay of the surrounding hills, that have been worn by wind and rain into a strange, wild roughness all over this huge prospect.   Fierce ridges, only a few hundreds of feet in height, are worked into a whole Himalaya of peaks and chains, and where the feet cannot walk for a few breaths without having to climb up or down these steep and crumbling crevasses, necessity has made a dangerous path, from which not even the modern science of road-making has removed the thrill of danger, along the very summit of the ridge towards the isolated peninsula where the monastery stands.   It may have been some small dell among these rocks that gave Signorelli his occasion for the picture of Pan and Apollo.   The view over this strange region is not like anything else in the world, and this incursion into its midst of Totila and his Goths is as appropriate in its unlikelihood as the more probable flutings of the shepherds, who have been changed by this magical solitude into kings and gods.

It is as strange and remote as the granite hills above the Escurial, which one could imagine as the scene of practice for the military ascetics of that stern, stone Thebaid, had it ever been peopled with the anchorites appropriate to its cold barracks.   There is only one other landscape that has such an inspiring effect upon the workings of the imagination.   This is in the Atlas mountains above Meknes, on the road that passes Azrou.

The forest, where snow is on the ground for more than half the year and wild crocuses and wild peonies grow in abundance between the wide-spaced cedars of Atlas, lies ahead, and this wonderful view comes before the forest begins, when the road has edged imperceptibly towards the edge of a precipice, the plateau dips and collapses, and suddenly half the world lies below you on the right. The vast landscape of this other earth, lying beneath, is revealed, in a second. It is a huge circle rimmed with mountains and filled with great volcanic cones, several of which hold lakes in their cups. It seems impossible that the dead lunar world, thus shown, should contain even a nomad tribe, and its inaccessibility is dramatized by a great eagle, almost as wide as an aeroplane in its wing-spread, that hovers above, patrolling the gale and making sudden descents into the gulf beneath, though these never take it into any near contact even with the peaks of that submerged world, and the eagle is soon floating once more high above this other earth on which we are moving. Indeed, these two earths seem to be rubbing shoulders as if a collision had taken place between them and they were forced to travel along side by side with each other for some space of time, giving a near and unreal view of the improbabilities of this ghostly satellite. These are the three most tremendous settings of nature's scene that it has ever been my fortune to set eyes upon, and this third Thebaid is not the least inspiring of them, though it is the only one of them that has not been given some work of art in temperament with its strangeness.

But smaller worlds, contained all within the compass of the eyes, can be found in which every single detail has been worked into harmony with the mind directing them. Such a one is the Tyranny of Rimini, and since it contains further evidence of my theories we can delay for a moment within its borders. This was the work of Sigismondo Pandolfo Malatesta, and the hard gains of his hired wars were used for its creation. Sigismondo employed the military engineer, L. B. Alberti, for the building of his church, which was conceived on a plan, and within a symbolism that no other mind has ever attempted.(8) It was called after, and designed upon, a temple of the ancient world, but this could only be true of the general lines of its structure, for all the detail was left to craftsmen who had too many of their own ideas, and too little knowledge of anyone else's, to attempt anything but an original creation.

The situation of Rimini on the Adriatic coast opposite Greece facilitated Sigismondo in his Hellenism, and enabled him to procure the bones of a number of Greek scholars and philosophers whom he caused to be buried in sarcophagi that were built into the exterior sides of the temple between its classical bays. This was a very poetical perversion from the saints' bodies necessary to the erection of any Catholic church. A spiritual fragrance of more pleasing odour might be felt to emanate from the dust of such flower-fed minds, and the sanctity of this walled space was no less assured from the crumbled honey, as of asphodel and thyme, that the harmonious mind let linger in this holy air made sacred by death.

Within the church Sigismondo prepared a tomb for himself and his mistress, Isotta degli Atti. This is supported on the backs of four elephants, and imposed upon this symbolism that was, of necessity, Indian in form, the exquisite linear sculptures of the Florentine craftsmen who worked inside the church have attained to something of definitely the same character. Effects quite outside anything else in experience have been reached by them, and these figures of fair-haired maidens, many of them still bearing traces of the original gilding with which they were embellished, carry this dramatization of the legendary North into the furthest regions that it ever arrived at. In this distant place there is something of the surprise and admiration that fair colouring is still greeted with in countries where it is never seen and is as rare as the sight of a black man in the snow. It has become the accepted concomitant of beauty. But, here, its truths are asserted out of the midst of a strange agglomerate of circumstance, for this Italian attempt at the symmetry and balance of Hellenism has found itself carried far beyond those near borders into a kind of Alexandrian India, colonized by that meteoric arrival, and with the conspicuous paleness of the white man given a more telling contrast with the dark races he had subdued by this insistence upon his fair hair. The Indian Kings, glittering in a steady tremolo of gems, and with their swarthy, heathen darkness made emphatic by rich raiment, and by the jewelled turrets put as a throne for them upon the elephant's back, have their tawdry splendour, which is not more strongly hinted at in these sculptures than by the mere showing of the elephant without a sign of its master or attendants, raised into a strong accent of useless extravagance and vain pomp by the absolute simplicity in which this Northern myth is apparelled.

These maidens wear nothing more solid than a shift, hardly patterned, or if at all, with flowers, and its light transparency reveals all the grace of their limbs beneath, and hardly veils the line of their bodies. A ruthless economy of effort has brought them into being, but this rises, not from an exhausted imagination, but out of the depthless and brimming wells of poetry, which ran with so strong an inspiration that in their haste to hurry on to the next thing the craftsmen strived for the most rapid and simple expression of the images flowing from their

hands. They were born with a natural and easy beauty
that had nothing difficult about its shape, and the wind
playing with their gowns billowed them into folds that
ran smoothly with the blown sails, curved beaches, and
the heads of foam shaken from the waves, and drew them
into a natural parallel with the round fruits of the cornucopia, the sheafs of corn, and the whole landscape
trembling into a line that summed up its distance.

These are queer products for what is, without dispute,
one of the most complete tyrannies in history. We find
the ideals born out of five centuries of Northern chivalry
occupying a quite decisive share in this formation of
physical principles, and these types of their admiration
are fully borne out in the heads of hair, dramatically
curbed and thickened, that appear on the beautiful
medals designed for this state by the great Pisanello.
If any further proof of this contention is needed, it may
be found in the portrait coming from a state whose
capital is not more than fifteen miles away from Rimini.
This is the portrait by Piero della Francesca of Battista
Sforza, Duchess of Urbino, the daughter of the tyrant
of Pesaro, and wife of the Condottiero Federico, Duke
of Urbino. This is the greatest presentment of a Gothick
aristocrat that has ever been achieved. Her fair hair,
tapering hands, and high-bridged nose, epitomize everything that history, or the imagination, could tell about
this type of person, and they are related in this instance
by an artist whose partiality lay in other directions and
who had no trace of feudality in his attitude, which
merely reported truthfully this thing lying before his
eyes. The wonderful landscape on the back of the panel
where the Duchess and her husband are drawn in a
chariot by unicorns, with emblematical figures accom-

panying them, through a romantic plain hemmed in by
hills, completes that extraordinary appearance by lifting
it into another age and making it belong to the plays of
Dekker, or of Roberto Greene. In the distance we may
imagine the new castle of Urbino, built by her husband
and herself, and into which it is now too late for us to
enter. That is the first palace built with no room for
ghosts in its dark corners, being the most beautiful expression of sanity, and of necessary and indispensable beauty,
that the hands of men have ever contrived. The glories
of its doorways, its mantelpieces, and its ceilings are
triumphs that no other age, or race, has ever approached ;
and we see the physical embodiment of all that the fair-
haired races accomplished working in their seclusion
without the help of the Italian, enshrined, now, in the
culmination of those opposite, Italian principles.

It may be found in lesser degree, but only because
this is the supreme instance of their stage-craft, everywhere that the Italian genius found its patrons. After
Urbino, the most beautiful palace is that of Mantua,
but here a change of proportion has come over the scheme,
due, we may imagine, to the finding of the Farnese
Hercules, and to the fulfilment of that giant canon of
strength in the bearded, lusty Teutons of the Imperial
army that sacked Rome in 1527, and who were on the
march through Italy for a generation to come. As might
be expected, the beginnings of this muscular distortion
were in Rome. Their strange effect, which is less peculiar
to eyes that have grown used to the monumental females
of Picasso's pictures, the dark sisters of this fair Hercules,
who bathe or play on the shores of the blue Mediterranean, was soon allowed an architectural setting to
accord with its inflated scale. The halls and corridors

of the Palazzo Farnese were designed by Michelangelo
for persons of this size and importance.* A dismantled
guardroom is still shown with high coffered ceiling of
cypress wood designed by the hand of the master, and
here a dozen of these monsters may be imagined sleeping
in the dim aureole thrown by a lantern set high in the
wall; the noise of their breathing seems to fill the room,
and the light catches the blades of their halberds that
lean, tall as flagstaffs, against the sides of the hall.

From this, it was an immediate step into the gardens
of the time, where this huge scale, and the natural silence
of such giants, suggested their facile transference into
sylvan deities and water-gods. Caprarola, the summer
castle of the Farnese, and Villa Lante, near Viterbo,
are two examples of this. The gardens at both these
places were designed by Vignola, and, in either place,
the stone gods recline wearily at their duties, grown over,
now, by moss and lichen. Water still drips from their wide
mouths, opened as if in invocation, or pours from their
urns. Their scale has exalted them out of the ordinary
nicety of the floral world into something that is really
elemental. Their majestic and overwhelming sadness,
giving birth, none the less, to laughing water and nodding
flowers, is a thing that the mind can never forget and
this solemn poetry that they produce leads without any
undue emphasis, at Caprarola, to the terraced garden at
the summit of the hill which is ringed round with the
statues of the twenty-four choephoræ, fauns who carry
baskets of fruits and flowers upon their heads, and whose

---

* The Palazzo Farnese was begun in the first years of the sixteenth century
by Sangallo the younger for Cardinal Farnese, afterwards Pope Paul III. When
Sangallo died Michelangelo carried on the work, and Bramante, Giacomo della
Porta, and Vignola, all had a share in its construction.

parted lips, with the varying expression of their sinister features, seem to make them sing or speak to each other in some undertone that the hour of day will not allow to be audible.

To their protection these fair-haired giants have been doomed, who are never allowed away from their posts and have assumed, because of this, something of the ferocity of the watch-dog who is never allowed off his chain. They are a little frightening in their silence, and their quiet persistence. Some among them are so worn by the rains and winds of time that they keep only the rough resemblance to features that a hill may have, whose rocks must be looked at a long time before the face coming out of them can be seen. Their feet and hands are broken, the stone clubs they hold are cracked and fallen, and their urns and cornucopiæ flourish with the secondary and desert growths of the damp, with trailing ferns, and parasite moss and lichen. Water falls from them and runs down its prepared channels of twisted stone, with purposeful impediments put in its course and down its bed, so as to vary the noise of waters and make them more melodious and of a richer compass. This perpetual dirge is at any rate a more beautiful accompaniment to these dying giants than anything that the chatter and bawled information of a museum-room can provide; but the Gothick colours and the other, supporting inspiration, as of Totila and his Goths, pictured in the frescoes described not far back, that confirmed and governed their creation into this stone reality, has by now left them, long ago, so that they seem the uncertain works of an age that no knowledge can help to identify.

The rumours of these things were soon dissipated far

and wide from Rome and were carried to Mantua by Giulio Romano. This neglected painter and architect had the greatest renown in his generation and even won the curious fame of being the only painter that Shakespeare mentions by name. His architectural skill, which later generations have nearly ignored, is evident all over the city of Mantua, and he was the most fervent apostle of these giantist principles. This is evident in the twelve giant caryatids with whom he decorated the façade of the Palazzo di Giustizia, and is made more manifest still in the courtyard for tournaments, called the Cortile della Cavallerizza, in the Palazzo Ducale.* This huge affair, with its twisted pillars and its balconies looking over the lagoons, is calculated to show off the struggles, not of ordinary horses and men, but of that family of giants. Because of their impossibility and non-existence, the opposite extreme of height became a curiosity that the wealth of the Gonzaga could easily collect. The Mantuan dwarves, bred in the palace for buffoons and pets, had their own apartments designed by Giulio Romano, with tiny doors and low ceilings suited to their stature; which, after all, must have seemed as improbable, and as far removed from ordinary humanity, as the non-existent giants to whose scale these greater buildings were accommodated.

In his frescoes, Giulio Romano showed the same predilection for this bolstered majesty, induced, perhaps a little too easily, from girth and muscle. Out of so much

---

* It is impossible in this reference not to draw attention to the palace of Charles V on the Alhambra hill at Granada. This, and the delightful fountain in the Alhambra Park, were the work of Pedro Machuca (d. 1550), a native of Granada, educated at Rome. The magnificent colonnaded circular court of the palace, and the sculptured doorways of the façade, are entirely in the Mantuan manner and are worthy of Giulio Romano.

that was designed by him it is difficult to deduce a particular instance, but the Sala di Troia is certainly a conspicuous example. Here, his principles have found an easy subject in the Wooden Horse. This incident has been lifted easily into the epical region, though the plumed warriors are fully as big as the animal that was to carry them, and it is not easy to imagine how even a single one of them could find room for himself in that hollowed belly. These heroic protagonists are all alike gifted with the fair hair that we should expect of them, and, indeed, by this time another influence that tended to make this a certainty was in operation. But that must be considered shortly, when this Mantuan splendour has been sufficiently described. For these different episodes from the Iliad reveal the utmost extension of all the conventions that this heroic subject could inspire in a painter. Furious battles are in progress which are doomed for ever to remain indecisive. White stallions, chosen specimens, no doubt, from the famous Mantuan stud, draw the chariots into the thick of the fight, and the crested helmets give a tragic dignity to their wearers. Those ancient wars were without the weapon of fire, and so fine summer trees blow uninjured over the scene and the boughs throw a trembling shade upon the dying. They have been granted perpetual sunny weather for their combats, broken only by clouds, that make a pretty echo to the white stallions reared up with snorting nostrils in their arrested speed.

These points of interpretation are carried still further in the Palazzo del Té, the summer villa of the Gonzaga, designed by Giulio Romano and built just outside the town. There are two rooms here that deserve our particular attention. In the first of them the pupils of Giulio Romano have painted under his direction the six favourite horses of Federico Gonzaga. These have a monumental, rather unpleasant importance, and have been emphasized as if they made a dramatic occasion and were not merely the pet animals of their master. They mark the first arrival in the land of Brobdingnag, and are part of the reactions of a painter's overworked nervous system that gives undue prominence to inanimate, or at any rate dumb, objects. This same neurotic fatigue, in our own generation, has given us the swollen hands in certain of Picasso's figures, the inflated forms of one whole period of his work, and the lay figures, sensitive chairs and tables, and spectral statues, with whose help Giorgio de Chirico has formed his most individual mannerisms.

Passing through a room with a frieze of Roman soldiers on the march, and another room frescoed with four battles of Centaurs, Amazons, and Tritons, we come to the second of our two objects. This is called the Sala dei Giganti. Walls and ceiling, alike, are frescoed with the Battle of the Giants, drawn by Giulio Romano and coloured under his supervision by three of his pupils. The giants are in rebellion against Jupiter, and huge rocks, uptorn trees, and the terrors of thunder and lightning are the weapons in use. This room was finished in 1532, and the discovery of the Farnese Hercules eight years later must have come as a curious justification of its apparent eccentricity. The peculiarities of it were made the more observable, as I have hinted, by the dwarves of the palace, who were no further removed from the normal scale than these men fifteen feet high. The usual tendency to still further blacken a villain's character by painting him dark and swarthy is very noticeable, while the stronger the poetic association the more certain is it that its embodiment will be allowed fair hair and Northern colouring. In fact, the North now begins to be the home from which poetry comes forth.

The lesser and dependent Gonzaga Duchies have the same things to show, but reduced in a proportionate scale. The model town of Sabbioneta, the creation of Charles V's general, Vespasiano Gonzaga (1531–1591), has the same equine interest in its palace, but these frescoes, and that statue, are more truly simple in their appeal and have lost the strange flavour of their original. The actual town of Gonzaga, the ancient seat of an independent marquisate of the family down till the year 1737, has a bronze statue by Leone Leoni in its market-place of Ferdinando Gonzaga (d. 1559) trampling down envy and rebellion, symbolized by a satyr who struggles under his feet. The general wears the kilt of a Roman Emperor, and this strange statue in that crowded market-place is a most typical example of the complicated imagery that had become the jargon and the ordinary conversation of the time.

Just beyond the Po valley, and its Gonzaga Duchies, the town of Piacenza has the last two specimens of this cult that we need pause to investigate, in the shape of a pair of statues of horsemen, again in its market-place. These represent Alessandro and Ranuccio Farnese ; and they have over and above those qualities that we should by now expect of them, a new and final interest of a double origin. For the costume of these two cavaliers is decidedly Spanish in its fashion, a trait which is no longer puzzling when it is remembered that Cremona is near Milan, that had been for a long period under Spanish rule. And there is, also, it may be thought, some echo of the statues of the Can Grande and his family at Verona. These horsemen, high upon their tombs, with their persons altogether hidden in plate armour so that even the horse has trappings down to his feet, until the tyrant's person is only recognizable by his armour and the badge above his shield, these are direct spiritual ancestors of this later pair of cavaliers, garbed more for conspiracy than tyranny, and with cloak and plumed hat doing duty for shield and visor. They are of the date and style of Callot and form an admirable assurance as to his truth of observation regarding the Spanish pomp and braggadocio of that epoch. The wind from the street corner fills out their sleeves and scarves into lines much more suggestive of the tattered rags of war than the billowy curves and blown-out insolence of Bernini's marble. Their dressed hair, and the starched Spanish collars that they wear, are modelled upon the Habsburg Court dress, so that we can see a suggestion of the blanched skins and flaxen locks of the Austrian race coming into these statues. Gothick features and dynastic chins were an anachronism of the seventeenth century, influencing all its history till the invention of the periwig gave birth to another age. In their flattery of imitation this pair of statues bear out that survival of mediaeval appearance, and they have, therefore, a belated contingency to my subject.*

But, by now, the predilection of the Italians for the Northern type, and its consequent fixation as the ideal

---

* Alessandro Farnese was the son of Ottavio Farnese and Margaret of Parma, natural daughter of the Emperor Charles V. Ranuccio was the son of Alessandro. This explains their Habsburg appearance. The statues of this brother and nephew of Phillip II are by Francesco Mocchi of Tuscany, and their date is 1620-1625.

had become definitely and for ever established.* The
town in which this was decided was Venice, which has
always had among its population a certain proportion
of fair, or red-haired, inhabitants, but it was the second
generation of great painters who achieved this, and even
then we must only associate it with two among them,
Veronese and Palma Vecchio. The Venetian women
who had red hair were in the habit of bleaching it into
as flaxen a condition as possible by exposing their heads
to the sun in a very wide-brimmed hat from which
they cut out the crown, allowing their hair to come out
through this, and only keeping the broad rims of the hat
for a protection to their necks and faces. This explains
the exaggerated paleness of hair in Palma Vecchio, more
especially in his portraits at Vienna, and in the group of
three women, supposed to be his daughters, at Dresden.
The latter picture, so unfashionable from a contemporary
point of view, is of the deepest interest in what it reveals
of the life and admirations of its period.

The reputation of Venice for intrigue and gallantry
was brought about by these soft colossi, wide-bosomed,
and requiring of their lovers energetic dispute and
dangerous jealousies among themselves in keeping with
the ardent courtship necessary to keep them amused
and attentive. The poems these three sisters must have
had by heart, and the songs they sang to the vibrating
lute, will have been of a pungent subtlety as strongly

* Its essential untruthfulness to what really lived in their midst is best exemplified in the paintings of Caravaggio. There is not a single person with fair
hair among the gallants and contadini who were his models ; but Caravaggio
worked in Rome, Naples, Sicily, and Malta, and shows no direct influence of
the Venetian school. On the other hand, the most particular contradiction
to this reality is to be found in the painting of Correggio, who, for the blond
prettiness of his types, might well be contemporary with Mr. Ziegfeld and the
Film Corporations.

flavoured as the sweetmeats, eaten in quantity, and responsible for some flaccidity in their physical shape. It may be imagined that the three of them together, walking on their high pattens, will have filled any Venetian alley and captured the high instep of each bridge they came to. Their reflections, leaning over the parapet into the weedy mirror below, came back to them and seemed in the beating sunlight like a group of parhelions settled on the water, or wherever the eyes look, after a mistaken catch of sun from looking up at some window cusped with Gothick fire above its openings. Or they may be thought of in a boat charged with fruit from the mainland crossing the limpid sky of the lagoons that echo every cloud in their shallows.

Their gallantry, parcelled into three divisions, occupied all the dark shadows of the house. If, as is probable, they were courtesans, foreign visitors of importance will have been sent to see them under police instruction as to their charges and conduct. Their culture and learning are, by this, the more assured, and the freedom of their profession made them into friends and models for the painters of the town without the ordinary and difficult trammels surrounding such association. Every circumstance helped to make this easy, and the gondoliers had rope-ladders which they mentioned to strangers and then hired out, so that the primitive embarrassment and explanation necessary at a door could be dispensed with by a quick climb in at the window.

If we leave these large heroines and look for their equivalent in the pictures of Veronese, we find a difference in essentials, for his women have all the virtues of parade and tenure as though they had been raised from the earliest age to be hostesses, and to take their places in a

cloudy pageantry designed for their display. The arts
of the theatre and of music could not yet effect an
apotheosis, so that this had to be brought about by the
alternation between rounded arms, deep bosoms, coiled
and gilt hair, and the gorgeous brocades and damasks
that were the product of Venice, and of which Veronese
is known to have kept a large wardrobe constantly by him
for this purpose. Perhaps this side of his art is best
seen where it is least expected, and the little church
of San Sebastiano, at Venice, which is entirely filled
with his paintings will reveal his method and its practice
to a better advantage than his work in the Doge's Palace,
or the great scenic compositions in Paris and Dresden.
His contemporary fame, down to the dispersion of Venice
at the hands of Napoleon, rested chiefly upon the four
banqueting scenes, or " Cene," great machineries painted
at the ends of refectories. The first of these, the Marriage of Cana, painted for the refectory of S. Giorgio
Maggiore, is now in the Louvre ; the second, the Call
of St. Matthew, was painted for the refectory of SS.
Giovanni and Paolo ; the third was the Feast of Simon
in the Church of S. Sebastiano ; and the fourth, of the
same subject, was painted for the refectory of the Servi,
but was sent to Louis XIV and placed at Versailles.
The background of architecture in all of these is due to
his friendship with Palladio, and it was when these two
men came into a close contact that restrained the
luxuriant imagination of the first, while it coloured and
enriched the fugal, dry fancy of the second, that both of
them produced their master-work.

This fortunate mating of two talents was responsible for
several villas of the Venetian nobles, and we may bid
farewell to our subject in those porticoes. They were

designed by two of the finest, and ultimate, minds of the
Renaissance as a shell to contain this physical type that we
have followed to such lengths through history.   In all,
there are about a dozen villas that Palladio designed
upon the Venetian terra firma, and Veronese painted the
frescoes and decorations in about half of these.   His
pupil and associate, Zelotti, helped him in some of them
and worked by himself in others ; while a great sculptor,
Vitoria, the friend of both architect and painter, embellished more than one villa with his work.

Out of all these houses it will be sufficient to speak of
the Villa Maser, or Giacomelli, where all three artists
worked together.   Let it be known, once and for all,
that this is the most beautiful private dwelling ever
produced by the genius of the white races !   It satisfies
every luxury of the mind and senses without distortion,
enervation, or luxury.   It has dignity without pomposity,
unstinted beauty, the solid poetries of volume and
proportion, and the association of great artists working
together within pleasant limits of smallness.   There
is no extravagance in scale or in material, no ruin of the
client, and no unwillingness, or inability, on his part ever
to finish the project put before him.   This is the last
alien home into which we can pursue the altered embodiment of all the qualities we set out to discover and
preserve, and it must be admitted that, by now, all things,
except the mere fallacies of pigmentation, have changed.

All the delights of harmony are in the very plan of
the villa.   The cornice, bold and judiciously sufficient ;
the doorway, just dramatic enough, and giving no unlikely emphasis to the figures that were to pass in and
out of it ; the aerial elaboration of the frescoes, letting
light into the room with a field, a flashing fountain, or

the coolness of a hill, or bringing the blank spaces of the wall into reality with a dog, a man in livery, or the image of some member of the family; these things are the privacies of each room, for there is hardly one of them that has not been given this consideration by painter and architect. They worked here during the summer and early autumn of each year when the canals were dry and stagnant, so that something of this recreation and holiday has entered into each conception, and governed its creation into these planned and painted fictions. The plain colonnade of the exterior, and the answering portico of the church that they designed, express very well the needs of this hot weather, for the pale shadows of white upon white seem to be contrived especially for a day unbroken by clouds and with nothing better for shade than cypress and plane tree.

The real persons dwelling in this paradise as guests were the senators of the Republic. Portraits by Titian and Tintoretto have preserved the image of these dark-bearded men in their robes of office, curtained from the sea, more often than not, by a drapery of red or green. There is a frugal magnificence about their bearing and manner, a luxury of externals which the Palladian Villas confirm and make evident. But poetic optimism intended a different population, and of this we can find idea and suggestion in the sculpture. In order to sur-mount its stint and economy, for in the Villa Maser the delights of necessity have been made use of to whet the appetite, and none of the three artists concerned have put their clients in any danger of a surfeit, it is important to think of this sculptor's more elaborate opportunities, and the occasion for these was in the Doge's Palace. There, it is not possible to doubt the nature of the ideal figures with whom he and his friends would have liked the numbers in the villa to have been swelled. They are distinctively of the Northern race, with no doubt left open as to this by the argument of their hair, which is coloured. Thus, an almost entirely alien population was requested, for people of genuine fair hair were most uncommon, being of no greater frequency than the usual proportion of red-haired persons in every race.

By this time, the creations of Ariosto and Tasso had made this orientation towards the North more certain, and had put into permanence the legends upon which it was supported. This is the least understood among all the channels into which the waters of the Renaissance ran. By a sudden and strange reversal of fortune the North became the source from which poetry flowed forth, and the Italians no longer looked to Greece, or into their own midst, for inspiration. This dramatic change of direction had a final importance in establishing the Northern type as desirable canon and fixed ideal of physical beauty. The influences of this poetry are most visible in the paintings of Dosso Dossi, a citizen of Ferrara and the countryman of Ariosto. He was much employed by Alphonso and Ercole II, Dukes of Ferrara, and, in his pictures, this turn about of interest towards the mythology and chivalry of the North is very clearly portrayed. There is a sighing after the mysteries of a dead age that had become extinct almost within the memory of living men. But these two poets, out of all the great names that were once a power in Europe, are the least read; although their predominance lasted for at least a century and a half after their deaths, and it should not be possible in picture, book, or tapestry, to see a curtain corded into a tree giving shade to an armoured warrior without thinking of the epics of chivalry that made this so familiar a convention.

The walls of Troy had burned down quite into the ground, and the triremes flashed their oars on other seas. The mediaeval mingling of names, when Troy and Jerusalem were joined into one epoch, came true again, for the armies of the North now marched into the sun for a set of wars as tiring and ineffective as the Trojan series, yet poet and painter armed his warriors as for the Greek wars, since the heroic costume, apparently, knew no changes and always kept its rigours of convention. So this poetry, of Northern origin, was poured into a classical mould, and we find these fresh heroes and their women domiciled in the porticoes and colonnades of Palladio.

Here, as I have said, we must bid farewell to them. This Italian, or other half of the European world, devoting itself more to things of the spirit than to commerce and prosperity, had ended by assuming to itself a physical inferiority to the shadows out of a colder sun. The very age, then, that surrendered the management of its arts to Italy, gave these hostages, that dwelt in the midst of the Italian ferment and influenced every idea and concept that came out of it.

A new and triumphant vindication came with the arrival of Rubens. He was the first man, of non-Italian race, able to co-ordinate his schemes into the great and intricate machinery of Veronese. But, in order to do this, an unimaginable physical vitality had to be shared out among his figures, and a quality, typical, almost, of the circus-tent weighed them out of the ordinary terrestrial plane into capacity with his plans for them. The noise and speed of his hunting of the wild-boar must have shaken the woods and brakes; while the Sabine women raped from their husbands demanded an appetite, on the part of all three parties concerned, such as has never existed, and that no climate could stimulate into activity. His finest work, the altar-piece of the Nuptials of St. Catherine with the Infant Jesus, in the church of St. Augustine at Antwerp, is a composition of such magnitude as no other painter has ever achieved. Its ascending and returning spirals are seen from the door of the church long before the figures can be made out, but they give the exact impression of the drama that is going on, just as an accident, or men fighting, can be guessed in their action and purposes while they are still too far off to be identified. On coming nearer to the high altar, this tremendous ceremony is manifested while in movement; the figures are not so still, posed in positions made lively and moving by the gorgeous silk and brocade of their dresses, as with Veronese. Nor is the melodrama of thunder and darkness, of figures jumping in and out of the picture with startling and correcting aim, as if thrown in these directions by the force of some blow or missile, made use of in order to intensify the story, after the manner of Tintoretto.

But the liveliest parade, and the climax of his invention, is the Galerie Medicis of the Louvre. Indeed, this is the apotheosis of Celt and Teuton, and it sums up every quality and advantage of the race, contrasted to the Latins. This overpowering conception, filling a huge hall with great scenes painted out of its walls, represents the whole Renaissance dragged back into the North by the power and personality of one man. It has been done, too, without the attractive theatrical trickery of the Italians, a thing about them which stultifies and at last diminishes their value, so that, in the " Cene " of Veronese, the chickens, eggs, and bread upon the table begin to appal by the counterfeit of their present-ment, and finish by reminding the eyes of the wax-works of the Sacro Monte at Varallo. Instead of this, the incidentals, the furnishings of the scenes, are of a more fluid importance, made subservient to the figures. As to the blonde character of all the protagonists who could not be argued with historical certainty to be dark, it is omnipresent and incontestable. The supernumeraries are allowed no other choice but this, and the victory of the fair-haired race is secure and unquestioned.

It is celebrated in its last phase by Tiepolo, whose style, founded out of Veronese and Rubens, was calculated from its very origins towards this end. But his adapta-tion omitted their heaviness. The heroic qualities that first appeared in the Trojan scenes of Giulio Romano, two centuries before, attains in him to the climax of its splendour ; that heap of dead names which Dr. Burney terms the Augustan period of music (singers like Faustina, Cuzzoni, Farinelli, composers like Hasse, Leo, Jomelli) ; the poetry of Dryden and Pope and their foreign con-temporaries ; architects, including even Sir Christopher Wren ; all these different phases of that lapse of time are set forth and expressed in his frescoes. He was the finest artist of his century, and, even now, his eminence and merit are not recognized at their true value. He marks the last and greatest contingency to my theme, as all eyes will know that have ever seen the banquet of Cleopatra in the Labia Palace, or the staircase and Kaisersaal at Würzburg. In these works the choice and predilection of his line of painters for the Northern, non-Italian races, is proved over and over again, just before the death of this long-lived school.

The Queen landing from her barge, attended by a page of her race, and then seen at the banquet with Antony, is my contention, made alive and personal. The balcony of musicians, the Egyptian obelisk, the cypresses and statues, the crowd of Moors and Roman soldiers, all these accessories give point and emphasis to my argument. This is further advanced by the ceiling of the great stair at Würzburg, where the four quarters of the globe, each given one wall of the ceiling to itself, are contrasted with the nymphs and goddesses of Olympus who occupy the whole heavenly vault. The marriage of Barbarossa which is the subject of his frescoes in the Kaisersaal is, by its very nature, of the same scope. So this expiring Italian art, for nothing more was to come after this, celebrated these virtues of the North with its dying breath.

The fresco of Apollo riding his chariot in the clouds, which occupies the ceiling of the Kaisersaal above the panels of the red-bearded Emperor in his nuptials, is perhaps the most beautiful abstraction of nude figures ever painted by this master. It has a physical poetry that no imagination can surpass, and we may finish our vindication and alarm among those clouds and in that unencumbered air. The chariot is axle-deep in cloud, and, as though this were Neptune and his mermen, the nymphs break their number in every direction and pose themselves upon, or against, the wind. It is this, and not the elemental air, that supports them, and the sum of their different attitudes depends upon its stream and rides sunwards with the painting of the chariot. The whole affair depends for its focus and correct perspective upon a corner of cloud caught on to the ceiling, which gives it all the scale it has and is as useful for this purpose as the string between a kite and the person flying it. But every inhabitant of this air is given the fair colouring essential to the abstract element in which the god and his attendants dwell.

This was a rule never contradicted. Many years later, in a book of letters from Naples and the Campagna Felice published in the year of Waterloo, there is one particular aquatint, among the illustrations by Rowlandson, that deserves our attention. It depicts a public letter-writer at his stall surrounded by a bevy of seven young women who are availing themselves of his presence to send messages to their lovers. The background is filled with an admirable screen of palaces and churches, so typical of Naples, though apparently the artist never visited the town, that it is probable a print of one of the chief streets was copied by him to give an air of veracity to his drawing. In opposition to this careful accuracy of the caricaturist the whole of that group of young women have been drawn and coloured in his usual manner, giving them the fair hair that would have made them an object of curiosity, and, indeed, of persecution, had they made an authentic appearance on the scene.

But this piece of carelessness on his part would seem to be not unjustified if any ceiling or painted wall in church or palace were examined for the same evidence. The school of painters associated with Luca Giordana and Solimena were apparently of the same opinion as the English caricaturist, and the dark Neapolitan reality was altogether ignored by them. These are among the last works of the old European art, and they show the permeation of this ideal into the alien South, where it was as foreign as a fall of snow.

The Italians, who lived through the eighteenth century in a poverty and untidiness like that in the studio of an unsuccessful painter, old furniture and bric-à-brac, carved frames, pieces of brocade, were sensible of this Northern superiority, physical and material. And they had the testimony to this effect of nearly every artist who had worked among them. This, then, was a shadowy, unprofitable victory, winning back some kind of renown against the breakdown of all the architecture and life of the North in favour of the new inventions coming out of Italy. For without wealth or conspicuous power, the Italians had made a spiritual conquest over the great kingdoms lying to the north of the mountains, but they acknowledged the greater resources of their enemy and paid this tribute to the strength they had subdued.

As to the efficacy of these principles in the countries most concerned at their greatest period, it will only be necessary to point for an example to the Elizabethan age in England. This was the only time in our history when the aristocrats proved their purpose and produced the writers, poets, and military or naval leaders, whom it was the duty of their wealth and leisure to provide against this privilege. The miniatures of Hilliard, that give an almost complete picture of the Court of Elizabeth, contain an overwhelming preponderance of fair hair, and as this class lost its caste, and its Norman blood was dispersed, it can be argued that they lost with it all their talents and everything that made their privilege defensible. Thus, the thinning of the Gothick strain meant the loss of the isolation and peculiarity of their race.

So we come back to the first effects that the North

produced upon strangers to its history, and the claim of
this ancient chivalry is at least reinforced by evidence
of the homage paid to it by painters. We find the gold
backgrounds of the primitives fading with new invention
into a mere halo, which circles a head of hair not much
less gilded than that mark of sanctity. Those in whom
virtue and beauty were supposed to dwell were given,
inevitably, this attribute; and the secular legends
moving up behind the religious, preserved the same
qualities and allowed a similar licence of improbable
appearance to their heroes. A chain of instances has
been given, and this Italian flattery of the North has
been proved in all its examples. Two chapters : on the
tapestries that were the greatest product of long winters,
and upon the monasteries that were the most ambitious
practitioners of architecture, and to whom nearly all
mediaeval building is due, are now confirmed and coloured
in an account of how this energy impressed the great
artists who conquered it.

Alas ! now, both these ages are dead ; the one of them
not being more remote from us than the other A third
has been laboriously begun, mostly in poverty and
persecution, with only the posthumous honours of the
sale-room to comfort men who died in defeat. Till the
present, painters and writers of fiction have been its only
progenitors, and the much more needed architects,
musicians, and poets have worked little anarchy and no
construction. For their inspiration, the past must build
up its store of anecdote in a new accumulation of imagery,
and this has been the only purpose, though but half the
pleasure, of my pages. But now these old ruins must be
left cold and empty once more, for the sound of voices,
and a lighted window, beckon us back to the living.

III

FINALE

AND what has been the use of it all ? The uncertain mists, resolved for a time into something
no more solid than the mirage on a plain, hold
nothing, and have nothing left. The quivering distance
we imaged into an elbow of sea, shining, now here, now
there, with no more burden than its shallows, scarcely
deep enough to sail upon. Lying above it, we carved a
cliff of chalk, and upon that a castle hung with gossamer
histories. The shore below this had an infinity of shells,
freshly strewn by the morning sea. These crackled as
each step destroyed them. It was more idyllic than any
field of grass, while, far away, making a more substantial
poetry, the skeleton of a whale lay like a great ship, and
its timbers were falling apart in the salt wind.

Behind the castle, the dells were full of deer. The
clashing of their antlers sounded like a battle of wooden
swords. As for the hounds, they ran baying through
the woods, with red tongues lolling from their mouths.
Trumpets and horses could hardly be heard for those
clamouring throats. The haunting of the woods was
after this nature, for what the sleepless dreaded to hear
was the winding of a horn in the moonlight. No adventure by day could explain this terror from the hanging
wood.

Then the moon climbed above that bank of trees and the walls of the castle shone out at once, as does marble if water is dashed upon it. But the shadows became more sombre still from this milk of the moonlight poured upon their flesh of black. A high tower could have topped the tree-cliff, and its bells would sound out clearly over the forest. Wherever the noise of bells could reach to had some measure of spiritual safety, and the dangers of darkness were dispelled, or at any rate warned off in such manner. The sacred colleges mumbled their youth away to this same purpose, and the noddings of dotage had an identical meaning.

That was one side of life, and for the other, steep doorways, borrowed from the church, rose to a point in their height as though to allow passage to plume and tiara. These brushed against, or clattered upon, the Gothick arch, while those more familiar figures from playing-card and chess-board reached only to the breadth of the door before it narrowed into character. This is our universal ancestry, and who has not shared in it, has at any rate seen these things with his unborn eyes, scaled through many incarnations till the present realities of touch and sound have been reached. These are fabulous and legendary truths, differing, because of this, from the intangible, unrelated past of Angkor or the Parthenon, dead things that have always been alien to us.

Every dawn puts that distance further behind us, till what is called the Middle Ages, lying half way between the start of the Christian religion and the present, will soon be a long way to one side of that watershed of time. Then, but little of the sleepy past of street and church will be left to us, and poetry will have to find new dwellings for its adepts. But, when that happens, this strange fermentation of the spirit, which is unquenchable, and which seems to live more especially in our own race, must find inevitably, a fresh direction for the relief of its agonies and pleasures. Even the age in which this beauty was rediscovered now seems dusty and remote from us, nearly invested with an antiquity of its own. To look at it through the eyes of the brother and sister I created for this end is to experience, for this reason, a double set of emotions. Such, apparently, are the only uses of the past, and its traces can have lasted for no other end than this, that they should sharpen our sentiment and put the fiction of life into things irremediably dead.

I could have taken my pair of witnesses with me wherever I went, but the sum of their saddening enthusiasm would have brought me to ground long before my wings were exhausted. So it was better they should stay away; and we can find them, where they have so often been found before, in the orchard at the back of that village inn, or behind the mullions in a lighted room.

The men and women out of that past are as children to us with our mechanical inventions, but we are in the same stature to them, dwarfed before their giant eminence where the poetry of the senses is concerned. Therefore, not only is antiquity sad because it is so old, ageing a little even as we think of it, but, also, its living force was something that we have missed. The massed effects and properties of those expired centuries give the illusion of something existing parallel to, but divided from, ourselves. It is the very world in which we want to live, lying near to us, but impossible to touch, or be in communion with; separated from us, so it seems, by some barrier whose nature we cannot either define, or overcome. Thus, its whole total is, in a sense, contemporary with us, and yet by no effort can we break into its area, and it is kept away from us by some infrangible rule that neither body nor mind can contradict.

It is easy enough to personify this loss. The casting for its characters need go no further than the fair-haired sept whose various energies this book has been written to celebrate. In a sense it is a sisterhood of Ophelias, for this nunnery encloses a race, all alike, and of one pattern. The thin distension and elaboration of their form is as though they were only to be seen through a film of water, which has combed back their long, flat hair with its weedy fingers and pressed their whole symmetry into its own limpid convenience. The fine hands, pale as milk and tapering to the nail-points, seem to have been rubbed with honey from the dropped flowers floating on the stream, or from the lilies that live of their own volition upon the waters. If the hair is not blonde and fluid, then it is coiled into some water-fixity after the pattern left by a rilled shell upon wet sand. These will be ornaments to the shells of each ear. As to the mind hidden behind this chastity and its defences, the very extent of its shortcomings is an absorbing mystery, which becomes still stranger on investigation. Then, this veil between ourselves and the past is lifted a little, but only to that point of comprehension which might be reached if speech was only possible with the eyes and any understanding of the lips was still forbidden. But no further point than this is ever arrived at, and, here, only half-way into words, this communion is interrupted and can never be improved into permanence.

The body of this beautiful and strange mystery lies so close to us that we can feel the warm emanation coming

B 2

from it, but our eyes, the only contact we have with it, never tell us of any change, though such lover's blindness is unwarranted and the gradual, slow decay of this ideal should be visible even to ourselves. If this is not so, it must be because of the inviolate sanctity, the sacred nunnery, in which this embodiment has been immured. This cloister is the work of our own hands and we are loath to destroy it. Only shadows, timed to the fateful clock, build here, and not even the spider hangs his nets. We may only look upon the outside walls and can never gain entrance, so that the ghost at a window is all the reward of vigilance.

Here, indeed, in this familiar orchard I was in the same predicament, but with this difference, that the window was lit, not with moonlight, but by authentic means called into being at a touch of the finger, and that the spider's web stretched from bough to bough, crossing even that gulf of ocean the path on which I walked. These lines, laid by him at night, the spider can have just completed, but already the dew was strung upon them, brushing the face and hands, while his web hid its strength behind that gentle, static rain, and the moisture seemed to be not dew strung upon the spider's web, but the corner of a shower caught in the green air and held there. After a time, the broken nets must have trailed along both sides of the path, blowing after me as I went and drawn back again each time I came back, but the wise conspirator who had made them moved his schemes into another direction and never tried to repair his damaged plans.

A poignant, insufferable tension held the nerves and locked the senses, keeping every other thought out of mind. All this search among the dead was ended ; the looting of their tombs was finished, and two whole years crumbled in my fingers into a stretch of moments. Apart from what life the pages of this book can give it, all the body of that investigation and discovery imprisoned itself into a sequence so small and rapid that its effect was simultaneous. In the same way a journey of many hours or an illness lasting months will compress themselves into the memories of a few seconds. This is time seen through a diminishing glass, that dwindles alike its pains and heroics and shrinks the stature of all things in proportion.

This was the last evening, the ending episode; and after it was over some other direction would open in front of me. Just now, it was not the start of the new, but the finish of the old, that lay before me. I should never want to come back here again, being more happy if I thought of it than ever I could be if I made the resolution to arrive again, to ask for my room, and to walk out quickly into the garden while my luggage was taken upstairs. But I could well imagine the breathless, painful silence in which I should be walking along this path, hardly daring to make a noise for fear it should dispel, or interrupt, any of the things I wanted to remember. As for the pair of artists, sitting upstairs, now, behind that lighted window, certainly even in the imagination I never allowed them to be here once more, for their shadows must be kept away from this reality in which I had seen them. The very possibility of these things made one of the saddest moments in life, more dreadful by far than this true farewell to the substance on which my fancy had fed itself for so long.

By now, the darkness had broken into a loud starlight which put little moats and castles on every leaf, while the apples looked dark and heavy as stones, and their bright skins, and the sweetness of their bodies piercing into the very core of their being, were difficult to believe in. The trees were tall enough to stand beneath and the branches made a fretted roof, not thick enough for shelter but intended more for a capricious thinning of the heat, as in some pavilion of the torrid East where rain was not to be hoped for and its imitation, made by artifice, might play at a wish through the diapers of the lattice. These apple trees were numerous as the tents of the plain, with only their difference of height and girth by which to tell them one from another, but their shade was never lived in for long enough to do this. Nor were the castles of the light to be known at a glance, for they were innumerable, hiding their towers, sometimes, in serried ranks behind each other, and throwing down their reflection, as you shook them, upon the grass of the tree-foot. The peculiar factor in all this lively play was the entire silence of everything concerned, as though sound was no part of their universe.

It was nearly time to go indoors and tell Carl and Hilda that this drama was at an end. Then, they must pack away their sketches and start off, like myself, towards some new destiny. Of the old, there were a few moments, and no more, to run. These built themselves, as the thoughts of a drowning man are said to do, into an epitome of all their actions.

Great towers rose up in every direction with their higher reaches hidden in mist. To give scale to them, the birds who nested in those airy chambers, whether rooks or jackdaws I know not, but I should prefer them to be ravens, flew in and out of the stone arcades, cawing loudly, and intent upon the comfort of the nests they were building. It seemed nearly impossible that one should be able to climb to that height, and the thought of this seemed to open a door at the top of a winding and endless stair into a vaulted porch. Instead of this leading to anywhere, it lay open to the sky with only enough wall to hang the roof upon. I could step straight off the floor into upper or lower gulfs of air, the one alternative being as dangerous as the other; and the birds, seen so impersonally from below, now loomed big and black with threatening wings, each of them so true to character that they could be known one from the other. If I walked as near as heart and mind would allow me to the dreadful edge of this floor the birds flew in an angry chain out of the archway, seeming to be thrown by myself into the air, for they kept in a rhythmical arrangement as though balanced on strings tied to my fingers, and they came back again mechanically into the porch once I had walked back to the middle of the floor. The stone monsters who also dwelt at this altitude, leaning on a balustrade and looking down upon the town, I could only see by holding to the stone wall and peering out over the abyss; but a bat's wing, an aquiline nose and thin lips, a horny hand with a head propped against it, or a hoof, like the sylvan satyr's but thicker of ankle, could be taken in even with a quick glance. And there among them were some of this tribe of birds, indeed, the statues were marked with their droppings and it appeared as if they lived perched on the backs of the stone cattle, and moved to their pastures with them.

But the roofs of the town, each with its twist of smoke, had too accustomed a truth for the imagination to be able to draw much material out of them. It was essential to leave this cathedral-close and travel towards some place less imprisoned in perpetual Sunday quiet. Anyone who has glanced through the pages of this book will be able to guess the sort of direction that is implicit in this change of scene.

Into these lands the Corders had never travelled, and they may be thought of as having arrived at a climate where it is nearly impossible to make a drawing of a tower because of the blinding radiance of its climb. The Moslems, who hated the sound of bells as a Christian invention, are so near at hand that the shrill voices calling from the towers of their mosques can almost be heard. There is no sea, no river, and hardly a mountain-range between. So this is a land of military pride, with a more florid heraldic magnificence than is to be met with anywhere else. These bright myths are wrapped in darker shadow than the Northern eyes can find, and the scale of complexity and depth is increased portentously, so that the intricate and laboured wins a deeper degree of admiration than the more pure projections of a plainer mind. The land is nearly treeless, and that leafy, flickering shade is inappropriate to bare hills and dun fields. The Northern variety of this architecture, working for midday, the zenith and climax of light, is here exchanged for a scheme of things taking that hour as an accepted rest, when no one is abroad out of the shade of his house or wall. Instead, the early part of the morning was considered, with its corresponding decline down the opposite slope of the heavens, and, as well as this, buildings were given the emphatic relief that looks best by starlight. But, also, a winter as long and stark as any in the North had to be endured, and those old enemies of the stone, wind and rain, had to be allowed their wear and destruction of all that the hands accomplished. The snow might drift its goose feathers into a crushing weight of softness, breaking down the vaults it collected upon, and vertical slides where it might roll down and drop long before it assumed a dangerous bulk, were designed and prepared for this purpose.

It was almost a cruelty to the Corders to construct their enthusiasm in this fresh environment, and to think of their happy assurance in this perfection of which they had dreamed. Its profuse and copious detail would be the delight of their eyes, and the Moorish or Manoeline perversion of the style they loved would afford them endless, half-shocked pleasures. But then, its uselessness, which would never dawn on them, obsessed me, and I could no longer envy a satisfaction which was so unprofitable, leading into so complete a bankruptcy of invention that they were for ever content with the imaginings of other minds, and had no desire to create of their own accord. This view of them soured and saddened any ambition I held for them, and made me feel that whatever happened they should not be allowed into this paradise. Their presence in it would only turn it into a mild, but eternal, hell; of that sort dwelt in by Tantalus and Sisyphus, for ever working at some useless thing which could never cease its torments. The sketches of the Corders were but a means to an end. Its finality was never reached by them, and was forgotten, ignored even, in the endless reaches of time devoured in its most initial stages.

At all costs they must be prevented, but this was the last moment that I should ever walk here under the apple-boughs, and until the clock struck its twelve dead hours, and this was due in a breath or two of time, I found it impossible to leave the starlight and the little secrecies of its action upon leaf and branch, that made a richer and more enchanting field for the imagination to work upon than could ever be found in the red embers of a domestic fire. Too often coals are simply bloated masks, with not even a neck to support their hideous bulk ; whereas, in this alternate world, these little things, changing before the eyes, become the long moonlight upon a summer land, a cluster of shining lakes, a rippled sea, and there is space beyond these diminutive boundaries for all the beauties that could exist in an enlargement of these principles into the detail proper to their suggestion.

But no time was left for this process to get to work. Like booming, vibrant thunder the bell began, and its echoes were just allowed their death before once again that doom was proclaimed. Its monotonous terror drove all other things out of mind. The appointed measures of that noise and silence built an authentic truth behind the artifice by which it was accomplished. Something real and actual depended upon this measurement by bells, and while their note distinctly sent the past further back into the distance, there was no denying that it, also, brought the past right up to the breath dying on one's lips. Stroke upon stroke had rung out, so that one might think the bells had exceeded their duty, but, at last, the shuddering echo was left unchallenged and this new division of time, for which I was waiting, began in solemn and earnest silence. So I went at once into the house, and climbed the stair.

They were busy packing, and the floor of the room was littered with paper. Apparently the sketches were left

till last, because their boxes were shut and strapped, but
the portfolios were being interleaved with sheets of paper,
and the corners of each sketch were carefully guarded so
that they should not be turned down and spoilt. They
expected me, and did not look round at once when I
came in.

S. S.: Well! I'm off to-morrow morning, like you
are, but we don't travel the same way, I'm afraid.

H. C.: No. We shall have left before you're called.
We must be in time to catch the midday boat, you see.

S. S.: Have you finished everything you wanted to
do ?

C. C.: Yes! More, or less. And you ?

S. S.: This very moment is the finishing touch to
what I have been working on for a couple of years, and
more. Once I've said " good-night " to you, the whole
thing is ended.

C. C.: What happens after this ?

S. S.: First of all a little rest, I hope, but that won't
be for long. Some other project will begin worrying
me, soon.

H. C.: How unlucky you are not to have a subject
which can last you for ever, like Carl and I have ! We
can go on with ours, every summer ; and if we could
travel all the year it would last us all that time, too.
Sometimes there seems so much to do that I feel over-
whelmed with it.

S. S.: I suppose you neither of you ever feel, like I do,
that you can't go inside a church again ! That is only
when I've been seeing ten or a dozen of them a day ;
and, then, the moment I am back in England I find
myself longing for the smell of incense and the sight of
a tomb ; if one is not content in the present—and who

could be, I should like to know ?—then the past becomes
a drug that one cannot be without for long.   But this
particular past that you both love is now, just to-day
perhaps, almost unendurable to me.   I feel I can't stand
it one moment longer.   My memories of it are too painful.

H. C.: You are disillusioned.

S. S.: Not in the slightest.   That is the very last
thing I am.   But what on earth has been the use of it
all ?   And another thing which annoys me is that, at the
same time, I should find myself in agreement with you
both about the dirty, drab gutter we are living in ourselves.   As for some of the horrors of the present, no
wonder the " bus-conductors " call out " Holloway
Gaol " when they stop in front of the Grosvenor House
Flats.   Perhaps we had better let the " bus-men " design
something, themselves !

C. C.: I entirely agree with you.

S. S.: Yes !   I thought you would, and that is what
is so irritating !   But it is nearly quarter-past, and I must
be going to bed.

H. C.: We can't have been talking for a quarter of an
hour, surely ?   It had just struck midnight when you
came in.

S. S.: That is so, but this has taken a quarter of an
hour in writing, and that is the limit I set myself.   Ah !
well !   I suppose we shall meet again one day !   Perhaps
in another fifteen years' time I shall find you at work
somewhere.   I shall come round a corner and there you
will both be, pencil in hand, head in air.   But there'll
be a difference somewhere !   Your hair will be white,
Hilda, and Carl will have not so much grown older as
swollen two or three sizes bigger than he is now.

H. C.: Don't, don't !

S. S. : You expect to be just the same, do you ?

C. C. : Remember, please, that half our lives were wasted, and we were saved when it was too late. You mustn't taunt us ! Give us back what we lost ; why are all the scales weighted against us ? Do you grudge us the little money we were left, and the few pleasures we've waited for so long ?

S. S. : I deny you nothing since I shall never see you again.

H. C. : How can you be certain of that ?

S. S. : Because I make it a rule never to go back on experience. Once I have been happy anywhere I never want to return again. For that reason if you took a leaf from my book and went sketching into the places I knew when I was twenty-one, or twenty-two, you would never find me there. Nor is it very likely that we should ever meet in a place equally unfamiliar to all three of us. You haven't the initiative for that. Think how everything has changed, even in the few years since I last saw you ! The streets in little places like this were full of subjects for you, but there is all the difference in the world when they are declared national property and become a kind of museum exhibit. Already, to take Notre Dame, for example, it is no longer the culmination of a whole lot of old houses and narrow streets, but it stands absolutely at contradiction with its surroundings. It is simply an old heathen temple, only that word " heathen " destroys my meaning because you know it was a Christian church. Still, there's no denying it was the resort of idolaters ; and, except for some familiar things that the eyes can interpret, it might be the work of Hindus, or of any of the true races of temple-builders. It is a whole millennium away from us. What profit can you find in its worn stones ? Can't you try to live altogether in your own orbit without having a picturesque background that you can dip into whenever you feel weak ? And I suggest that, if there must be one, it had better take the more dematerialized forms of music and poetry, where you can't hurt yourself wandering about, and which, by their very unsubstantial nature, if they exist at all, are likely to do so in a more inspired air. They are made of nothing, like a magical omelette made without eggs. They won't waste so much of your time. But this change of plan comes too late in your case ; I can't expect you to alter at your age !

C. C. : This must be good-bye, then !

H. C. : Stay a moment longer !

S. S. : No, it is too late. The new quarter has already struck.

And I climbed up another flight of stairs into my room.

This was the last I saw of them. A few moments later I stood in the window for a last look at the trees, and just then a light on the floor below was put out. It was from one of their rooms, and there was a little sound of sudden darkness when this happened as if something heavy had been dropped. There was not a whisper, not a sigh to be heard. Probably as we all three lay trying to sleep we thought over the same projects ; but my mind was already made up, and at any rate I had reached a decision. Therefore I slept soundly and had no dreams.

NOTES

1. The Church of St. Simeon the Stylite is some eight hours' ride from Aleppo. It is called Kal'at Sim'ân, and was built in the fifth century on the establishment, in this place, of a convent of the order of Stylites, or "pillar-hermits." St. Simeon, the founder of the Order, and the son of a peasant, was born in 391 and died in 459. He began at an early age to practise the strangest and most stringent austerities. In 422 he ascended a column of moderate height, upon which he spent seven years; after which he established himself on the top of a column 38 feet high, where he passed most of the remaining thirty years of his existence. The highest altitude that he ever reached was one of sixty feet, but this was inconvenient because out of earshot. A railing ran round the capital of his pillar, and a ladder enabled his disciples to take him the necessaries of life. Exposed here to all the inclemency of the weather, he delivered lectures on the Holy Scriptures from his lofty station, answered questions and attracted thousands of hearers and pupils.

The ruins of this church and monastery occupy the whole of a plateau lying among desolate mountains. The plan of the church answers so well to the description given by Procopius of the church of the Apostles erected by Constantine in his new capital, and intended for his burial place, that it would appear to be a copy of that older building. It consists of four great arms, built in the shape of a Greek cross, and each containing two rows of six columns. Where these four arms meet a great octagonal space is formed. In the centre of this there still lies the pedestal of a huge column, probably that upon which St. Simeon passed three decades of his life. But, in the great court, behind the east wing of the church, there is a large mass of rock, approached by steps, and this may equally well be the rock on which his pillar stood. Traces of the monastery, less well preserved than those of the church, still remain ; and to the south of this there is another church of the same style, the interior of which is occupied by several Arab families. Apart from the romantic interest of these relics of the Stylite, the Church of St. Simeon is an architectural masterpiece of a very high order, and in all that region of the world there are only two things that can compare with it, the temples of Petra and of Baalbek. (Cf. " Les Stylites," by H. Delahaye the Bollandist, Paris, 1895.)

2. With regard to this manuscript the name of a celebrated primitive painter must be mentioned. Simon Marmion of Amiens, 1425–1480, is recorded as at work in his native city in the years 1449–1458. In 1454 he was called with thirty-four other painters from Bruges, Audenarde, Ghent, Tournai, and Arras, to Lille, in order to work upon the decorations for the celebrated Banquet du Faisan. In 1458 he settled at Valenciennes, where he stayed till his death, painting pictures, also, for Cambrai and Tournai. One of his best works is " The Legend of St. Vincent," in twelve sections, arrived by some strange chance at the church of S. Pietro Martire at Naples. He was, as well, a celebrated miniaturist, and among other works of this kind the frontispiece to this volume has been attributed to his hand. This manuscript (Huth XIII, Add. MS. 38126) is one of the best extant specimens of Flemish illumination. It contains twenty-four full page and seventy-four smaller miniatures, with full, or partial, borders of flowers and insects upon every page.

3. Maria Sibylla Merian, the daughter of Matthaeus Merian the engraver, and sister to the well-known painter of the same name, was born at Frankfort in 1647. She became the pupil of Abraham Mignon, and devoted herself entirely to painting reptiles, flowers and insects. She finished an astonishing number of these in water-colours upon vellum. In 1679 and 1683 were published the two parts of her book upon European insects, but, later in life, she was not content with this vast field for observation but undertook, in 1698, a voyage to the Dutch colony of Surinam in South America. Here she stayed for two

years, discovering numerous flowers and animals unknown to the learned world, and was the first person to study the transformation of the chrysalis, for which reason she has a scientific renown as well as her fame as a painter. Her daughter, Dorothea Henrietta Graff, accompanied her to Surinam, helped her with her designs, married a rich Dutch merchant of the colony, and assisted her mother on their return to Europe with the publication of two great volumes of engravings. These were handcoloured by the two of them. M. S. Merian died in 1717, and when she was dead her daughter collected and published a third volume of fifty engravings from her designs. (Cf. Pilkington's " Dictionary of Painters," 1810.)

4. Tulips were introduced into Holland from Turkey by Clusius in 1575. The speculation in bulbs reached its height in 1637. For the Semper Augustus 10,000 florins was given; for the Admiral Liefkens 4,500; for the Viceroy 4,500; while one Dutch town is said to have cleared ten million florins in one year by the sale of bulbs, and a private investor sixty-eight thousand florins in a few weeks. The government eventually suppressed this form of gambling, and prices fell so rapidly that many people were ruined. A century later there was a similar craze for hyacinths. (Cf. " The Netherlands Display'd," by Marjorie Bowen, 1926, p. 210.)

5. The poetess Christine de Pisan, 1364–1430, was born at Venice. Her father was the Italian astrologer to Charles V of France. She married Etienne du Castel, notary to Charles V, and on his death, in 1389, being left with three children, she took to writing in order to gain a living. Her most celebrated works are the " Cité des Dames " and the " Livre des Trois Vertus," two books which contain many portraits of her contemporaries. She composed a poem in honour of Joan of Arc in 1429. She adopted France for her native country and lived there all her life, in spite of invitations from Henry IV of England, and Galeazzo Visconti, the Tyrant of Milan.

The manuscript in question (Harleian MS. 4431) is one of the most beautiful manuscripts in the British Museum Library. The frontispiece shows the poet presenting her book to the wife of Charles V, Elizabeth, daughter of Stephen II of Bavaria, whose name was Gallicized into Isabeau. The bed in this frontispiece is bright red in colour, and the walls are hung with blue brocade, with chequers, or golden fleurs-de-lys. Throughout the manuscript there is an astonishing clearness of colour, more especially when blue is used, and the whole manuscript provides in its miniatures the most interesting evidence as to the daily life and surroundings of that time.

6. Although Batavia was founded in 1618 the Dutch did not obtain full possession of Java till they dissolved the important Moslem Sultanate of Mataram in 1755. Out of its ruins they formed the two Sultanates of Djojka and Solo. The capital of the first of these, Djojkacarta, has a population of 60,000, and a royal walled town, or kraton, lived in by 15,000 soldiers, eunuchs, wives, and royal attendants. In this enclosure is the "Water-casteel," a palace built in the eighteenth century by European architects on an artificial island, with statues, fountains, pavilions, and underground galleries. It was destroyed by an earthquake in 1867. Soeracarta, the capital of Solo, has 120,000 inhabitants, and a kraton lived in by 10,000 persons. Near to it is the kraton of the Mangkoe-Negoro, or second king, who is powerless and has no function. These two States are famous for their marionette-plays, and for the live dramas in which the princes and princesses of the Sultan's family take the part of marionettes.

In Cambodia, on the other hand, the authentic bayadères from the sculptures of Angkor are still to be seen. This is at Phnom-Penh, the capital of the kingdom. In the palace here, the sacred sword of the State, a blade damascened with gold, is still preserved, and this has been the Royal insignia ever since the time of the Khmer emperors who built Angkor. The only other relic of that civilization is the corps of choreutes, or ballet-dancers, belonging to the king. This is a part of the ancient Brahminic liturgy, and the dances are given in honour of the god Siva, or to please the gods of Indra, i.e., paradise. The gods, who are personified in the king, are thus satisfied in his personal pleasures. This dancing is said to be of the most exquisite beauty, in no way lessened by the static graces of the bayadères. The stables of the sacred white elephant, also part of the palace, are another indication of the curious nature of this sacred establishment.

7. The Cartuja de Miraflores was founded by Juan II and rebuilt in the years after 1454 by Hans and Simon of Cologne. D. Juan II and his wife Isabella of Portugal are buried here in tombs erected for them by their daughter, Isabella the Catholic. Externally, the chapel, as pointed out by Street in his " Gothic Architecture in Spain," has a strong resemblance in scale and in plan to Eton College Chapel. The cloister, refectory, and library are not shown, but evidently they do not contain much of interest. The Cartuja is now occupied by about thirty French monks, driven out of their country by the laws of 1903. The present prior is an Englishman. (Cf. Francisco Tarin y Juaneda, "La Real Cartuja de Miraflores," Libreria Rodriguez, Burgos, 1927.) The work of Gil de Siloe in this monastery, the royal tombs, that is to say, and the retablo of the altar, are the finest existing works of the last part of the fifteenth century, exactly contemporary with, but how different to, the temple of the Malatesta at Rimini !

8. The Temple of the Malatesta was begun, under the direction of Alberti, in 1447. The tomb of Sigismondo, built while he was still living, in 1468, was made by Bernardo Ciuffagni. This is immediately to the right on entering the church. The first chapel on the right, dedicated to St. Sigismund, King of Hungary, was designed by Francesco Laurana, or, according to Vasari, by Simone, the brother of Donatello. The arch of the chapel rests on pilasters supported by elephants, two on each side. The first chapel on the left is the most beautiful of all. It has the same two pillars supported upon four elephants, by Simone. The chapel is covered with beautiful sculpture, and contains the tomb in which Sigismondo wished that the bones of his ancestors and descendants might repose. This has two bas-reliefs : Pallas Athene surrounded by heroes of the Malatesta family, and Sigismondo drawn on a chariot by four horses, preceded by prisoners, under a triumphal arch. This tomb, and the whole chapel, are attributed by Vasari to Luca della Robbia.

C 2

Another chapel contains the tomb of Isotta, supported on two elephants. The arch of yet another contains eighteen bas-reliefs in Greek marble of the Liberal Arts; while the chapel next to this has an archway, the two pillars of which, divided each into nine sections, show the signs of the zodiac and of the planets on an azure ground. In these two chapels the pillars are supported by great baskets of white marble on red bases, and embellished with cupids and garlands. Above every basket are bronze wreaths of grapes, apples and leaves, with lizards, frogs, and butterflies among them. These are by Lorenzo Ghiberti, or by Matteo de Pasti. Lastly, the inside wall of the locked reliquary room has a fresco, by Piero della Francesca, of Sigismondo Malatesta kneeling before St. Sigismund, King of Hungary. Two greyhounds are by his side, and the fortress he had but lately built is shown in the background.

As to the tombs built into the arches on the outside of the church, the first four of them contain the ashes of Basinio Parmense, author of various Latin poems; of Giusto de Conti, a Roman, and the writer of a ballad " La Bella Mano," in honour of Isotta; of Roberto Valturi of Rimini, author of a book, " De re militari," and counsellor to Sigismondo; and, lastly, of the famous Gemistio, a Byzantine philosopher whose bones were carried away from the Morea, in 1465, by Sigismondo when he was leading the Venetian armies against the Turks. (Cf. Rimini in the series " L'Italia Monumentale," Milan, Bonomi, 1915.)

INDEX

INDEX